Middle School 2-1

중간고사 완벽대비

KB084801

적중100

영어 기출 문제집

중2

시사 | 박준언

Best Collection

구성과 특징

교과서의 주요 학습 내용을 중심으로 학습 영역별 특성에 맞춰 단계별로 다양한 학습 기회를 제공하여 단원별 학습능력 평가는 물론 중간 및 기말고사 시험 등에 완벽하게 대비할 수 있도록 내용을 구성

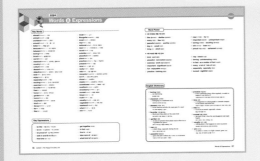

Words & Expressions

Step1 Key Words 단원별 핵심 단어 설명 및 풀이
Key Expression 단원별 핵심 숙어 및 관용어 설명
Word Power 반대 또는 비슷한 뜻 단어 배우기
English Dictionary 영어로 배우는 영어 단어

Step2 실력평가 단원별 수시평가 대비 주관식, 객관식 문제풀이

Step3 서술형 대비 학업성취도 및 수행능력평가 대비 서술형 문제풀이

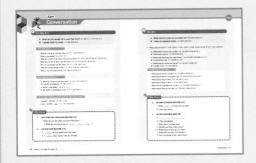

Conversation

Step1 핵심 의사소통 의사소통에 필요한 주요 표현 방법 요약
핵심 Check 기본적인 표현 방법 및 활용능력 확인

Step2 대화문 익히기 상황에 따른 대화문 활용 및 연습

Step3 기본평가 시험대비 기초 학습 능력 평가

Step4 실력평가 단원별 수시평가 대비 주관식, 객관식 문제풀이

Step5 서술형 대비 학업성취도 및 수행능력평가 대비 서술형 문제풀이

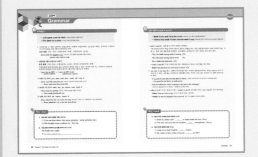

Grammar

Step1 주요 문법 단원별 주요 문법 사항과 예문을 알기 쉽게 설명

핵심 Check 기본 문법사항에 대한 이해 여부 확인

Step2 기본평가 시험대비 기초 학습 능력 평가

Step3 실력평가 단원별 수시평가 대비 주관식, 객관식 문제풀이

Step4 서술형 대비 학업성취도 및 수행능력평가 대비 서술형 문제풀이

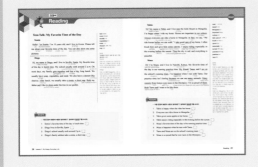

Reading

Step1 구문 분석 단원별로 제시된 문장에 대한 구문별 분석과 내용 설명
확인문제 문장에 대한 기본적인 이해와 인지능력 확인

Step2 확인학습A 빈칸 채우기를 통한 문장 완성 능력 확인

Step3 확인학습B 제시된 우리말을 영어로 완성하여 작문 능력 키우기

Step4 실력평가 단원별 수시평가 대비 주관식, 객관식 문제풀이

Step5 서술형 대비 학업성취도 및 수행능력평가 대비 서술형 문제풀이
교과서 구석구석 교과서에 나오는 기타 문장까지 완벽 학습

Cmposition

|영역별 핵심문제|

단어 및 어휘, 대화문, 문법, 독해 등 각 영역별 기출문제의 출제 유형을 분석하여 실전에 대비하고 연습할 수 있도록 문제를 배열

|서술형 실전 및 창의사고력 문제|

학교 시험에서 점차 늘어나는 서술형 시험에 집중 대비하고 고득점을 취득하는데 만전을 기하기 위한 학습 코너

|단원별 예상문제|

기출문제를 분석한 후 새로운 시험 출제 경향을 더하여 새롭게 출제될 수 있는 문제를 포함하여 시험에 완벽하게 대비할 수 있도록 준비

|단원별 모의고사|

영역별, 단계별 학습을 모두 마친 후 실전 연습을 위한 모의고사

INSIGHT on the textbook

교과서 파헤치기

- 단어Test1~2 영어 단어 우리말 쓰기와 우리말을 영어 단어로 쓰기
- 대화문Test1~2 대화문 빈칸 완성 및 전체 대화문 쓰기
- 본문Test1~5 빈칸 완성, 우리말 쓰기, 문장 배열연습, 영어 작문하기 복습 등 단계별 반복 학습을 통해 교과서 지문에 대한 완벽한 습득
- 구석구석지문Test1~2 지문 빈칸 완성 및 전문 영어로 쓰기

Contents

Lesson 1

Manage Yourself!

의사소통 기능

- 슬픔, 불만족, 실망의 원인에 대해 묻기
  What's the matter?
- 제안·권유하기
  I think you should use a planner.

언어 형식

- to부정사의 형용사적 용법
  You will have more work **to do**.
- 접속사 that
  I think **that** using my time to prepare for my future is important.

Words & Expressions

Key Words

- **achieve** [ətʃíːv] 동 달성하다, 성취하다
- **again** [əgen] 부 다시
- **always** [ɔ́ːlweiz] 부 항상
- **appointment** [əpɔ́intmənt] 명 약속
- **attention** [əténʃən] 명 주의, 집중
- **before** [bifɔ́ːr] 접 ~하기 전에
- **check** [tʃek] 동 확인하다
- **chef** [ʃef] 명 요리사
- **due** [djuː] 형 ~하기로 되어 있는[예정된]
- **easily** [íːzili] 부 쉽게
- **finish** [fíniʃ] 동 끝내다
- **focus** [fóukəs] 동 집중하다
- **forget** [fərgét] 동 잊다
- **free time** 자유 시간
- **future** [fjúːtʃər] 명 미래
- **help** [help] 동 도움이 되다 명 도움
- **helpful** [hélpfəl] 형 도움이 되는
- **history** [hístəri] 명 역사
- **important** [impɔ́ːrtənt] 형 중요한
- **instead** [instéd] 부 대신에
- **join** [dʒɔin] 동 가입하다
- **lesson** [lésn] 명 수업, 강습
- **master** [mǽstər] 동 ~을 완전히 익히다, ~에 숙달하다
- **monthly** [mʌ́nθli] 형 매월의 부 매월
- **nervous** [artwərk] 형 긴장되는, 불안한
- **planner** [plǽnər] 명 일정 계획표, 플래너
- **posting** [póustiŋ] 명 포스팅, (인터넷이나 SNS에 올리는) 글
- **practice** [prǽktis] 동 연습하다
- **prepare** [pripɛ́ər] 동 준비하다
- **present** [préznt] 명 선물
- **probably** [prábəbli] 부 아마 (= perhaps)
- **quiz** [kwiz] 명 퀴즈, 시험, 테스트
- **recipe** [résəpi] 명 조리[요리]법
- **regularly** [régjulərli] 부 규칙적으로
- **remember** [rimémbər] 동 기억하다
- **save** [seiv] 동 절약하다, 구하다
- **schedule** [skédʒuːl] 명 일정
- **spend** [spend] 동 (돈을) 쓰다, (시간을) 소비하다
- **step** [step] 명 걸음
- **textbook** [tekstbuk] 명 교과서
- **tired** [taiərd] 형 피곤한
- **toward** [tɔːrd] 전 (목적·준비) ~을 위해, ~을 향하여
- **try** [trai] 동 해 보다, 노력하다
- **warm** [wɔːrm] 형 따뜻한
- **weekly** [wíːkli] 형 매주의 부 매주
- **while** [hwail] 접 ~하는 동안
- **wisely** [wáizli] 부 현명하게
- **worried** [wɔ́ːrid] 형 걱정하는

Key Expressions

- **a lot of** 많은
- **a type of** 일종의
- **all day long** 온종일
- **at a time** 한 번에
- **be good at** ~을 잘하다, ~에 능숙하다
- **be worried about** ~에 대해 걱정하다
- **because of** ~ 때문에
- **get along with** ~와 잘 지내다
- **have a cold** 감기에 걸리다
- **in front of** ~ 앞에
- **make a plan** 계획을 세우다
- **prepare for** ~을 준비하다
- **put aside** ~을 한쪽에 두다
- **put off** 미루다, 연기하다
- **search for** ~을 찾다
- **see a doctor** 병원에 가다
- **set a goal** 목표를 세우다
- **set the alarm** 알람을 맞춰 놓다
- **stop -ing** ~하는 것을 멈추다
- **take[have] a lesson** 수업[강습]을 받다
- **these days** 요즘
- **used to** ~하곤 했다

Word Power

※ 명사에 -ful, -y 등을 붙여 형용사가 되는 단어

- [ ] **beauty** (아름다움) → **beautiful** (아름다운)
- [ ] **care** (주의) → **careful** (주의 깊은)
- [ ] **cloud** (구름) → **cloudy** (흐린)
- [ ] **harm** (해) → **harmful** (해로운)
- [ ] **help** (도움) → **helpful** (도움이 되는)

- [ ] **luck** (행운) → **lucky** (운이 좋은)
- [ ] **mess** (엉망인 상태) → **messy** (지저분한)
- [ ] **star** (별) → **starry** (별이 총총한)
- [ ] **thirst** (갈증) → **thirsty** (갈증이 나는)
- [ ] **wonder** (경이) → **wonderful** (경이로운)

※ 형용사에 -ly를 붙여 부사가 되는 단어

- [ ] **easy** (쉬운) → **easily** (쉽게)
- [ ] **careful** (주의 깊은) → **carefully** (주의 깊게)
- [ ] **kind** (친절한) → **kindly** (친절하게)
- [ ] **loud** (소리가 큰) → **loudly** (큰 소리로)

- [ ] **special** (특별한) → **specially** (특별히)
- [ ] **sudden** (갑작스러운) → **suddenly** (갑자기)
- [ ] **regular** (규칙적인) → **regularly** (규칙적으로)
- [ ] **wise** (현명한) → **wisely** (현명하게)

English Dictionary

- [ ] **achieve** 달성하다, 성취하다
  → to get or reach something by working hard
  열심히 일해 뭔가를 얻거나 이루다

- [ ] **appointment** 약속
  → an arrangement to meet with someone at a particular time
  특정한 때에 어떤 사람을 만나기로 하는 약속

- [ ] **attention** 주의
  → the act of listening to, looking at, or thinking about something or someone carefully
  어떤 것 또는 누군가에 대해 주의 깊게 듣고, 보고, 생각하는 행위

- [ ] **due** ~하기로 되어 있는[예정된]
  → expected to happen or arrive at a particular time
  특정 시간에 발생하거나 도착할 것으로 예상되는

- [ ] **focus** 집중하다
  → to direct your attention or effort at something specific
  관심이나 노력을 특정한 대상에 기울이다

- [ ] **future** 미래
  → the period of time that will come after the present time
  현재 시간 이후에 올 시간[시기]

- [ ] **join** 가입하다
  → to become a member of a group or organization
  집단이나 단체의 구성원이 되다

- [ ] **lesson** 수업, 강습
  → an activity that you do in order to learn something
  어떤 것을 배우기 위해 하는 활동

- [ ] **master** ~을 완전히 익히다
  → to learn something completely
  어떤 것을 완전히 익히다

- [ ] **prepare** 준비하다
  → to make yourself ready for something that you will be doing
  앞으로 하려는 일을 위해 자신을 준비시키다

- [ ] **present** 선물
  → something that you give to someone especially as a way of showing affection or thanks
  특히 애정이나 감사의 표시로 누군가에게 주는 것

- [ ] **recipe** 조리[요리]법
  → a set of instructions for making food
  음식을 만들기 위한 일련의 지시 사항

- [ ] **save** 절약하다
  → to keep something from being lost or wasted
  어떤 것이 손실되거나 낭비되지 않게 하다

- [ ] **schedule** 일정
  → a plan of things that will be done and the times when they will be done
  할 일에 대한 계획 및 그 일을 할 때

01 다음 중 〈보기〉와 같이 변화하는 단어가 <u>아닌</u> 것은?

┌─ 보기 ─┐
help → helpful

① harm
② color
③ danger
④ wonder
⑤ beauty

02 다음 빈칸에 공통으로 알맞은 것은?

• There is a church in front _____ the school.
• She closed the door because _____ the rain.

① at
② of
③ on
④ by
⑤ from

03 다음 영영풀이에 해당하는 단어로 알맞은 것은?

to get or reach something by working hard

① check
② focus
③ master
④ achieve
⑤ prepare

서답형

04 다음 짝지어진 두 단어의 관계가 같도록 빈칸에 알맞은 말을 쓰시오.

easy : difficult = remember : _____

05 다음 빈칸에 들어갈 동사가 바르게 짝지어진 것은?

• I _____ the alarm clock for 7 o'clock.
• I will _____ a plan to visit you next year!

① keep – give
② set – take
③ get – make
④ keep – have
⑤ set – make

서답형

06 다음 영영풀이에 해당하는 단어를 쓰시오.

a set of instructions for making food

➡ _____

서답형

07 다음 우리말에 맞게 빈칸에 알맞은 말을 쓰시오.

Ann은 하루 종일 집에 있었어.
➡ Ann stayed home _____ _____ _____.

08 다음 빈칸에 알맞은 말이 바르게 짝지어진 것은?

• I must prepare _____ the exam.
• Carrie never puts _____ doing her homework.

① at – on
② for – off
③ from – up
④ about – out
⑤ with – down

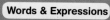

01 다음 짝지어진 두 단어의 관계가 같도록 빈칸에 알맞은 말을 쓰시오.

(1) before : after = _____ : cool

(2) delicious : tasty = gift : _____

(3) cloud : cloudy = help : _____

02 다음 우리말에 맞게 빈칸에 알맞은 말을 쓰시오.

(1) 나는 영어에 능숙하고 싶다.

➡ I want to _____ _____ _____ English.

(2) 나는 반 아이들과 잘 지낼 거야.

➡ I'll _____ _____ _____ my classmates.

(3) 마지막 목표는 스마트폰 게임을 멈추는 것이다.

➡ The last goal is to _____ _____ smartphone games.

03 다음 빈칸에 들어갈 알맞은 말을 〈보기〉에서 골라 쓰시오.

┌─── 보기 ───┐
achieve future manage appointment
└──────────────┘

(1) Let's change our _____ to 7 o'clock.

(2) What do you want to be in the _____?

(3) You need to _____ your time well.

(4) I set small goals and _____ them every day.

04 다음 괄호 안의 단어를 문맥에 맞게 고쳐 쓰시오.

(1) I want to spend money _____. (wise)

(2) Listen _____ to what I say. (careful)

(3) We all need to exercise _____. (regular)

05 다음 빈칸에 알맞은 말을 〈보기〉에서 골라 쓰시오.

┌─── 보기 ───┐
put aside   put off
at a time   because of
└──────────────┘

(1) I was late _____ a traffic jam.

(2) Don't _____ today's work until tomorrow.

(3) I will achieve my big goal, one step _____.

(4) I _____ my smartphone when I do my homework.

06 다음 영영풀이에 해당하는 단어를 주어진 철자로 시작하여 쓰시오.

(1) l_____ : an activity that you do in order to learn something

(2) s_____ : to keep something from being lost or wasted

(3) f_____ : to direct your attention or effort at something specific

(4) d_____ : expected to happen or arrive at a particular time

교과서 Conversation

1 슬픔, 불만족, 실망의 원인에 대해 묻기

> **A** Emily, you look sad. What's the matter? Emily, 너 슬퍼 보여. 무슨 일 있니?
> **B** I lost my cat. 고양이를 잃어버렸어.

■ What's the matter?는 '무슨 일 있니?'라는 뜻으로 상대방의 슬픔, 불만족, 실망의 원인에 대해 물을 때 사용하는 표현이다. 상대방의 응답에 이어 That's too bad. 나 I'm sorry to hear that. 등과 같은 동정이나 유감을 나타내는 표현이 주로 이어진다.

- A: What's the matter? 무슨 일이야?
  B: I broke my smartphone. 내 스마트폰이 고장 났어.
  A: That's too bad. 그것 참 안됐구나.

슬픔, 불만족, 실망의 원인에 대해 묻는 표현

- What's wrong (with you)? 무슨 일 있니?
- What's the matter (with you)?
- What happened (to you)?
- What's the problem (with you)?
- What's going on?
- Is (there) something wrong with you? 무슨 문제라도 있니?
- Why are you sad[disappointed]? 왜 슬픈[실망한] 거야?

슬픔, 불만족, 실망의 원인에 대해 답하기

- I have a cold. 감기에 걸렸어.
- My team lost the game. 우리 팀이 경기에서 졌어.
- She's in the hospital. 그녀는 지금 병원에 입원해 있어.
- My puppy is sick. 내 강아지가 아파.
- I failed the test. 나는 시험에 떨어졌어.

핵심 Check

1. 다음 우리말과 일치하도록 빈칸에 알맞은 말을 쓰시오.

(1) A: What's the _____? (무슨 일 있니?)

B: I _____ my cellphone. (나는 휴대전화를 잃어버렸어.)

A: That's _____ _____. (그거 참 안됐구나.)

(2) A: What's wrong _____ Mr. Han? (한 선생님에게 무슨 문제가 있니?)

B: He _____ his _____. (그분은 손가락을 다치셨어.)

A: _____ _____ to hear that. (그거 참 안됐구나.)

② 제안 · 권유하기

> **A** I want to be good at speaking English. 나는 영어를 잘하고 싶어.
>
> **B** I think you should join an English conversation club.
> 내 생각에 너는 영어 회화 동아리에 가입해야 할 것 같아.

■ '내 생각에 넌 ~해야 할 것 같아.'라고 상대방에게 무언가를 제안하거나 권유할 때에는 I think you should ~. 표현을 사용하여 말할 수 있다.

> • A: I want to be good at cooking. 나는 요리를 잘하고 싶어.
> B: I think you should search for recipes. 내 생각에 넌 조리법을 찾아봐야 할 것 같아.

제안 · 권유하기 표현

- I think (that) you should[ought to]+동사원형 ~. 나는 네가 ~해야 한다고 생각해.
- You should[must / have to] + 동사원형 ~. 너는 ~해야 해.
- You'd better + 동사원형 ~. 너는 ~하는 게 좋겠어.
- I advise you to + 동사원형 ~. 나는 네가 ~하길 조언해.
- If I were you, I'd + 동사원형 ~. 내가 너라면 ~할 텐데.
- Why don't you + 동사원형 ~? ~하는 게 어때?
- How[What] about + -ing ~? ~하는 게 어때?

핵심 Check

2. 다음 우리말과 일치하도록 빈칸에 알맞은 말을 쓰시오.

(1) **A**: I have a _____. (이가 아파.)

  B: I _____ you _____ _____ to a dentist. (내 생각에 넌 치과에 가야 할 것 같아.)

(2) **A**: _____ eat hamburgers. (햄버거를 먹자.)

  B: You'd _____ eat some vegetables. (너는 채소를 좀 먹는 것이 좋겠어.)

(3) **A**: _____ _____ we drink soft drinks? (우리 탄산음료를 마시는 게 어때?)

  B: You _____ _____ milk. (너는 우유를 마셔야 해.)

(4) **A**: Shall we _____ computer games? (컴퓨터 게임을 할까?)

  B: I think you _____ _____ do your homework first.
  (넌 먼저 숙제부터 해야 한다고 난 생각해.)

A. Listen & Speak 1 - A - 1

G: ❶You look worried, Sam. ❷What's the matter?

B: ❸I don't hear my alarm in the morning these days.

G: ❹Why don't you set the alarm on your clock and on your smartphone?

B: ❺That's a good idea.

G: 걱정이 있어 보여, Sam. 무슨 일 있니?
B: 요즘 아침에 알람을 못 들어.
G: 네 시계와 스마트폰에 알람을 맞춰 놓는 게 어때?
B: 좋은 생각이야.

❶ look+형용사: ~하게 보이다
❷ What's the matter?: 무슨 일 있니?(슬픔, 불만족, 실망의 원인에 대해 묻기) = What's the problem?=What's wrong?=Is something wrong?
❸ these days: 요즈음
❹ Why don't you + 동사원형 ~?: ~하는 게 어때? (권유나 제안하기) / set the alarm: 알람을 맞춰 놓다
❺ That's a good idea. = I think so, too.=I'm with you on that.=That sounds good.=You can say that again. (동의하기)

Check(√) True or False

(1) Sam looks happy these days. T ☐ F ☐

(2) Sam will set the alarm on his clock and on his smartphone. T ☐ F ☐

Conversation B

Hana: ❶What's the matter, Jiho?

Jiho: I didn't bring my uniform. ❷I forgot I have soccer practice today.

Hana: Again?

Jiho: ❸My second year in middle school is busier than my first year, and ❹I often forget things.

Hana: ❺I think you should use a planner. Here's mine.

Jiho: ❻Oh, can I see it?

Hana: Sure. I write my class schedule and appointment in my planner.

Jiho: That's great. ❼Maybe I should buy one.

하나: 무슨 일 있니, 지호야?
지호: 나는 내 유니폼을 가져오지 않았어. 오늘 축구 연습이 있다는 걸 잊고 있었어.
하나: 또?
지호: 중학교 2학년은 1학년보다 더 바쁘고, 나는 종종 어떤 것들을 잊어버려.
하나: 내 생각에는 너는 일정 계획표를 사용해야 할 것 같아. 여기 내 것이 있어.
지호: 오, 내가 봐도 될까?
하나: 물론. 나는 일정 계획표에 나의 수업 일정과 약속을 적어.
지호: 정말 좋구나. 나도 하나 사야 할까 봐.

❶ What's the matter?: 무슨 일 있니?(슬픔, 불만족, 실망의 원인에 대해 묻기)
❷ I forgot와 I 사이에 목적절을 이끄는 접속사 that 생략
❸ busier than: 비교급 + than(~보다 더 …한)
❹ 빈도부사 often은 일반동사 앞이나 be동사와 조동사 뒤에 위치한다.
❺ I think you should ~.: 내 생각에 너는 ~해야 할 것 같아. (제안이나 권유하기) = You'd better + 동사원형 ~. = Why don't you + 동사원형 ~? = How[What] about + -ing ~?
❻ Can I ~?: 내가 ~해도 될까?(허락 요청하기) / it=a planner
❼ Maybe I should + 동사원형 ~.: (아마) ~해야겠지, ~할까 봐. / one = a planner

Check(√) True or False

(3) Jiho always forgets things. T ☐ F ☐

(4) Hana advises Jiho to use a planner. T ☐ F ☐

Listen & Speak 1 - A - 2

G: ❶Phew, what should I do?
B: ❷What's the matter, Julie?
G: I spend money too fast.
B: ❸Well, I always make a plan before I buy things.
G: ❹Maybe I should do the same.

❶ What should I do?: 내가 어떻게 해야 하니? / phew: 휴, 후유
❷ What's the matter? = What's wrong? = What's the problem? = What happened?
❸ 빈도부사 always는 일반동사 앞이나 be동사와 조동사 뒤에 위치한다.
❹ Maybe I should + 동사원형 ~.: (아마) ~해야겠지, ~할까 봐.

Listen & Speak 2 - A - 1

G: ❶Jason, are you okay? You don't look good today.
B: ❷I have a cold.
G: ❸That's too bad. ❹ I think you should see a doctor.
B: You're right. Thank you.

❶ Are you okay?: 너 괜찮니?
❷ have a cold: 감기에 걸리다(=catch[get/take] a cold)
❸ That's too bad.: 그것 참 안됐구나. (유감을 나타내는 표현) = I'm sorry to hear that.
❹ I think you should + 동사원형 ~.: 내 생각에 너는 ~해야 할 것 같아.

Listen & Speak 2 - A - 2

G: You look worried. ❶What's going on?
B: ❷I'm worried about tomorrow's history quiz. What should I do?
G: I think you should read your textbook again.
B: ❸That's a good idea.

❶ What's going on?: 무슨 일 있니?(슬픔, 불만족, 실망의 원인에 대해 묻기) = What's the problem?=What's wrong?=Is something wrong?
❷ I'm worried about ~: 나는 ~이 걱정돼.
❸ That's a good idea.: 좋은 생각이야.

Listen & Speak 2 - A - 3

B: I'm so tired.
G: Why?
B: ❶I don't sleep well these days.
G: ❷I think you should drink a glass of warm milk before you sleep. ❸It will help.
B: Okay, I will try.

❶ these days: 요즈음
❷ a glass of: 한 잔의
❸ It = to drink a glass of warm milk before you sleep

Conversation A

B: ❶This is a type of book. I write my daily, weekly, and monthly plans here. ❷I also write important dates like my friends' birthdays and homework due dates here. Every night, I check this for the next day. Do you want to remember things easily? ❸Then I think you should use this.

❶ a type of: 일종의(=a kind of, a sort of)
❷ like: ~와 같은 / due: ~하기로 되어 있는[예정된]
❸ I think you should + 동사원형 ~.: 내 생각에 너는 ~해야 할 것 같아.

Wrap Up - ❶

W: ❶What's the matter, Sam? Are you sick?
B: ❷Ms. Green, I think I have a cold.
W: Did you go to the school nurse?
B: Yes. ❸She said I need to go to the hospital. ❹ Can I leave school now?
W: Okay, Sam. I'll call your mom and tell her about it.

❶ What's the matter? = What's wrong? = What's the problem? = What happened?
❷ have a cold: 감기에 걸리다(=catch[get/take] a cold)
❸ need to: ~할 필요가 있다
❹ Can I + 동사원형 ~?: 제가 ~해도 될까요? (허락 요청하기)

Wrap Up - ❷

B: I'm so nervous.
G: Why? ❶Is it because of the dance contest?
B: Yes. I practiced for many days, but I'm still nervous. ❷What should I do?
G: ❸I think you should practice in front of your family. ❹It will be very helpful.
B: That's a good idea. Thank you.

❶ because of: ~ 때문에
❷ What should I do?: 내가 어떻게 해야 하지? (충고 구하기)
❸ in front of: ~ 앞에서
❹ It=to practice in front of your family

Conversation 교과서 확인학습

● 다음 우리말과 일치하도록 빈칸에 알맞은 말을 쓰시오.

Listen & Speak 1 - A

1. **G:** You look _____, Sam. What's the _____?

   B: I don't _____ my alarm in the morning _____ _____.

   G: _____ _____ you _____ the alarm on your clock and on your smartphone?

   B: That's a good _____.

2. **G:** Phew, what _____ I do?

   B: _____ the matter, Julie?

   G: I _____ money too _____.

   B: Well, I always _____ a plan _____ I buy things.

   G: Maybe I _____ do the _____.

Listen & Speak 2 - A

1. **G:** Jason, are you _____? You _____ _____ good today.

   B: I have a _____.

   G: That's too bad. I _____ you _____ _____ a doctor.

   B: You're _____. Thank you.

2. **G:** You look _____. What's _____ _____?

   B: I'm _____ _____ tomorrow's history quiz. _____ should I _____?

   G: I think you _____ _____ your textbook again.

   B: That's a good _____.

3. **B:** I'm so _____.

   G: Why?

   B: I don't sleep well _____ _____.

   G: _____ _____ you should drink _____ _____ _____ warm milk _____ you sleep. It will _____.

   B: Okay, I _____ _____.

해석

1. G: 걱정이 있어 보여, Sam. 무슨 일 있니?
   B: 요즘 아침에 알람을 못 들어.
   G: 네 시계와 스마트폰에 알람을 맞춰 놓는 게 어때?
   B: 좋은 생각이야.

2. G: 휴, 어떻게 해야 하지?
   B: 무슨 일인데, Julie?
   G: 나는 돈을 너무 빨리 써.
   B: 음, 난 항상 물건을 사기 전에 계획을 세워.
   G: 나도 똑같이 해야 할 것 같아.

1. G: Jason, 괜찮니? 오늘 안 좋아 보여.
   B: 감기에 걸렸어.
   G: 그거 참 안됐구나. 내 생각에 너는 병원에 가 봐야 할 것 같아.
   B: 네 말이 맞아. 고마워.

2. G: 걱정 있어 보여. 무슨 일이야?
   B: 내일 역사 시험이 걱정돼. 어떻게 해야 하지?
   G: 내 생각에 너는 교과서를 다시 읽어야 할 것 같아.
   B: 좋은 생각이야.

3. B: 나 너무 피곤해.
   G: 왜?
   B: 요즘 잠을 잘 못 자.
   G: 내 생각에는 너는 잠을 자기 전에 따뜻한 우유 한 잔을 마셔야 할 것 같아. 그것은 도움이 될 거야.
   B: 알았어, 한번 해 볼게.

Conversation A

B: This is a _____ of book. I write my _____, weekly, and _____ plans here. I also write important dates _____ my friends' birthdays and homework _____ _____ here. Every night, I _____ this for the next day. Do you want _____ _____ things _____? Then I think you _____ _____ this.

Conversation B

Hana: What's the _____, Jiho?

Jiho: I _____ _____ my uniform. I _____ I have soccer practice today.

Hana: Again?

Jiho: My _____ year in middle school is _____ _____ my _____ year, and I often forget things.

Hana: I think _____ _____ _____ a planner. Here's _____.

Jiho: Oh, _____ I see it?

Hana: Sure. I write my class _____ and _____ in my planner.

Jiho: That's great. _____ I _____ buy one.

Wrap Up - ❶

W: _____ the matter, Sam? _____ you _____?

B: Ms. Green, I think I _____ _____ _____.

W: Did you go to the _____ _____?

B: Yes. She said I _____ _____ go to the hospital. _____ I _____ school now?

W: Okay, Sam. I'll _____ your mom and _____ _____ about it.

Wrap Up - ❷

B: I'm so _____.

G: Why? Is it _____ _____ the dance contest?

B: Yes. I practiced _____ many days, but I'm _____ nervous. What _____ I _____?

G: I _____ you _____ practice _____ _____ _____ your family. It will be very _____.

B: That's _____ _____. Thank you.

해석

B: 이것은 일종의 책이야. 나는 여기에 매일, 매주, 그리고 월간 계획을 써. 나는 또한 여기에 내 친구들의 생일이나 숙제 예정일과 같은 중요한 날짜를 적어. 매일 밤, 나는 다음 날을 위해 이것을 확인해. 무언가를 쉽게 기억하고 싶니? 그러면 내 생각에 너는 이것을 사용해야 할 것 같아.

하나: 무슨 일 있니, 지호야?
지호: 나는 내 유니폼을 가져오지 않았어. 오늘 축구 연습이 있다는 걸 잊고 있었어.
하나: 또?
지호: 중학교 2학년은 1학년보다 더 바쁘고, 나는 종종 어떤 것들을 잊어버려.
하나: 내 생각에는 너는 일정 계획표를 사용해야 할 것 같아. 여기 내 것이 있어.
지호: 오, 내가 봐도 될까?
하나: 물론. 나는 일정 계획표에 나의 수업 일정과 약속을 적어.
지호: 정말 좋구나. 나도 하나 사야 할까 봐.

W: 무슨 일이야, Sam? 어디 아파?
B: Green 선생님, 제가 감기에 걸린 것 같아요.
W: 보건 선생님한테 갔었니?
B: 네. 보건 선생님이 병원에 갈 필요가 있다고 하셨어요. 지금 하교를 해도 될까요?
W: 그럼, Sam. 내가 어머니한테 전화해서 그것에 대해 말할게.

B: 나 너무 긴장돼.
G: 왜? 댄스 경연 대회 때문이니?
B: 응. 며칠 동안 연습을 했지만 여전히 긴장돼. 어떻게 해야 하지?
G: 내 생각에 너는 가족 앞에서 연습을 해야 할 것 같아. 그것은 아주 도움이 될 거야.
B: 좋은 생각이야. 고마워.

01 다음 대화의 밑줄 친 말과 바꾸어 쓸 수 있는 것은?

> A: You look worried today. <u>What's the matter?</u>
> B: My puppy is sick.

① What's wrong?　　② What about you?
③ How are you doing?　④ What do you do?
⑤ What are you doing?

02 다음 대화의 빈칸에 알맞은 것은?

> A: I have a bad cold.
> B: _____

① You'd better eat less.
② You'd better study harder.
③ You'd better go to bed late.
④ You'd better go to see a doctor.
⑤ You'd better get up late.

03 다음 중 의도하는 바가 나머지 넷과 <u>다른</u> 것은?

① What's wrong with Jinsu?
② What do you think of Jinsu?
③ What's the matter with Jinsu?
④ What's the problem with Jinsu?
⑤ Is something wrong with Jinsu?

04 다음 대화의 ⓐ~ⓓ를 자연스러운 대화가 되도록 바르게 배열하시오.

> ⓐ Oh, you are right.
> ⓑ No. I have a bad cold.
> ⓒ You should see a doctor.
> ⓓ You look sick. Are you okay?

➡ _____

see a doctor 병원에 가다

[01~05] 다음 대화를 읽고, 물음에 답하시오.

> Hana: ⓐ<u>What's the matter, Jiho?</u>
>
> Jiho: I didn't bring my uniform. I forgot I have soccer practice today.
>
> Hana: Again?
>
> Jiho: My second year in middle school is ⓑ<u>busy</u> than my first year, and I often forget things.
>
> Hana: ⓒ<u>I think you should use a planner.</u> Here's mine.
>
> Jiho: Oh, can I see ⓓ<u>it</u>?
>
> Hana: Sure. I write my class schedule and appointment in my planner.
>
> Jiho: That's great. Maybe I should buy one.

서답형

01 다음 대화의 밑줄 친 ⓐ와 같은 의미가 되도록 빈칸에 알맞은 말을 쓰시오.

> What's the _____, Jiho?

➡ _____

서답형

02 위 대화의 밑줄 친 ⓑ를 알맞은 형태로 고쳐 쓰시오.

➡ _____

위 대화의 밑줄 친 ⓒ와 바꿔 쓸 수 있는 것은?

① Do you think I should use a planner?
② Do you want to use a planner?
③ Why don't you use a planner?
④ Why do you use a planner?
⑤ If I were you, I wouldn't use a planner.

서답형

04 위 대화의 밑줄 친 ⓓ가 가리키는 것을 쓰시오.

➡ _____

05 위 대화를 읽고, 답할 수 <u>없는</u> 질문은?

① What didn't Jiho bring today?
② Does Jiho often forget things?
③ Where does Jiho practice soccer?
④ What does Hana think Jiho should use?
⑤ Does Hana write her class schedule in her planner?

[06~09] 다음 대화를 읽고, 물음에 답하시오.

> G: You looked worried. What's going __ⓐ__ ?
>
> B: I'm worried about tomorrow's history quiz. _____ⓑ_____
>
> G: ⓒ<u>I think you should read your textbook again.</u>
>
> B: That's a good idea..

서답형

06 위 대화의 빈칸 ⓐ에 알맞은 것을 쓰시오.

➡ _____

위 대화의 빈칸 ⓑ에 알맞은 것은?

① What is it?
② What's the matter?
③ What's wrong?
④ What should I do?
⑤ What happened?

08 위 대화의 밑줄 친 ⓒ를 다음과 같이 바꿔 쓸 때 빈칸에 알맞은 말을 쓰시오.

> You'd _____ _____ your textbook again.

09 위 대화를 읽고, 다음 질문에 완전한 문장으로 답하시오.

> Q: What does the girl think the boy should read?
>
> A: _____

[10~12] 다음 대화를 읽고, 물음에 답하시오.

> B: I'm so nervous. (①)
> G: Why? Is it because _____ⓐ_____ the dance contest? (②)
> B: Yes. I practiced for many days, but I'm still nervous. (③)
> G: I think you should practice in front _____ⓑ_____ your family. ⓒIt will be very helpful. (④)
> B: That's a good idea. Thank you. (⑤)

10 위 대화의 ①~⑤ 중 주어진 문장이 들어갈 알맞은 곳은?

> What should I do?

①   ②   ③   ④   ⑤

11 위 대화의 빈칸 ⓐ와 ⓑ에 공통으로 알맞은 말을 쓰시오.

➡ _____

12 위 대화의 밑줄 친 ⓒ가 가리키는 말을 우리말로 구체적으로 쓰시오.

➡ _____

[13~15] 다음 대화를 읽고, 물음에 답하시오.

> G: You look worried, Sam. _____ⓐ_____
> B: I don't hear my alarm in the morning these days.
> G: _____ⓑ_____ set the alarm on your clock and on your smartphone?
> B: ⓒThat's a good idea.

13 위 대화의 빈칸 ⓐ에 들어갈 말로 적절하지 <u>않은</u> 것은?

① What's wrong?
② What's the problem?
③ What happened to you?
④ What's the matter with you?
⑤ What do you hope to do?

14 위 대화의 빈칸 ⓑ에 알맞은 것은?

① How about   ② How come
③ What about   ④ What makes you
⑤ Why don't you

15 위 대화의 밑줄 친 ⓒ와 바꿔 쓸 수 <u>없는</u> 것은?

① I think so, too.
② I'm afraid I can't.
③ I'm with you on that.
④ That sounds good.
⑤ You're right.

[01~03] 다음 대화를 읽고, 물음에 답하시오.

> G: You look worried. <u>What's going on?</u>
> B: I'm worried about tomorrow's history quiz. What should I do?
> G: ⓑI think you should read your textbook again.
> B: That's a good idea.

01 위 대화의 밑줄 친 ⓐ와 바꿔 쓸 수 있는 표현을 두 가지 이상 쓰시오.

➡ _____

_____

위 대화의 밑줄 친 ⓑ를 다음과 같이 바꿔 쓸 때 빈칸에 알맞은 말을 쓰시오.

> _____ _____ you read your textbook again?

03 What is the boy worried about? Answer in Korean.

➡ _____

[04~05] 다음 대화를 읽고, 물음에 답하시오.

> G: Jason, are you okay? You don't look good today.
> B: I have a cold.
> G: <u>That's too bad.</u> I think you should see a doctor.
> B: You're right. Thank you.

04 위 대화의 밑줄 친 ⓐ와 바꿔 쓸 수 있는 표현을 쓰시오.

➡ _____

_____

05 What does the girl think Jason should do? Answer in English.

➡ _____

[06~09] 다음 대화를 읽고, 물음에 답하시오.

> W: What's the (A)[wrong / matter], Sam? Are you sick?
> B: Ms. Green, ⓐ(cold / a / have / I / I / think).
> W: Did you go to the school nurse?
> B: Yes. She said I need to go to the hospital. (B)[Can / Should] I leave school now?
> W: Okay, Sam. I'll call your mom and tell her about ⓑit.

06 위 대화의 괄호 ⓐ를 의미가 통하도록 단어를 바르게 배열하시오.

➡ _____

07 위 대화의 괄호 (A)와 (B)에서 알맞은 것을 골라 쓰시오.

(A) _____ (B) _____

08 What did the school nurse say to Sam? Answer in English.

➡ _____

09 위 대화의 밑줄 친 ⓑ가 가리키는 것을 우리말로 쓰시오.

➡ _____

Grammar

교과서

① to부정사의 형용사적 용법

- You will have more work **to do**. 너는 할 일이 더 많아질 것이다.
- He has many books **to read**. 그는 읽을 책을 많이 가지고 있다.
- Would you like something **to drink**? 마실 것 좀 드릴까요?

- to부정사가 명사나 대명사를 뒤에서 꾸며주는 형용사의 역할을 할 때는 '~할', '~해야 할'로 해석한다.
  - Seho needs some water **to drink**. 세호는 마실 물이 필요하다.
  - He had no friends **to help** him. 그는 자기를 도와줄 친구가 하나도 없었다.
  - You feel that you have nothing **to wear**. 너는 입을 것이 아무것도 없다고 느낀다.
- **명사+to부정사+전치사**: 수식받는 명사가 전치사의 목적어인 경우는 to부정사 뒤에 반드시 전치사를 쓴다.
  - I need some paper **to write on**. 나는 쓸 종이가 좀 필요하다.
  - She's looking for a chair **to sit on**. 그녀는 앉을 의자를 찾고 있다.
  - They will need a house **to live in**. 그들은 살 집이 필요할 것이다.
  - He needs a friend **to talk to**. 그는 말할 친구가 필요하다.
  - She has a pen **to write with**. 그녀는 쓸 펜을 가지고 있다.
- *cf.* **-thing+형용사+to부정사**: -thing으로 끝나는 부정대명사는 형용사가 뒤에서 수식하며, 이를 다시 to부정사가 뒤에서 수식한다.
  - I want something **hot to drink**. 나는 뜨거운 마실 것을 원한다.

핵심 Check

1. 다음 괄호 안에서 알맞은 것을 고르시오.
   (1) It's time (go / to go) to school.
   (2) Jack has a lot of friends (helping / to help).
   (3) Give me a pen (to write / to write with).
   (4) Would you like something (to drink cold / cold to drink)?

2. 다음 괄호 안에서 알맞은 것을 고르시오.
   (1) There are so many places _____ _____ in my town. (visit)
   (2) I have something important _____ _____ you. (tell)
   (3) Is there nobody _____ _____ to my story? (listen)

② 접속사 that

- I think **that** using my time to prepare for my future is important.
  나는 미래를 준비하기 위해 시간을 사용하는 것이 중요하다고 생각한다.

- He knows **that** I want to be a writer. 그는 내가 작가가 되고 싶어 한다는 것을 알고 있다.

- Imagine **that** you can fly like a bird. 새처럼 날 수 있다고 상상해 보라.

■ 접속사는 절과 절을 연결하는 역할을 하므로 접속사 that은 「주어+동사+that+주어+동사 ~」의 형태로 쓰인다.

- I hope **that** she likes the flowers. 그녀가 그 꽃들을 좋아하면 좋겠어.

- I think **that** he is a genius. 나는 그가 천재라고 생각해.

■ 접속사 that이 이끄는 절은 문장 안에서 주어, 목적어, 보어의 역할을 하므로 이때 that을 명사절 접속사라 한다. 목적어 역할을 하는 명사절을 이끄는 that은 생략 가능하다.

- **That** he plays soccer well is true. [주어 역할] 그가 축구를 잘한다는 것은 사실이다.

- He knows (**that**) I got up early this morning. [목적어 역할]
  그는 내가 오늘 아침에 일찍 일어났다는 것을 알고 있다.

- My problem is **that** I'm poor at English. [보어 역할] 내 문제는 내가 영어를 못한다는 것이다.

cf. that은 '저것'을 뜻하는 지시대명사나 지시형용사로 사용될 수도 있으므로, 문장 안에서 명사 역할을 하는 접속사 용법과 구분하도록 한다.

- I need **that** pen. [지시형용사] 나는 저 펜이 필요해.

- I want **that** blue shirt. 나는 저 파란색 셔츠를 원해.

■ 접속사 that 이하의 내용이 부정일 때, that 앞에 있는 동사를 부정으로 만든다.

- He doesn't think **that** she is rich. 그는 그녀가 부자라고 생각하지 않는다.

- We don't hope **that** you will like it. 우리는 네가 그것을 좋아하기를 바라지 않는다.

핵심 Check

3. 다음 괄호 안에서 알맞은 것을 고르시오.

(1) I think (what / that) he is honest.

(2) I know (that / which) she was a teacher.

4. 다음 문장에서 that이 들어갈 수 있는 곳에 V표 하시오.

(1) I heard she would go to the Philippines.

(2) Our teacher thought we were good at math.

(3) Miss Susan says the Han River is beautiful.

01 다음 문장의 빈칸에 알맞지 <u>않은</u> 것은?

> be good at ~을 잘하다

> I _____ that Jane is good at playing the piano.

① think ② know ③ mind
④ heard ⑤ believe

02 다음 괄호 안에 주어진 단어를 바르게 배열하시오.

(1) There are _____ _____ _____ _____.
(do / things / to / many)

(2) He is the only person _____ _____ _____.
(help / to / us)

03 다음 우리말과 같도록 괄호 안의 단어를 바르게 배열하여 문장을 완성하시오.

(1) 나는 Jenny가 집에 있다고 생각한다.
(at / is / home / Jenny / that)
➡ I think _____.

(2) 그녀는 그가 돌아올 거라고 믿었다.
(he / back / believed / come / that / would)
➡ She _____.

(3) 나는 Alice가 Mason을 좋아할 거라고 생각하지 않았다.
(Mason / didn't / Alice / think / like / that / would)
➡ I _____.

04 다음 우리말과 일치하도록 빈칸에 알맞은 말을 쓰시오.

(1) 우리는 계획을 바꿀 시간이 없다.
➡ We have no time _____ _____ the schedule.

(2) 그는 우리나라를 방문한 최초의 미국인이었다.
➡ He was the first American _____ _____ our country.

(3) 그는 풀어야 할 수학 문제가 많다.
➡ He has a lot of math problems _____ _____.

01 다음 문장의 빈칸에 알맞은 것은?

> We want to introduce _____ water.

① saving a way　　② to save a way
③ a way save　　④ a way saving
⑤ a way to save

중요

02 다음 문장의 빈칸에 알맞지 <u>않은</u> 것은?

> I _____ that he is sick today.

① know　　② believe
③ heard　　④ think
⑤ made

서답형

03 다음 빈칸에 공통으로 알맞은 말을 쓰시오.

> • He knows _____ the room is clean.
> • My mom said _____ the story was true.

04 다음 문장의 빈칸에 알맞은 것은?

> I bought some books _____.

① to read at night
② to drink after running
③ to eat in the morning
④ to wear after swimming
⑤ to keep in the refrigerator

중요

05 다음 중 밑줄 친 부분의 쓰임이 나머지와 <u>다른</u> 하나는?

① It's time <u>to say</u> goodbye.
② I have a lot of work <u>to do</u>.
③ She needs a chair <u>to sit</u> on.
④ Please give me something <u>to eat</u>.
⑤ When does the snow start <u>to melt</u>?

서답형

06 다음 문장의 빈칸에 알맞은 말을 쓰시오.

> 나는 그가 현명한 아빠가 될 것이라고 믿는다.
> ➡ I _____ _____ he will be a wise father.

07 다음 밑줄 친 that 중 쓰임이 <u>다른</u> 하나는?

① I think <u>that</u> the movie was terrible.
② I know <u>that</u> Sally doesn't have a job.
③ I think <u>that</u> bag is yours.
④ I hope <u>that</u> he will be my boyfriend.
⑤ I know <u>that</u> she will go abroad to study.

서답형

08 다음 두 문장을 한 문장으로 바꿀 때, 빈칸에 알맞은 말을 쓰시오.

> I will bring some snacks. + I will eat them during the hike.
> ➡ I will bring some snacks _____ _____ during the hike.

09 다음 문장의 빈칸에 알맞은 것은?

> She has good news _____ you.

① tell ② to tell
③ tells ④ telling
⑤ to telling

10 다음 밑줄 친 that 중 생략할 수 없는 것은?

① I think that you are so beautiful.
② I hope that I will get good grades.
③ I didn't know that Jenny was sick.
④ I believe that he will be a great engineer.
⑤ I know that man is Jack's father.

서답형

11 다음 우리말에 맞도록 빈칸에 알맞은 말을 쓰시오.

> Ann은 그 없이는 살 수 없을 것이라는 사실을 몰랐다.
> ➡ Ann _____ _____ _____ she wouldn't be able to live without him.

12 다음 중 밑줄 친 부분의 쓰임이 다른 하나는?

① I have the project to finish.
② I need some food to eat.
③ We went out to have lunch.
④ She has no money to buy a new dress.
⑤ I have a lot of homework to do today.

서답형

13 다음 우리말과 같도록 주어진 어휘를 바르게 배열하시오.

> 나는 진우가 훌륭한 리더가 될 것이라고 생각한다.
> (Jinwoo / great / be / will / that / think / I / a / leader).

➡ _____

14 다음 중 어법상 어색한 것은?

① He has no friends to talk to.
② I have no time to play.
③ She's looking for something reading.
④ I need something to write on.
⑤ I have lots of homework to do.

서답형

15 다음 우리말과 뜻이 같도록 주어진 단어를 알맞게 배열하시오.

> 너에게는 읽을 흥미로운 것이 있니?
> (interesting / something / you / do / have / read / to)

➡ _____

16 다음 중 밑줄 친 that의 쓰임이 다른 하나는?

① I think that honesty is the most important thing.
② I think that Jinny has a dog.
③ Do you know that woman over there?
④ Susan thinks that he is very smart.
⑤ Runa believes that her hometown is New York.

17 다음 문장의 괄호 안의 말을 바르게 배열한 것은?

> She needs (paper, to, on, write).

① on paper to write
② paper on to write
③ to write paper on
④ paper to write on
⑤ on write to paper

[18~19] 다음 괄호 안에 주어진 단어를 이용하여 우리말에 맞도록 문장을 완성하시오.

서답형
18

> 차가운 마실 것 좀 주세요. (something)
> ➡ Give me _____ .

서답형
19

> 그녀는 앉을 의자가 필요하다. (sit)
> ➡ She needs _____ .

20 다음 중 밑줄 친 that과 쓰임이 같은 것은?

> He thinks that science is a useful subject.

① Look at that old temple.
② Where did you find that pencil?
③ He walked this way and that way.
④ I am not that interested in music.
⑤ I believe that everything will be fine.

21 다음 빈칸에 들어갈 말로 알맞지 <u>않은</u> 것은?

> I think _____ .

① it is easy
② he is honest
③ is she fine
④ that he likes you
⑤ that she is taller than you

서답형
22 다음 주어진 단어를 이용하여 우리말을 영어로 바꿔 쓰시오.

> 나는 James가 여행을 갔다고 생각한다.
> (think, go on a trip)

➡ _____

 23 다음 중 밑줄 친 부분의 쓰임이 바르지 <u>않은</u> 것은?

① There are no benches to sit on.
② I have no money to give you.
③ Judy has a lot of friends to talk.
④ She doesn't have a house to live in.
⑤ Do you have a pen to write with?

서답형
24 다음 우리말과 뜻이 같도록 주어진 단어를 이용하여 영작하시오.

> 그 소녀에게는 그 개에게 먹일 음식이 좀 있다.
> (have, some, feed)

➡ _____

[01~02] 다음 빈칸에 공통으로 알맞은 말을 쓰시오.

01
- Mike had no time _____ do his homework.
- We are going to buy a house _____ live in.

02
- I believe _____ the story is true.
- I'm reading the book _____ I bought yesterday.
- Does your mother know _____ boy in the room?

03 다음 두 문장을 to부정사를 이용하여 한 문장으로 고쳐 쓰시오.

(1) I bought some cookies. I will eat them in the afternoon.
➡ _____

(2) They need four chairs. They'll sit on the chair.
➡ _____

04 다음 주어진 두 문장을 that을 사용하여 한 문장으로 만드시오.

(1) My brother says something. He didn't eat the bananas.
➡ _____

(2) They think something. They are proud of themselves.
➡ _____

05 다음 〈보기〉에서 알맞은 단어를 골라 문장을 완성하시오.

보기
sit eat drink talk buy wear

(1) I'm hungry. I need some food _____ _____.

(2) I'm very thirsty. I need something _____ _____.

(3) There's no chair here. I need a chair to _____ _____.

(4) Tony feels lonely. He needs friends to _____ _____.

06 다음 우리말과 같도록 괄호 안의 단어를 바르게 배열하시오.

(1) 나는 네가 모든 것을 할 수 있다고 생각한다.
(everything / do / you / can / that)
➡ I think _____.

(2) 너는 그녀가 예쁘다고 생각하니?
(is / think / she / pretty / that / you)
➡ Do _____?

07 다음 문장에서 어법상 어색한 부분을 찾아 바르게 고쳐 쓰시오.

(1) He needs a pen to write.
_____ ➡ _____

(2) There are many places visiting in Paris.
_____ ➡ _____

08 다음 괄호 안에 주어진 단어와 that을 이용하여 바르게 배열하시오.

(1) (is / wife / know / I / a / wise / she)

➡ _____ that _____.

(2) (Chinese / I / is / think / he)

➡ _____ that _____.

(3) (we / we / world / the / can / change / believe)

➡ _____ that _____.

09 다음 우리말과 같도록 주어진 단어를 바르게 배열하시오.

그녀는 입을 뭔가가 필요하다.
(put / something / on / she / needs / to)

➡ _____

10 다음 괄호 안에 주어진 단어를 이용하여 우리말을 영어로 옮기시오.

(1) 그녀는 딸이 아프다고 생각한다.
(think, that, sick)

➡ _____

(2) 나는 Nick이 파티에 올 것이라고 믿지 않는다.
(believe, that)

➡ _____

11 다음 우리말에 맞게 빈칸에 알맞은 말을 쓰시오.

나는 묵을 호텔을 찾고 있다.
➡ I'm looking for _____ _____ _____ _____ _____.

12 다음 괄호 안에 주어진 단어를 이용하여 우리말을 영어로 옮기시오.

(1) 그녀는 가수가 되려는 강한 욕망을 갖고 있다.
(strong desire, be, singer)

➡ _____

(2) 우리는 이야기할 것이 있었다.
(something, talk about)

➡ _____

(3) 나는 쓸 종이를 한 장 원한다.
(want, write)

➡ _____

(4) 제게 뜨거운 마실 것을 좀 주십시오.
(please, something, drink)

➡ _____

13 다음 우리말을 괄호 안의 단어를 이용하여 영작하시오.

(1) 나는 나의 영어 선생님이 예쁘다고 생각한다.
(pretty)

➡ _____

(2) 많은 사람들은 지구가 둥글다고 믿는다.
(round)

➡ _____

14 다음 주어진 단어를 바르게 배열하여 문장을 완성하시오.

(1) (a / of / to / homework / I / do / have / lot)

➡ _____

(2) (family / your / is / to / introduce / turn / it / your)

➡ _____

Manage Your Time Well

Welcome to the new school year. In the second grade, you will have
more work to do. You need to manage your time well. How do you do
that?

Subin: I set small goals and achieve them every day. I do not say,
"I will master English." With such a big goal, I will probably put off
working on it until tomorrow, next week, or next month. Instead, I say,
"I will learn three new English words every day." I will achieve my big
goal, one step at a time.

work 일
manage 관리하다
well 잘
grade 학년
goal 목표
achieve 성취하다, 달성하다
master ~을 완전히 익히다
such 그런, 그러한
probably 아마(=perhaps)
instead 대신에
learn 배우다
step 걸음, 단계
at a time 한 번에

📎 확인문제

● 다음 문장이 본문의 내용과 일치하면 T, 일치하지 <u>않으면</u> F를 쓰시오.

1 First graders will have more work to do. ☐

2 In the second grade, you need to manage your time well. ☐

3 Subin sets big goals and achieves them every day. ☐

4 Subin does not say, "I will master English." ☐

5 Subin says "I will learn a lot of English words every day." ☐

6 Subin will achieve her big goal quickly. ☐

Minsu: When I do something, I give it my full attention. I used to read
SNS postings while I was doing my homework. It slowed me down
because I couldn't focus. Now, I put aside my smartphone when I
do my homework. It saves me a lot of time. These days, I finish my
homework quickly and enjoy my free time.

John: I regularly spend time working toward my dream. I want to
become a chef. Every Saturday morning, I go to cooking classes or
search for recipes. I think that using my time to prepare for my future
is important.

Time is a present. Everyone has the same present to spend every day.
Manage your time well, and you will be happier in the new school
year!

---

attention 주의, 집중

posting 포스팅, 게시 글

focus 집중하다

save 절약하다

finish 끝내다

regularly 규칙적으로

toward ~을 위하여

chef 요리사

cooking class 요리 강좌

recipe 요리[조리]법

future 미래

important 중요한

present 선물

everyone 모든 사람

every day 매일

확인문제

● 다음 문장이 본문의 내용과 일치하면 T, 일치하지 않으면 F를 쓰시오.

1 Minsu used to read SNS postings while he was doing his homework. ☐

2 Minsu uses his smartphone when he does his homework. ☐

3 These days, Minsu finishes his homework quickly. ☐

4 John always spends time working for his dream. ☐

5 John wants to become a chef. ☐

6 John goes to cooking classes every morning. ☐

7 Everyone has different presents to spend every day. ☐

● 우리말을 참고하여 빈칸에 알맞은 말을 쓰시오.

1 _____ _____ the new school year.

2 _____ the _____ grade, you will have more work _____ _____.

3 You _____ _____ manage your time _____.

4 _____ do you _____ that?

5 Subin: I _____ small goals and _____ them every day.

6 I do not say, "I _____ _____ English."

7 _____ such a big goal, I will probably _____ _____ working on it _____ tomorrow, next week, _____ next month.

8 _____, I say, "I _____ _____ three new English words _____ _____."

9 I _____ _____ my big goal, one step _____ _____ _____.

10 Minsu: _____ I do something, I give it my _____ _____.

11 I _____ _____ _____ SNS postings _____ I was doing my homework.

1 새 학년이 된 걸 환영해.

2 2학년에서, 여러분은 할 일이 더 많을 거야.

3 여러분은 시간을 잘 관리할 필요가 있어.

4 여러분은 시간 관리를 어떻게 하는가?

5 수빈: 나는 작은 목표들을 세우고 매일 그것들을 성취해.

6 나는 "나는 영어를 마스터할 거야."라고 말하지 않아.

7 그렇게 큰 목표를 가지면, 나는 아마 그것을 위해 노력하는 걸 내일, 다음 주, 혹은 다음 달까지 미룰 거야.

8 대신에 나는 "나는 매일 세 개의 새로운 영어 단어를 배울 거야." 라고 말해.

9 나는 한 번에 한 단계씩 나의 큰 목표를 달성할 거야.

10 민수: 나는 무언가를 할 때 그것에 모든 주의를 기울여.

11 나는 숙제를 하는 동안 SNS 게시 글을 읽곤 했어.

12 It _____ me down _____ I couldn't focus.

13 Now, I _____ _____ my smartphone _____ I do my homework.

14 It saves me _____ _____ _____ time.

15 _____ _____ , I finish my homework quickly and enjoy my _____ _____ .

16 John: I regularly _____ time _____ toward my dream.

17 I want _____ _____ a chef.

18 _____ Saturday morning, I go to cooking _____ or _____ _____ recipes.

19 I think _____ using my time _____ _____ for my future is important.

20 Time is a _____ .

21 Everyone _____ the same present _____ _____ every day.

22 _____ your time well, _____ you will _____ _____ in the new school year!

---

12 집중할 수 없었기 때문에 그것은 나의 속도를 늦추었어.

13 지금 나는 숙제를 할 때 스마트폰을 한쪽에 치워 놔.

14 그렇게 하면 시간이 많이 절약돼.

15 요즈음, 나는 숙제를 빨리 끝내고 자유 시간을 즐겨.

16 John: 나는 내 꿈을 위해 노력하며 규칙적으로 시간을 사용해.

17 나는 요리사가 되고 싶어.

18 토요일 아침마다 나는 요리 강습에 가거나 요리법을 찾아봐.

19 나는 나의 미래를 준비하기 위해 시간을 쓰는 것이 중요하다고 생각해.

20 시간은 선물이다.

21 모든 사람은 매일 소비할 똑같은 선물을 가지고 있다.

22 시간을 잘 관리하면 여러분은 새 학년에 더 행복해질 것이다!

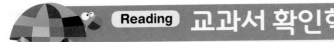

• 우리말을 참고하여 본문을 영작하시오.

1 새 학년이 된 걸 환영해.

➡ _____

2 2학년에서, 여러분은 할 일이 더 많을 거야.

➡ _____

3 여러분은 시간을 잘 관리할 필요가 있어.

➡ _____

4 여러분은 시간 관리를 어떻게 하는가?

➡ _____

5 수빈: 나는 작은 목표를 세우고 매일 그것들을 성취해.

➡ _____

6 나는 "나는 영어를 마스터할 거야."라고 말하지 않아.

➡ _____

7 그렇게 큰 목표를 가지면, 나는 아마 그것을 위해 노력하는 걸 내일, 다음 주, 혹은 다음 달까지 미룰 거야.

➡ _____

8 대신에 나는 "나는 매일 세 개의 새로운 영어 단어를 배울 거야."라고 말해.

➡ _____

9 나는 한 번에 한 단계씩 나의 큰 목표를 달성할 거야.

➡ _____

10 민수: 나는 무언가를 할 때 그것에 모든 주의를 기울여.

➡ _____

11 나는 숙제를 하는 동안 SNS 게시 글을 읽곤 했어.

➡ _____

12▶ 집중할 수 없었기 때문에 그것은 나의 속도를 늦추었어.

➡ _____

13▶ 지금 나는 숙제를 할 때 스마트폰을 한쪽에 치워 놔.

➡ _____

14▶ 그렇게 하면 시간이 많이 절약돼.

➡ _____

15▶ 요즈음, 나는 숙제를 빨리 끝내고 자유 시간을 즐겨.

➡ _____

16▶ John: 나는 내 꿈을 위해 노력하며 규칙적으로 시간을 사용해.

➡ _____

17▶ 나는 요리사가 되고 싶어.

➡ _____

18▶ 토요일 아침마다 나는 요리 강습에 가거나 요리법을 찾아봐.

➡ _____

19▶ 나는 나의 미래를 준비하기 위해 시간을 쓰는 것이 중요하다고 생각해.

➡ _____

20▶ 시간은 선물이다.

➡ _____

21▶ 모든 사람은 매일 소비할 똑같은 선물을 가지고 있다.

➡ _____

22▶ 시간을 잘 관리하면 여러분은 새 학년에 더 행복해질 것이다!

➡ _____

[01~05] 다음 글을 읽고, 물음에 답하시오.

Subin: I ⓐ_____ small goals and achieve ⓑthem every day. I do not say, "I will master English." With such a big goal, I will probably ⓒput off working on it until tomorrow, next week, or next month. ⓓ_____, I say, "I will learn three new English words every day." I will achieve my big goal, one step at a time.

01 위 글의 빈칸 ⓐ에 알맞은 것은?

① put   ② set
③ get   ④ take
⑤ win

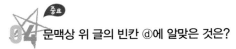

02 위 글의 밑줄 친 ⓑ가 가리키는 말을 찾아 영어로 쓰시오.

➡ _____

03 위 글의 밑줄 친 ⓒ와 바꿔 쓸 수 있는 것은?

① quit   ② finish
③ carry   ④ postpone
⑤ establish

04 문맥상 위 글의 빈칸 ⓓ에 알맞은 것은?

① So   ② However
③ Instead   ④ Besides
⑤ Therefore

05 위 글의 내용으로 보아 수빈이에 대한 진술이 올바른 것은?

① 매일 큰 목표들을 성취한다.
② 영어를 빨리 익히고 싶어 한다.
③ 영어 공부하는 것을 자주 미룬다.
④ 매일 많은 영어 단어를 배우고 싶어 한다.
⑤ 차근차근 그녀의 큰 목표를 성취하기를 원한다.

[06~10] 다음 글을 읽고, 물음에 답하시오.

Welcome ⓐ_____ the new school year. In the second grade, you will have more work ⓑto do. You need to manage your time well. How do you do that?
John: I regularly spend time ⓒwork toward my dream. I want to become a chef. Every Saturday morning, I go to cooking classes or search for recipes. I think ⓓ_____ using my time to prepare for my future is important.

06 위 글의 빈칸 ⓐ에 알맞은 말을 쓰시오.

➡ _____

07 위 글의 밑줄 친 ⓑ와 쓰임이 같은 것은?

① I have no pen to write with.
② My dream is to be a doctor.
③ I did my best to pass the test.
④ They want to go hiking together.
⑤ I went to the bakery to buy some bread.

서답형

08 위 글의 밑줄 친 ⓒ를 알맞은 형태로 고쳐 쓰시오.

➡ _____

09 위 글의 빈칸 ⓓ에 알맞은 것은?

① as　　　　　② if
③ that　　　　④ while
⑤ when

10 위 글의 내용으로 보아 John에 대한 진술이 잘못된 것은?

① 꿈을 위해 시간을 규칙적으로 사용한다.
② 요리사가 되고 싶어 한다.
③ 토요일 아침마다 요리 수업을 듣는다.
④ 매일 요리법을 찾아본다.
⑤ 미래를 준비하기 위해 시간을 사용하는 것이 중요하다고 생각한다.

[11~16] 다음 글을 읽고, 물음에 답하시오.

Minsu: When I do something, ⓐI give it my full attention. (①) I ⓑ _____ read SNS postings while I was doing my homework. (②) ⓒIt slowed me down _____ⓓ I couldn't focus. (③) Now, I put aside my smartphone when I do my homework. (④) These days, I finish my homework quickly and enjoy my free time. (⑤)

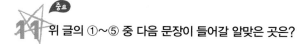

11 위 글의 ①~⑤ 중 다음 문장이 들어갈 알맞은 곳은?

| It saves me a lot of time. |

①　　②　　③　　④　　⑤

서답형

12 위 글의 밑줄 친 ⓐ를 다음과 같이 바꿔 쓸 때 빈칸에 알맞은 말을 쓰시오.

| I give my full attention _____ it |

➡ _____

13 위 글의 빈칸 ⓑ에 문맥상 알맞은 것은?

① could　　　② might
③ should　　　④ ought to
⑤ used to

서답형

14 위 글의 밑줄 친 ⓒ가 가리키는 것을 우리말로 구체적으로 쓰시오.

➡ _____

15 문맥상 위 글의 빈칸 ⓓ에 알맞은 것은?

① if　　　　　② while
③ when　　　④ though
⑤ because

16 위 글의 내용으로 보아 민수에 대해 알 수 없는 것은?

① 어떤 일을 할 때 그것에 모든 주의를 기울인다.
② 숙제하는 동안 SNS 게시 글을 읽곤 했다.
③ 스마트폰을 이용해서 숙제를 하곤 했다.
④ 지금은 숙제할 때 스마트폰을 한쪽에 치워 놓는다.
⑤ 요즈음은 숙제를 빨리 끝낸다.

[17~21] 다음 글을 읽고, 물음에 답하시오.

I regularly spend time working ⓐ_____ my dream. I want ⓑbecome a chef. Every Saturday morning, I go to cooking ⓒclasses or search ⓓ_____ recipes. ⓔI think that using my time to prepare for my future are important.

※ I = John

17 위 글의 빈칸 ⓐ에 알맞은 것은?

① against ② within
③ toward ④ through
⑤ along

서답형

18 위 글의 밑줄 친 ⓑ를 알맞은 형태로 고쳐 쓰시오.

➡ _____

19 위 글의 밑줄 친 ⓒ와 같은 의미로 쓰인 것은?

① I will take a class on play.
② We were in the same class at school.
③ He is the tallest boy in the class.
④ He is ahead of his class in English.
⑤ The class listened and took notes.

20 위 글의 빈칸 ⓓ에 알맞은 것은?

① up ② for
③ in ④ into
⑤ with

서답형

21 위 글의 밑줄 친 ⓔ에서 어법상 틀린 부분을 찾아 바르게 고쳐 쓰시오.

_____ ➡ _____

[22~26] 다음 글을 읽고, 물음에 답하시오.

Welcome to the new school year. In the second ⓐgrade, you will have more work to do. You need to _____ⓑ_____ your time well. How do you do that?

Subin: I set small goals and achieve them every day. I do not say, "I will master English." With such a big goal, I will probably put _____ⓒ_____ working on it _____ⓓ_____ tomorrow, next week, or next month. Instead, I say, "I will learn three new English words every day." I will achieve my big goal, one step at a time.

22 위 글의 밑줄 친 ⓐ와 같은 의미로 쓰인 것은?

① I got a terrible grade in math.
② He is one grade above me.
③ His grade is almost at the bottom.
④ She's not in the first grade as a painter.
⑤ 70% of pupils got grade C or above.

23 위 글의 빈칸 ⓑ에 알맞은 것은?

① save ② spend
③ create ④ manage
⑤ design

24 위 글의 빈칸 ⓒ에 알맞은 것은?

① on
② out
③ down
④ up
⑤ off

25 위 글의 빈칸 ⓓ에 알맞은 것은?

① to
② within
③ until
④ during
⑤ among

서답형

26 위 글을 다음과 같이 요약할 때 빈칸에 알맞은 말을 쓰시오.

> Subin says, "I _____ small goals and _____ them every day. A _____ doesn't help me _____ it."

[27~32] 다음 글을 읽고, 물음에 답하시오.

> **Minsu:** When I do something, I give it my full ⓐ_____ . (①) I ⓑunderlined{used to} read SNS postings ⓒ_____ I was doing my homework. (②) Now, I put aside my smartphone when I do my homework. (③) It ⓓsaves me a lot of time. (④) These days, I finish my homework quickly and enjoy my free time. (⑤)

27 위 글의 ①~⑤ 중 다음 문장이 들어갈 알맞은 곳은?

> It slowed me down because I couldn't focus.

① ② ③ ④ ⑤

서답형

28 위 글의 빈칸 ⓐ에 다음 영영풀이에 해당하는 단어를 주어진 철자로 시작하여 쓰시오.

> the act of listening to, looking at, or thinking about something or someone carefully

➡ a_____

29 위 글의 밑줄 친 ⓑ와 바꿔 쓸 수 있는 것은?

① might
② could
③ should
④ would
⑤ ought to

30 위 글의 빈칸 ⓒ에 알맞은 것은?

① if
② since
③ because
④ though
⑤ while

31 위 글의 밑줄 친 ⓓ와 같은 의미로 쓰인 것은?

① I wanted to save my dog.
② She has to save this report to a file.
③ He saved many lives from the fire.
④ This is why we need to save energy.
⑤ You should save your work frequently.

서답형

32 위 글을 읽고, 다음 질문에 완전한 문장으로 답하시오.

> Q: These days, what does Minsu do after he finishes his homework quickly?
>
> A: _____

[01~06] 다음 글을 읽고, 물음에 답하시오.

Welcome to the new school year. In the second grade, ⓐ너는 할 일이 더 많을 거야. You need to manage your time well. How do you ⓑdo that?

Subin: I set small goals and achieve them every day. I do not say, "I will master English." With such a big goal, I will probably put off ⓒwork on it until tomorrow, next week, or next month. Instead, I say, "I will learn three new English words every day." ⓓI will achieve my big goal, one step at a time.

01 위 글의 밑줄 친 ⓐ의 우리말을 주어진 단어를 이용하여 영어로 옮기시오.

> (will / work / do)

➡ _____

02 위 글의 밑줄 친 ⓑ가 의미하는 것을 우리말로 쓰시오.

➡ _____

03 How often does Subin set small goals and achieve them? Answer in English.

➡ _____

04 위 글의 밑줄 친 ⓒ를 알맞은 형태로 고쳐 쓰시오.

➡ _____

05 How many new English words will Subin learn every day? Answer in English.

➡ _____

06 위 글의 밑줄 친 ⓓ를 우리말로 옮기시오.

➡ _____

[07~10] 다음 글을 읽고, 물음에 답하시오.

Minsu: When I do something, I give ⓐit my full attention. I (A)[used to / ought to] read SNS postings while I was doing my homework. It slowed me down (B) [though / because] I couldn't focus. Now, I put aside my smartphone when I do my homework. ⓑIt saves me a lot of time. These days, I finish my homework quickly and enjoy my free time.

07 위 글의 밑줄 친 ⓐit이 가리키는 것을 찾아 쓰시오.

➡ _____

08 위 글의 괄호 (A)와 (B)에서 알맞은 것을 골라 쓰시오.

(A) _____ (B) _____

09 위 글의 밑줄 친 ⓑIt이 가리키는 것을 우리말로 쓰시오.

➡ _____

10 What did Minsu use to do while he was doing his homework? Answer in English.

➡ _____

_____

[11~17] 다음 글을 읽고, 물음에 답하시오.

Welcome to the new school year. In the second grade, you will have more work (A) [doing / to do]. You need to manage your time well. How do you do that?

John: I regularly spend time (B)[working / to work] toward my dream. I want to become a chef. Every Saturday morning, I go to cooking classes or search for recipes. ⓐI think (　) using my time to prepare for my future (　) important.

Time is a present. Everyone has ⓑ(spend / same / to / the / present) every day. Manage your time well, and you will be happier in the new school year!

11 위 글의 괄호 (A)와 (B)에서 알맞은 것을 골라 쓰시오.

(A) _____ (B) _____

12 What do you need to do in the second grade? Answer in English.

➡ _____

13 What does John want to become? Answer in English.

➡ _____

14 위 글의 밑줄 친 ⓐ에서 괄호 안에 들어갈 말을 순서대로 쓰시오.

➡ _____

15 What does John do every Saturday morning? Answer in English.

➡ _____

16 위 글에서 시간의 중요성을 강조하기 위해 시간을 무엇에 비유했는지 우리말로 쓰시오.

➡ _____

17 위 글의 괄호 ⓑ의 단어들을 순서에 맞게 알맞게 배열하시오.

➡ _____

해석

Enjoy Writing B

My Goals for This Year

I have three goals to achieve this year. The first goal is to get along with my
　　　　　　　to부정사의 형용사적 용법 (～ 할)　　　　　　　　～와 잘 지내다

new classmates. The second goal is to get an A on the English speaking test.
　　　　　　　　　　　　　　　　　A를 받다

The last goal is to stop playing smartphone games. I hope that this year is
　　　　　　　　stop -ing: ～하는 것을 멈추다　　　　　명사절을 이끄는 접속사(생략 가능)

better than last year.
비교급+than: ～보다 더 ...한

구문해설 • this year: 올해　• goal: 목표　• second: 두 번째의　• last year: 지난해

올해의 나의 목표

"나는 올해 달성해야 할 목표가 세 가지 있다. 첫 번째 목표는 새로운 반 친구들과 잘 지내는 것이다. 두 번째 목표는 영어 말하기 시험에서 A를 받는 것이다. 마지막 목표는 스마트폰 게임을 중단하는 것이다. 나는 올해가 작년보다 더 낫기를 희망한다.

Project - Step 1

A: I think we should make our group's motto about dreaming and doing.
나는 ～해야 한다고 생각해. (무언가를 제안하거나 권유하는 표현)　　　　전치사+동명사

B: That's a good idea. I believe that dreaming and doing are different.
　　상대방의 의견에 동의하는 표현　　명사절을 이끄는 접속사　　동명사 주어

C: Yes. I think that doing is more important than dreaming.
　　　　　　　　동명사 주어는 단수 취급　　～보다 더 중요한(비교급)

D: That's right.

구문해설 • motto: 좌우명　• dream: 꿈을 꾸다　• different: 다른

A: 나는 우리가 꿈을 꾸고 행동하는 것에 대한 우리 모둠의 좌우명을 만들어야 한다고 생각해.

B: 좋은 생각이야. 나는 꿈과 행동이 다르다고 믿어.

C: 맞아. 나는 꿈을 꾸는 것보다 행동하는 것이 더 중요하다고 생각해.

D: 맞아.

Wrap Up - Writing

Jenny is going to go to the grocery store today. She is going to buy three
　　　　　～할 것이다

apples to eat. She is going to buy two bottles of water to drink. She is going to
　　to부정사의 형용사적 용법 (～ 할)　　　　두 병의　　　to부정사의 형용사적 용법 (～ 할)

buy one fashion magazine to read.
　　to부정사의 형용사적 용법 (～ 할)

구문해설 • grocery: 식료품, 잡화류　• buy: 사다　• magazine: 잡지

Jenny는 오늘 식료품점에 갈 거야. 그녀는 먹을 사과 세 개를 살 거야. 그녀는 마실 물 두 병을 살 거야. 그녀는 읽을 패션 잡지를 하나 살 거야.

01 다음 중 단어의 성격이 <u>다른</u> 것은?

① wisely   ② loudly
③ kindly   ④ lovely
⑤ regularly

02 다음 영영풀이에 해당하는 단어는?

> to direct your attention or effort at something specific

① check   ② focus
③ master   ④ join
⑤ prepare

03 다음 짝지어진 두 단어의 관계가 같도록 빈칸에 알맞은 단어를 쓰시오.

> probably : perhaps = gift : _____

04 다음 문장의 빈칸에 알맞은 것은?

> • I want to be good _____ English.
> • Please do one thing _____ a time.

① in   ② on
③ at   ④ by
⑤ for

05 다음 빈칸에 들어갈 말로 적절하지 <u>않은</u> 것은?

> • I will _____ my big goal.
> • I have soccer _____ today.
> • He is in the sixth _____.
> • You need to _____ your time well.

① grade   ② manage
③ finish   ④ practice
⑤ achieve

06 다음 문장의 밑줄 친 부분과 바꿔 쓸 수 있는 것은?

> We cannot <u>put off</u> decisions any longer.

① order   ② postpone
③ achieve   ④ demand
⑤ prepare

07 다음 대화의 밑줄 친 부분과 바꿔 쓸 수 <u>없는</u> 것은?

> A: I want to be good at cooking.
> B: I think you should <u>search for recipes</u>.

① What about searching for recipes?
② I advise you to search for recipes.
③ How about searching for recipes?
④ You'd better search for recipes.
⑤ Why didn't you search for recipes?

08 다음 대화의 빈칸에 들어갈 말로 어색한 것은?

> A: What's wrong with Jinsu?
> B: _____
> A: That's too bad.

① He has a terrible headache.
② He lost his new digital camera.
③ He broke his leg in the soccer game.
④ He won first prize on a science contest.
⑤ He got a really bad grade on his English test.

09 다음 대화의 순서를 바르게 배열하시오.

> (A) I have a cold.
> (B) You're right. Thank you.
> (C) That's too bad. I think you should see a doctor.
> (D) Jason, are you okay? You don't look good today.

➡ _____

10 다음 대화의 빈칸에 알맞지 않은 것을 모두 고르면? (2개)

> A: _____
> B: He failed the math test.
> A: I'm sorry to hear that.

① What's wrong with Kevin?
② What subject is Kevin good at?
③ Is something wrong with Kevin?
④ What's the matter with Kevin?
⑤ How do you feel about Kevin?

11 다음 주어진 표현을 이용하여 밑줄 친 우리말을 영작하시오.

> A: You looked worried. What's the matter?
> B: <u>나는 수학 시험이 걱정돼.</u> (math test)

➡ _____

[12~16] 다음 대화를 읽고, 물음에 답하시오.

> B: I'm so nervous. (①)
> G: Why? (②) Is it because ___ⓐ___ the dance contest?
> B: Yes. I practiced ___ⓑ___ many days, ___ⓒ___ I'm still nervous. (③) What should I do?
> G: I think you should practice ___ⓓ___ front of your family. (④)
> B: That's a good idea. Thank you. (⑤)

12 위 대화의 ①~⑤ 중 다음 문장이 들어갈 위치로 알맞은 것은?

> It will be very helpful.

①   ②   ③   ④   ⑤

13 위 대화의 빈칸 ⓐ와 ⓑ에 알맞은 말이 바르게 짝지어진 것은?

① of – during   ② for – for
③ to – for   ④ of – for
⑤ to – during

14 위 대화의 빈칸 ⓒ에 알맞은 것은?

① so   ② and   ③ but
④ for   ⑤ because

15 위 대화의 빈칸 ⓓ에 알맞은 말을 쓰시오.

➡ _____

16 Why is the boy nervous? Answer in English.

➡ _____

17 다음 문장의 빈칸에 알맞은 것은?

> I think _____ cars will fly in the sky someday.

① that   ② before

③ as   ④ after

⑤ when

18 다음 〈보기〉의 우리말을 영어로 바르게 옮긴 것은?

> ┤ 보기 ├
> 그는 살 좋은 집을 갖기를 원한다.

① He wants to have a good house live.

② He wants to have a good house live in.

③ He wants to have live in a good house.

④ He wants to have to live in a good house.

⑤ He wants to have a good house to live in.

19 다음 두 문장의 빈칸에 공통으로 알맞은 말을 쓰시오.

> • I believe _____ I can fly in the air.
> • We don't hope _____ you will like it.

20 다음 밑줄 친 부분의 쓰임이 나머지와 다른 하나는?

① This is the time to study.

② I bought some water to drink.

③ I studied hard to pass the exam.

④ Tom needs some books to read.

⑤ She has no money to buy a new dress.

21 다음 밑줄 친 부분 중 생략할 수 있는 것은?

① You can say that again.

② He said that was a correct answer.

③ She likes that brown bag on the shelf.

④ Do you know that boy in the corner?

⑤ I think that we should respect each other.

22 다음 문장의 밑줄 친 부분의 쓰임이 〈보기〉와 같은 것은?

> ┤ 보기 ├
> She has many bags to carry.

① I went to bed to sleep.

② He has a dog to walk.

③ I want to meet my friends.

④ My hobby is to collect stamps.

⑤ He went to her house to fix the computer.

23 다음 우리말과 일치하도록 주어진 단어를 바르게 배열하시오.

> Jane은 Kevin이 그 파티에 올 것이라고 믿지 않았다. (party / Jane / the / Kevin / come / to / that / would / didn't / believe)

➡ _____

24 다음 문장에서 어법상 어색한 부분을 찾아 바르게 고쳐 쓰시오.

> I need a pen to write.

_____ ➡ _____

25 다음 문장에서 어법상 어색한 부분을 찾아 고쳐 쓰시오.

> I don't know that he will come tomorrow.

_____ ➡ _____

26 다음 문장의 밑줄 친 부분의 쓰임이 나머지와 다른 하나는?

① I have a book to buy.
② There are many places to visit.
③ I went to the store to buy a jacket.
④ Do you have something to eat?
⑤ The man has three dogs to take care of.

27 다음 문장의 빈칸에 들어갈 말이 다른 하나는? (대 · 소문자 무시)

① Do you know _____ man?
② I think _____ she is pretty.
③ Do you know _____ he is sick?
④ _____ you finish it, let me know.
⑤ _____ he never came back is true.

28 다음 중 밑줄 친 부분의 쓰임이 같은 것끼리 묶인 것은?

> ⓐ I need something to drink.
> ⓑ She wants to become a teacher.
> ⓒ The girl had nothing to wear.
> ⓓ She went out to meet her boyfriend.

① ⓐ, ⓑ
② ⓑ, ⓓ
③ ⓑ, ⓒ
④ ⓐ, ⓒ
⑤ ⓒ, ⓓ

Reading

[29~35] 다음 글을 읽고, 물음에 답하시오.

> _____ⓐ_____ I do something, I give it my full attention. I ⓑused to read SNS postings while I was doing my homework. It slowed me down because I couldn't _____ⓒ_____. ⓓNow, I put aside my smartphone when I do my homework. It saves me a lot of time. ⓔThese days, I finish my homework quickly and enjoy my ⓕfree time.　　　　※ I = Minsu

29 위 글의 빈칸 ⓐ에 알맞은 것은?

① If
② That
③ When
④ What
⑤ Because

30 위 글의 밑줄 친 ⓑ를 한 단어로 바꿔 쓰시오.

➡ _____

31 위 글의 빈칸 ⓒ에 다음 영영풀이에 해당하는 단어를 주어진 철자로 시작하여 쓰시오.

> to direct your attention or effort at something specific

➡ f_____

32 위 글의 밑줄 친 ⓓ를 우리말로 옮기시오.

➡ _____

33 위 글의 밑줄 친 ⓔ와 바꿔 쓸 수 있는 것은?

① Instantly ② At once

③ Right now ④ Nowadays

⑤ Immediately

34 위 글의 밑줄 친 ⓕ와 의미가 같은 것은?

① Is this seat free?

② He was free as a bird.

③ I am now free from danger.

④ Children under five travel free.

⑤ An excellent lunch is provided free.

35 위 글을 읽고, 답할 수 <u>없는</u> 질문은?

① When Minsu does something, does he give it his full attention?

② What did Minsu use to do while he was doing his homework?

③ How long does Minsu use his smartphone a day?

④ Now, what does Minsu do when he does his homework?

⑤ What does Minsu do after finishing his homework quickly?

[36~40] 다음 글을 읽고, 물음에 답하시오.

I have three goals ⓐto achieve this year. The first goal is to get along ___ⓑ___ my new classmates. The second goal is to get an A on the English speaking test. The last goal is to stop ⓒplay smartphone games. I hope ___ⓓ___ this year is better than last year.

36 위 글의 밑줄 친 ⓐ와 쓰임이 같은 것은?

① His dream was to draw pictures.

② It's easy to memorize English words.

③ I have a lot of work to do today.

④ He wants to play tennis after school.

⑤ She studied very hard to pass the exam.

37 위 글의 빈칸 ⓑ에 알맞은 말을 쓰시오.

➡ _____

38 위 글의 밑줄 친 ⓒ를 알맞은 형태로 고쳐 쓰시오.

➡ _____

39 위 글의 빈칸 ⓓ에 알맞은 것은?

① if ② that

③ when ④ while

⑤ as

40 위 글을 읽고, 답할 수 <u>없는</u> 질문은?

① Does the writer have three goals to achieve this year?

② What is the first goal the writer wants to achieve?

③ What test does the writer want to get an A on?

④ What goals did the writer achieve last year?

⑤ What is the last goal the writer wants to achieve?

✎ 출제율 90%

01 다음 중 짝지어진 두 단어의 관계가 <u>다른</u> 것은?

① future : past
② sad : glad
③ gift : present
④ low : high
⑤ remember : forget

✎ 출제율 95%

02 다음 빈칸에 알맞은 말이 바르게 짝지어진 것은?

> • I _____ along with him very well.
> • He _____ aside his smartphone when the teacher came in.

① go – put
② make – got
③ take – made
④ get – turned
⑤ get – put

✎ 출제율 100%

03 다음 우리말에 맞게 빈칸에 알맞은 말을 쓰시오.

(1) 나는 많은 사람들 앞에서 말할 수 없다.
➡ I can't speak _____ _____ _____ many people.

(2) 그녀는 매우 슬퍼서 하루 종일 울었습니다.
➡ She was very sad and cried _____ _____ _____.

(3) 수지는 어렸을 때 안경을 썼었다.
➡ Suji _____ _____ wear glasses when she was a child.

(4) 그녀는 그 때문에 매우 화가 났다.
➡ She was very angry _____ _____ him.

✎ 출제율 85%

04 다음 중 영영풀이가 <u>잘못된</u> 것은?

① easy: not difficult
② master: to learn something completely
③ recipe: a set of instructions for making food
④ save: to use money to pay for something
⑤ due: expected to happen or arrive at a particular time

✎ 출제율 95%

05 다음 대화의 빈칸에 알맞은 것은?

> A: You look worried. What's wrong?
> B: I can't get good grades. _____
> A: How about making a study plan?

① What is it?
② What are you doing?
③ What should I do?
④ What happened?
⑤ What are you looking for?

✎ 출제율 90%

06 다음 대화의 빈칸에 알맞은 말이 바르게 짝지어진 것은?

> A: What's wrong?
> B: I have _____.
> A: That's too bad. Why don't you _____?
> B: OK. I will.

① a bad cold — see a doctor
② a pet — get some fresh air
③ a lot of homework — go to sleep
④ some stress — go to see a dentist
⑤ long hair — take some medicine

07 다음 짝지어진 대화 중 어색한 것은?

① A: What should I do?
   B: You should make a new study plan.
② A: You look down. What's wrong?
   B: My computer isn't working.
③ A: Would you give me some advice?
   B: Sure. What is it?
④ A: Why don't you take notes?
   B: Not yet. What should I do?
⑤ A: We should wait for the next showing.
   B: Sorry, it's all my fault.

[08~10] 다음 대화를 읽고, 물음에 답하시오.

G: You look ⓐworry. ⓑWhat's going on?
B: I'm ⓒworry about tomorrow's history quiz. What should I do?
G: _____ⓓ_____ read your textbook again?
B: That's a good idea.

08 위 대화의 밑줄 친 ⓐ와 ⓒ의 단어를 올바른 형태로 고쳐 쓰시오.

➡ _____

09 위 대화의 밑줄 친 ⓑ의 의도로 알맞은 것은?

① 안부 묻기   ② 경험 묻기
③ 주의 끌기   ④ 의견 묻기
⑤ 문제점 파악하기

10 위 대화의 빈칸 ⓓ에 알맞은 것은?

① Are you   ② How about
③ Do you want   ④ What about
⑤ Why don't you

11 다음 중 <보기>의 밑줄 친 부분과 쓰임이 같은 것은?

┤ 보기 ├
Do you have anything to eat?

① To ride a bike is fun.
② My hobby is to play soccer.
③ I want to go to Jeju-do.
④ She has no money to buy a ticket.
⑤ Tom went to Canada to learn how to snowboard.

12 다음 빈칸에 공통으로 들어갈 말은?

• I hope _____ you do well in the spelling bee.
• I'm sorry to hear _____.

① what   ② this   ③ that
④ it   ⑤ them

13 다음 문장에서 어법상 어색한 부분을 바르게 고쳐 쓰시오.

I can't find a peg to hang my coat.

_____ ➡ _____

14 다음 밑줄 친 부분의 쓰임이 나머지와 다른 것은?

① Look at that parrot.
② I think that boy is Jake's brother.
③ I know that he hurt his arm yesterday.
④ Wash your hands before eating that cake.
⑤ That skirt is more expensive than this one.

15 다음 문장에서 어법상 <u>어색한</u> 부분을 찾아 바르게 고쳐 쓰시오.

출제율 95%

> I hope if you will be a famous writer.

_____ ➡ _____

16 다음 괄호 안에 주어진 단어를 이용하여 우리말에 맞게 문장을 완성하시오.

출제율 85%

> 뜨거운 마실 것 좀 주세요. (something, hot)

➡ Give me _____.

17 다음 중 밑줄 친 부분을 생략할 수 <u>없는</u> 것은?

출제율 100%

① I think <u>that</u> he is American.
② He knows <u>that</u> she is rich.
③ We don't hope <u>that</u> you will like it.
④ I can't believe <u>that</u> you made this.
⑤ It is true <u>that</u> I'm poor at English.

18 다음 중 어법상 <u>어색한</u> 문장은?

출제율 95%

① I need a chair to sit.
② Columbus was the first man to discover the American continent.
③ We have no house to live in.
④ He has a wish to become a pilot.
⑤ She forgot to bring something to write with.

[19~26] 다음 글을 읽고, 물음에 답하시오.

> Subin: I set small goals and achieve ⓐ<u>them</u> every day. I do not say, "I will master English." With ⓑ(such / big / a / goal), I will probably put off working on ⓒ<u>it</u> until tomorrow, next week, or next month. Instead, I say, "I will learn three new English words every day." I will achieve my big goal, one step ___ⓓ___ a time.
>
> Time is a present. Everyone has the same present ⓔ<u>to spend</u> every day. Manage your time well, ___ⓕ___ you will be happier in the new school year!

19 위 글의 밑줄 친 ⓐthem이 가리키는 것을 우리말로 쓰시오.

출제율 90%

➡ _____

20 위 글의 괄호 ⓑ의 단어들을 순서대로 배열하시오.

출제율 85%

➡ _____

21 위 글에서 다음 영영풀이에 해당하는 말을 찾아 쓰시오.

출제율 90%

> to decide that something which had been planned for a particular time will be done at a later time instead

➡ _____

22 위 글의 밑줄 친 ⓒ가 의미하는 것을 우리말로 쓰시오.

출제율 95%

➡ _____

23 위 글의 빈칸 ⓓ에 알맞은 것은? ⟨출제율 95%⟩

① at   ② with
③ in   ④ on
⑤ for

24 위 글의 밑줄 친 ⓔ와 쓰임이 같은 것은? ⟨출제율 90%⟩

① There is no water to drink.
② I must hurry to the bus stop to meet Jack.
③ My hobby is to play computer games.
④ She was very happy to pass the exam.
⑤ We went to the store to buy some snacks.

25 위 글의 빈칸 ⓕ에 알맞은 말을 쓰시오. ⟨출제율 100%⟩

➡ _____

26 위 글을 읽고, 다음 질문에 완전한 문장으로 답하시오. ⟨출제율 90%⟩

Q: Instead of "I will master English," what does Subin say?
A: _____

[27~29] 다음 글을 읽고, 물음에 답하시오.

I regularly spend time working toward my dream. I want to become a chef. Every Saturday morning, I go to cooking classes or search for ⓐ_____ . I think that using my time ⓑto prepare for my future is important.

※ I = John

27 위 글의 빈칸 ⓐ에 다음 영영풀이에 해당하는 단어를 쓰시오. (복수형으로 쓸 것) ⟨출제율 95%⟩

a set of instructions for making food

➡ _____

28 위 글의 밑줄 친 ⓑ와 쓰임이 다른 것은? ⟨출제율 100%⟩

① Ann is coming to Seoul to visit us.
② Give me a pen to write with.
③ I'm going to the park to walk my dogs.
④ Paul drove very quickly to get there on time.
⑤ I went to the post office to send the parcel.

29 위 글을 읽고, 답할 수 없는 질문은? ⟨출제율 85%⟩

① Does John spend time working toward his future every day?
② What does John want to become?
③ Where does John take his cooking classes?
④ Does John search for recipes every day?
⑤ Does John think it is important to use his time to prepare for his future?

서술형 실전문제

01 다음 괄호 ⓐ와 ⓑ 안에 주어진 단어를 이용하여 대화를 완성하시오.

> G: You look worried. ⓐ(what, the matter)?
> B: I'm worried about tomorrow's history quiz. ⓑ(what, do)?
> G: I think you should read your textbook again.
> B: That's a good idea.

ⓐ _____

ⓑ _____

02 다음 대화의 순서를 바르게 배열하시오.

> (A) OK, I will.
> (B) What's wrong?
> (C) Well, I have a toothache.
> (D) That's too bad. Why don't you go see a dentist?

➡ _____

[03~04] 다음 대화를 읽고, 물음에 답하시오.

> A: ⓐWhat's the matter with you?
> B: I have a sore throat.
> A: That's too bad. ⓑI think you should drink some water.
> B: Okay, I will.

03 위 대화의 밑줄 친 부분과 바꿔 쓸 수 있는 표현을 두 가지 이상 쓰시오.

➡ _____

_____

04 위 대화의 밑줄 친 ⓑ와 유사한 표현을 3가지 이상 쓰시오.

➡ _____

_____

_____

05 다음 괄호 안에 주어진 단어를 이용하여 우리말을 영어로 옮기시오.

(1) 그는 그것이 매우 재미있을 것이라고 믿는다.
(believe / that / a lot of fun)
➡ _____

(2) 나는 그가 정직하다고 생각한다.
(think / that / honest)
➡ _____

(3) 나는 그녀가 선생님이었다는 것을 안다.
(know / that / teacher)
➡ _____

06 다음 두 문장을 한 문장으로 쓸 때 빈칸에 알맞은 말을 쓰시오.

> I need a friend. + I play with the friend.
> ➡ I need a friend _____ _____ _____.

07 다음 주어진 단어를 바르게 배열하여 문장을 완성하시오. (필요시 어형을 바꿀 것)

> (think / play / enjoy / he / soccer / I / that)

➡ _____

08 다음 〈보기〉에서 알맞은 단어를 골라 올바른 형태로 문장을 완성하시오.

> ┌ 보기 ┐
> eat live play take tell

(1) Sumi has good news _____ _____.
(2) He is looking for a house _____ _____ _____.

★**09** 다음 문장에서 어법상 **틀린** 부분을 찾아 바르게 고쳐 쓰시오.

(1) Here are the questions to answers.

_____ ➡ _____

(2) I'm lonely. I want some friends to talk.

_____ ➡ _____

(3) I'm eating pizza, but I don't have anything drink.

_____ ➡ _____

[10~12] 다음 글을 읽고, 물음에 답하시오.

> I have ⓐ(to / goals / achieve / three) this year. The first goal is to get along with Jiho and Sujin. ⓑThe second goal is to stop to play smartphone games. The last goal is to learn taegwondo. I hope that I achieve these goals this year.

10 위 글의 괄호 ⓐ 안의 단어들을 어법에 맞게 바르게 배열하시오.

➡ _____

★**11** 위 글의 밑줄 친 ⓑ에서 어법상 **어색한** 것을 찾아 바르게 고쳐 쓰시오.

_____ ➡ _____

12 What is the last goal the writer wants to achieve? Answer in English.

➡ _____

[13~17] 다음 글을 읽고, 물음에 답하시오.

> I ⓐregular spend time working toward my dream. I want to become a ___ⓑ___. Every Saturday morning, I go to cooking classes or search ___ⓒ___ recipes. I think that ⓓuse my time to prepare ___ⓔ___ my future is important.
>
> ※ I = John

13 위 글의 밑줄 친 ⓐ를 알맞은 형태로 고쳐 쓰시오.

➡ _____

14 위 글의 빈칸 ⓑ에 다음 영영풀이에 해당하는 단어를 쓰시오.

> a professional cook, especially the most senior cook in a restaurant, hotel, etc.

➡ _____

★**15** 위 글의 빈칸 ⓒ와 ⓔ에 공통으로 알맞은 말을 쓰시오.

➡ _____

16 위 글의 밑줄 친 ⓓ를 알맞은 형태로 고쳐 쓰시오.

➡ _____

★**17** When does John go to cooking classes? Answer in English.

➡ _____

창의사고력 서술형 문제

01 다음 주어진 상황에 맞게 〈to부정사〉와 괄호 안의 단어를 이용하여 〈보기〉처럼 문장을 완성하시오.

┌─ 보기 ───┐
│   I'm hungry. <u>I need some food to eat.</u> (eat) │
└──┘

(1) I'm very thirsty. _____ (drink)

(2) There's no chair here. _____ (sit)

(3) Tony feels lonely. _____ (talk)

02 다음 (A), (B), (C)에 주어진 단어를 이용하여 〈보기〉와 같이 문장을 4개 쓰시오.(필요하면 어형을 바꿀 것)

(A)	(B)	(C)
I	say that	it's delicious
He	think that	Jenny is kind
She	hear that	they need help
Mike	know that	everyone will be happy
They	hope that	many children are hungry

┌─ 보기 ───┐
│   I hope that everyone will be happy. │
└──┘

(1) _____

(2) _____

(3) _____

(4) _____

03 자신의 경우에 맞게 〈to부정사〉를 이용하여 〈보기〉와 같이 지금 필요한 것에 대해 써 보시오. (3문장 이상)

┌─ 보기 ───┐
│   I need something to drink. │
└──┘

(1) _____

(2) _____

(3) _____

단원별 모의고사

01 다음 영영풀이에 해당하는 단어로 알맞은 것은?

> to make yourself ready for something that you will be doing

① achieve　　② decide
③ prefer　　④ prepare
⑤ practice

02 다음 중 밑줄 친 우리말 뜻이 잘못된 것은?

① You should see a doctor.
　　　　　　병원에 가다
② He put off his homework.
　　　　끝냈다
③ I want to be good at cooking.
　　　　　～을 잘하다
④ This is a type of book.
　　　　일종의
⑤ I don't sleep well these days.
　　　　　　요즘

03 다음 빈칸에 공통으로 알맞은 것은?

> • We have to _____ water for the future.
> • We need to _____ pink dolphins in danger.

① recycle　　② share
③ store　　④ save
⑤ protect

04 다음 짝지어진 두 단어의 관계가 같도록 빈칸에 알맞은 말을 쓰시오.

> future : past = forget : _____

05 다음 영영풀이에 해당하는 단어를 쓰시오. (m으로 시작할 것)

> to learn something completely

➡ _____

06 다음 짝지어진 대화가 어색한 것은?

① A: Hey, Jenny. What's the matter?
　B: My bicycle doesn't work.
② A: I want to be friends with her. What should I do?
　B: You should say hello to her first.
③ A: I have too much homework.
　B: Don't worry. I will help you.
④ A: I left my homework at home. What should I do?
　B: You should bring it tomorrow, then.
⑤ A: You look sad today. What's the matter?
　B: I will help you.

07 다음 대화의 밑줄 친 부분과 같은 의미가 되도록 빈칸에 알맞은 말을 쓰시오.

> A: It's very cold outside.
> B: You'd better wear a warm coat.

➡ _____ _____ _____ wear a warm coat?

[08~11] 다음 대화를 읽고, 물음에 답하시오.

Hana: ⓐWhat's the matter, Jiho?

Jiho: I didn't bring my uniform. I forgot I have soccer practice today.

Hana: Again?

Jiho: My second year in middle school is busier than my first year, and I often forget things.

Hana: ⓑI think you should use a planner. Here's mine.

Jiho: Oh, can I see it?

Hana: Sure. I write my class schedule and ⓒ in my planner.

Jiho: That's great. Maybe I should buy one.

08 위 대화의 밑줄 친 ⓐ와 같은 의미가 되도록 빈칸에 알맞은 말을 쓰시오.

What's _____, Jiho?

09 위 대화의 밑줄 친 ⓑ와 바꿔 쓸 수 있는 것은?

① You had better
② You must not
③ You can rarely
④ You used to
⑤ You are able to

10 위 대화의 빈칸 ⓒ에 알맞은 단어를 다음 영영풀이를 참조하여 쓰시오. (주어진 철자로 시작할 것)

an arrangement to meet with someone at a particular time

➡ a_____

11 What does Hana think Jiho should use? Answer in English.

➡ _____

12 다음 문장의 빈칸에 알맞은 것은?

I'm looking for a friend to travel _____.

① at
② in
③ with
④ on
⑤ for

13 다음 중 밑줄 친 부분의 쓰임이 나머지와 다른 하나는?

① Do you know that she is from Turkey?
② This is a picture that I took yesterday.
③ We hope that Jenny will get better soon.
④ I believe that he read the book twice.
⑤ I think that Susan is good at playing tennis.

14 다음 괄호 안의 단어 형태가 바르게 짝지어진 것은?

• I have something (tell) you.
• Do you have anything (read)?

① tell – read
② tell – to read
③ to tell – read
④ telling – read
⑤ to tell – to read

15 다음 우리말에 맞게 주어진 단어를 바르게 배열하시오.

나는 나의 영어 선생님이 예쁘시다고 생각한다.
(teacher / is / that / English / think / my / pretty / I)

➡ _____

16 다음 중 어법상 알맞지 <u>않은</u> 것은?

① Let me get you a chair to sit on.
② She has no house to live in.
③ There's nothing to worry about.
④ Give me a pen to write with.
⑤ You seem to have important something to tell me.

17 다음 괄호 안에 주어진 단어를 이용하여 우리말에 맞게 문장을 완성하시오.

> 수진이는 머무를 호텔을 찾고 있다. (stay)

➡ Sujin is looking for a hotel _____.

18 다음 밑줄 친 부분의 쓰임이 나머지와 <u>다른</u> 하나는?

① I think <u>that</u> he is handsome.
② He believes <u>that</u> he can be a good doctor.
③ She hopes <u>that</u> there will be no more exams.
④ Do you know <u>that</u> handsome guy over there?
⑤ Professor Kim says <u>that</u> we should save energy.

19 다음 중 밑줄 친 부분의 쓰임이 같은 것끼리 묶인 것은?

> ⓐ I want something <u>to drink</u>.
> ⓑ I want <u>to become</u> a teacher.
> ⓒ There are many problems <u>to solve</u>.
> ⓓ <u>To clean</u> the house is really fun.
> ⓔ I'm standing here for three hours <u>to meet</u> her.

① ⓐ, ⓑ   ② ⓑ, ⓓ   ③ ⓑ, ⓒ
④ ⓐ, ⓓ   ⑤ ⓒ, ⓔ

[20~24] 다음 글을 읽고, 물음에 답하시오.

> Minsu: When I do something, I give it my full attention. I ___ⓐ___ read SNS postings while I was doing my homework. ⓑIt slowed down me because I couldn't focus. Now, I put aside my smartphone when I do my homework. ⓒIt saves me ⓓa lot of time. These days, I finish my homework quickly and enjoy my free time.

20 문맥상 위 글의 빈칸 ⓐ에 알맞은 것은?

① could   ② should
③ might   ④ used to
⑤ ought to

21 위 글의 밑줄 친 ⓑ에서 어법상 어색한 부분을 찾아 바르게 고쳐 쓰시오.

_____ ➡ _____

22 위 글의 밑줄 친 ⓒ가 의미하는 것은?

① 숙제할 때 SNS 게시 글을 읽는 것
② 숙제할 때 음악을 듣는 것
③ 숙제할 때 스마트폰을 한쪽에 치워 놓는 것
④ 빨리 숙제를 끝내는 것
⑤ 여가 시간을 즐기는 것

23 위 글의 밑줄 친 ⓓ를 한 단어로 바꿔 쓰시오.

➡ _____

24 위 글을 읽고, 다음 질문에 완전한 문장으로 답하시오.

> Q: Does Minsu finish his homework late these days?
>
> A: _____

[25~31] 다음 글을 읽고, 물음에 답하시오.

Welcome to the new school year. In the second grade, you will have more work ⓐ<u>to do</u>. You need to manage your time well. How do you do that?

John: I regularly spend time ⓑ<u>work</u> toward my dream. I want to become a chef. Every Saturday morning, I go to cooking classes or search for recipes. I think that using my time ___ⓒ___ for my future is important.

Time is a present. Everyone has the ⓓ<u>same</u> present to spend every day. ⓔ<u>Manage your time well, and you will be happier in the new school year!</u>

25 위 글의 밑줄 친 ⓐ와 쓰임이 같은 것은?

① He likes <u>to play</u> badminton.
② I didn't have time <u>to think</u>.
③ I want <u>to buy</u> some cheese.
④ <u>To study</u> English is not easy.
⑤ My dream is <u>to be</u> an English teacher.

26 위 글의 밑줄 친 ⓑ를 알맞은 형태로 쓰시오.

➡ _____

27 위 글에서 다음 영영풀이에 해당하는 단어를 찾아 쓰시오.

> to use your time, money, etc. sensibly, without wasting it

➡ _____

28 위 글의 빈칸 ⓒ에 알맞은 것은?

① prepare
② preparing
③ to prepare
④ for prepare
⑤ to preparing

29 위 글의 밑줄 친 ⓓ의 반의어를 쓰시오.

➡ _____

30 위 글의 밑줄 친 ⓔ를 다음과 같이 바꿔 쓸 때 빈칸에 알맞은 말을 쓰시오.

> ➡ _____ you manage your time well, you will be happier in the new school year!

31 위 글을 읽고, 답할 수 <u>없는</u> 질문은?

① What do second graders need to do?
② What does John do to become a chef?
③ Does John take his cooking class every day?
④ Why does John want to become a chef?
⑤ Does everyone have the same present to spend every day?

Lesson 2

All about Safety

의사소통 기능

- 상기시켜 주기
  Don't forget to get under the desk.
- 금지하기
  You'd better not use the elevator.

언어 형식

- 의문사+to부정사
  I learned **how to do** CPR.
- as + 형용사/부사의 원급 + as
  I was **as** scared **as** the others.

Words & Expressions

Key Words

- **almost** [ɔ́ːlmoust] 閉 거의
- **ambulance** [ǽmbjuləns] 명 구급차
- **angle** [ǽŋgl] 명 각도
- **announcer** [ənáunsər] 명 아나운서
- **around** [əráund] 전 ~ 주위에
- **audience** [ɔ́ːdiəns] 명 청중, 시청자
- **brave** [breiv] 형 용감한(= fearless)
- **breathe** [briːð] 동 숨을 쉬다, 호흡하다
- **carefully** [kɛ́ərfəli] 閉 주의 깊게
- **chance** [tʃæns] 명 기회, 가능성
- **chest** [tʃest] 명 가슴
- **CPR** 명 심폐소생술
- **dangerous** [déindʒərəs] 형 위험한(↔ safe)
- **degree** [digríː] 명 (각도의 단위인) 도
- **earthquake** [əːrθkweik] 명 지진
- **excited** [iksáitid] 형 신이 난
- **experience** [ikspíəriəns] 명 경험
- **floor** [flɔːr] 명 바닥(↔ ceiling)
- **forget** [fərgét] 동 잊다(↔ remember)
- **gear** [giər] 명 장비, 복장
- **grade** [greid] 명 학년
- **greatly** [gréitli] 閉 대단히, 크게
- **hard** [haːrd] 閉 세게, 힘껏 형 어려운, 딱딱한
- **heart** [haːrt] 명 심장
- **important** [impɔ́ːrtənt] 형 중요한(↔ unimportant)
- **impressive** [imprésiv] 형 인상적인

- **join** [dʒɔin] 동 함께하다
- **late** [leit] 閉 늦게(↔ early)
- **low** [lou] 閉 낮게(↔ high) 형 낮은
- **lower** [lóuər] 동 낮추다, 낮아지다
- **luckily** [lʌ́kili] 閉 다행히도
- **open** [óupən] 형 막혀 있지 않은, 개방된
- **perform** [pərfɔ́ːrm] 동 행하다, 실시하다
- **practice** [prǽktis] 동 연습하다
- **protect** [prətékt] 동 보호하다
- **remember** [rimémbər] 동 기억하다
- **safety** [séifti] 명 안전(↔ danger)
- **save** [seiv] 동 구하다
- **scared** [skɛərd] 형 무서워하는, 겁먹은
- **scary** [skɛ́əri] 형 무서운, 겁나는
- **shake** [ʃeip] 동 흔들리다
- **shoulder** [ʃóuldər] 명 어깨
- **shout** [ʃaut] 동 외치다
- **skill** [skil] 명 기술
- **stay** [stei] 동 유지하다
- **suddenly** [sʌ́dnli] 閉 갑자기
- **tap** [tæp] 동 (가볍게) 톡톡 두드리다[치다]
- **teenager** [tíːnèidʒər] 명 십대
- **training** [tréiniŋ] 명 교육, 훈련
- **wet** [wet] 형 젖은(↔ dry)
- **within** [wiðín] 전 ~ 이내에, ~ 안에
- **zoo keeper** 동물원 사육사

Key Expressions

- **all the time** 항상
- **as ~ as possible** 가능한 한 ~한[하게]
- **as soon as you can** 가능한 한 빨리
- **at first** 처음에
- **bump into** ~에 부딪히다
- **fall down** 넘어지다
- **get off** ~에서 내리다
- **get out** 나가다
- **get under** 밑에 들어가다, 밑에 숨다
- **hit ~ on the shoulder** ~의 어깨를 치다

- **hold on to** ~을 꼭 잡다, ~을 붙잡다
- **in case of** ~의 경우에
- **in front of** ~ 앞에서
- **out of** ~의 밖으로
- **push down** ~을 꽉[꼭] 누르다
- **put on** ~을 입다
- **run around** 뛰어다니다
- **stand in line** 줄을 서다
- **up and down** 위아래로
- **wait for** ~을 기다리다

Word Power

※ 동사에 -ive를 붙여 형용사로 만드는 단어

☐ **act** (행동하다) → **active** (활동적인)

☐ **attract** (마음을 끌다) → **attractive** (매력적인)

☐ **communicate** (의사소통을 하다) →
　　　　　　communicative (이야기하기 좋아하는)

☐ **create** (창조하다) → **creative** (창의적인)

☐ **impress** (깊은 인상을 주다) → **impressive** (인상적인)

☐ **talk** (수다를 떨다) → **talkative** (수다스러운)

※ 형용사에 -ly를 붙여 부사로 만드는 단어

☐ **careful** → **carefully** (주의 깊게)

☐ **easy** → **easily** (쉽게)

☐ **great** → **greatly** (대단히, 크게)

☐ **lucky** → **luckily** (다행히)

☐ **slow** → **slowly** (천천히)

☐ **sudden** → **suddenly** (갑자기)

English Dictionary

☐ **audience** 청중, 시청자
→ the people who watch, read, or listen to something
어떤 것을 보거나 읽거나 듣는 사람들

☐ **brave** 용감한
→ feeling or showing no fear
두려움을 느끼거나 나타내지 않는

☐ **breathe** 숨을 쉬다, 호흡하다
→ to move air into and out of your lungs
공기를 폐 안으로 들이마셨다가 내쉬다

☐ **chest** 가슴
→ the front part of the body between the neck and the stomach
목과 위 사이의 몸의 앞부분

☐ **degree** (각도의 단위인) 도
→ a unit for measuring the size of an angle
각의 크기를 측정하는 단위

☐ **earthquake** 지진
→ a sudden, violent shaking of the earth's surface
지구 표면의 갑작스럽고 격렬한 진동

☐ **experience** 경험
→ the process of doing and seeing things and of having things happen to you
자신이 일들을 하고 보고 자신에게 일어나는 일들을 겪는 과정

☐ **lower** 낮추다, 낮아지다
→ to reduce something in amount, degree, strength etc, or to become less
양, 정도, 강도 등을 줄이거나 적게 만들다

☐ **perform** 행하다, 실시하다
→ to do an action or activity that usually requires training or skill
대개 훈련이나 기술이 필요한 행동이나 활동을 하다

☐ **protect** 보호하다
→ to keep someone or something from being harmed, lost, etc.
누군가 또는 어떤 것이 해를 입거나 없어지거나 하지 않게 하다

☐ **save** 구하다
→ to keep someone or something safe from death, harm, loss, etc.
누군가 또는 무언가를 죽음, 위해, 상실 등으로부터 안전하게 지키다

☐ **shake** 흔들리다
→ to move sometimes violently back and forth or up and down with short, quick movements
짧고 빠른 동작으로 때때로 격렬하게 앞뒤로 또는 위아래로 움직이다

☐ **skill** 기술
→ the ability to do something that comes from training, experience, or practice
훈련·경험·연습에서 생기는 어떤 일을 할 수 있는 능력

☐ **tap** (가볍게) 톡톡 두드리다[치다]
→ to hit someone or something quickly and lightly
누군가 또는 무언가를 빠르고 가볍게 치다

☐ **wet** 젖은
→ not yet dry
아직 마르지 않은

☐ **zoo keeper** 동물원 사육사
→ a person who takes care of the animals in a zoo
동물원에서 동물을 돌보는 사람

01 다음 〈보기〉와 같은 형태로 변화하는 단어는?

┌─ 보기 ─────────────────────┐
│ act : active │
└────────────────────────────┘

① help
② stress
③ scare
④ harm
⑤ impress

서답형

02 다음 두 문장의 뜻이 같도록 빈칸에 알맞은 말을 쓰시오.

┌─────────────────────────────────────┐
│ You need to call 119 as soon as you can. │
│ = You need to call 119 as soon as _____ . │
└─────────────────────────────────────┘

 중요

03 다음 영영풀이에 해당하는 단어로 알맞은 것은?

┌─────────────────────────────────────┐
│ to move air into and out of your lungs │
└─────────────────────────────────────┘

① allow
② throw
③ defend
④ breathe
⑤ protect

서답형

04 다음 짝지어진 단어의 관계가 같도록 빈칸에 알맞은 말을 쓰시오.

┌─────────────────────────────┐
│ wrong : right = dry : _____ │
└─────────────────────────────┘

05 다음 빈칸에 알맞은 말이 바르게 짝지어진 것은?

┌─────────────────────────────────────┐
│ • He says he bumped _____ the wall. │
│ • I'll wait _____ you in front of the │
│   theater. │
└─────────────────────────────────────┘

① to – on
② up – for
③ in – with
④ into – for
⑤ over – on

서답형

06 다음 영영풀이에 해당하는 단어를 쓰시오.

┌─────────────────────────────────────┐
│ a sudden, violent shaking of the earth's │
│ surface │
└─────────────────────────────────────┘

➡ _____

 중요

07 다음 빈칸에 공통으로 알맞은 것은?

┌─────────────────────────────────────┐
│ • I'll _____ off at the first floor. │
│ • Don't forget to _____ under the desk │
│   when the earthquake occurs. │
└─────────────────────────────────────┘

① put
② get
③ take
④ turn
⑤ bring

서답형

08 다음 빈칸에 공통으로 알맞은 말을 쓰시오.

┌─────────────────────────────────────┐
│ • He's the person who can _____ your │
│   life. │
│ • You can _____ money by buying a │
│   one-day ticket. │
└─────────────────────────────────────┘

01 다음 짝지어진 두 단어의 관계가 같도록 빈칸에 알맞은 말을 쓰시오.

(1) late : early = important : _____
(2) easy : difficult = forget : _____
(3) strong : weak = floor : _____
(4) trash : waste = _____ : fearless

02 다음 우리말에 맞게 빈칸에 알맞은 말을 쓰시오.

(1) 자동차가 트럭 앞에 있다.
　➡ The car is _____ _____ _____ the truck.
(2) 우리는 버스 정류장에서 한 줄로 서야 한다.
　➡ We must _____ _____ _____ at a bus stop.
(3) 너무 빨리 뛰지 마. 넘어질 수 있어.
　➡ Don't run too fast. You may _____ _____.
(4) 그녀는 항상 해복해 보인다.
　➡ She looks happy _____ _____ _____.

03 다음 빈칸에 공통으로 들어갈 말을 〈보기〉에서 골라 쓰시오.

┌─── 보기 ───┐
grade　　save　　hard
└──────────┘

(1) • That test was _____.
　 • He hit the ball _____.
(2) • He risked his life to _____ her.
　 • She would rather _____ than spend.
(3) • He is in the second _____.
　 • I got a good _____ on my math test.

04 다음 빈칸에 들어갈 알맞은 말을 〈보기〉에서 골라 쓰시오.

┌─── 보기 ───┐
scared　　breathe　　practice
└──────────┘

(1) They usually _____ soccer after school.
(2) Humans need oxygen to _____.
(3) The rabbit was _____ when it met the lion.

05 다음 빈칸에 알맞은 말을 〈보기〉에서 골라 쓰시오.

┌─── 보기 ───┐
in case of　　put on　　run around
└──────────┘

(1) You should not _____ indoors.
(2) Don't forget to _____ hiking shoes.
(3) You'd better not use an elevator _____ _____ a fire.

06 다음 영영풀이에 해당하는 단어를 주어진 철자로 시작하여 쓰시오.

(1) d_____ : a unit for measuring the size of an angle
(2) c_____ : the front part of the body between the neck and the stomach
(3) p_____ : to do an action or activity that usually requires training or skill
(4) a_____ : the people who watch, read, or listen to something

Conversation

① 상기시켜 주기

> **A** I'm going to go hiking. 나는 등산하러 갈 거야.
>
> **B** Don't forget to put on hiking shoes. 등산화 신는 걸 잊지 마.
>
> **A** Okay, I see. 그래. 알았어.

- Don't forget to ~.는 '~하는 것을 잊지 마라.'라는 뜻으로 상대방에게 어떤 일을 상기시킬 때 사용하는 표현이다.
  - A: I'll buy a cake for my mom's birthday. 엄마 생일을 위해 케이크를 살 거야.
    B: Don't forget to bring some candles. 초 가져 오는 것을 잊지 말아라.

상기시켜 주기 표현

- Don't forget to bring your coat. 코트 가져오는 것을 잊지 마.
- Never forget to bring your coat 코트 가져오는 것을 잊지 마.
- Remember to bring your coat. 코트 가져오는 것을 기억해.
- Make[Be] sure you bring your coat. 코트를 반드시 가져오도록 해.

상기시켜 주는 말에 답하기

- Okay, I see.
- OK, I won't.
- I'll keep that in mind. 명심하도록 할게.
- All right. Thank you.
- I will remember (that).
- OK, thanks.
- Thank you for reminding me. 상기시켜 줘서 고마워요.

핵심 Check

1. 다음 우리말과 일치하도록 빈칸에 알맞은 말을 쓰시오.

   (1) **A:** I'm going bike riding. (나는 자전거를 타러 갈 거야.)

   B: Have fun and _____ _____ _____ wear a helmet.

   (재밌게 타고, 헬멧 쓰는 것을 잊지 마.)

   (2) **A:** May I _____ this book? (제가 이 책 빌려가도 될까요?)

   B: Sure. Just _____ _____ give it back in a week.

   (그럼요. 일주일 후에 돌려주는 것을 잊지 마세요.)

   A: Okay. I _____. (네. 그럴게요.)

   (3) **A:** _____ _____ you close the windows. (창문을 반드시 닫도록 해.)

   B: OK, I _____. (알았어. 잊지 않을게.)

② 금지하기

> **A** Peter, you'd better not play with a ball on the street.
> Peter, 길거리에서 공을 가지고 놀면 안 돼.
>
> **B** Okay, I see. 응, 알았어.

■ You'd better not ~은 '~하지 않는 게 좋겠어., ~하면 안 돼.'라는 뜻으로 어떤 일을 하지 말아야 함을 이야기할 때 사용하는 금지의 표현이다.

- A: Tony, you'd better not run when you cross the street. Tony, 길을 건널 때 뛰지 않는 게 좋겠어.
  B: Okay, I see. 응, 알겠어.

cf. You'd better ~는 '~하는 게 좋겠다.'라는 뜻으로 상대방에게 제안이나 충고를 할 때 사용한다.

- You had better have breakfast every day. 너는 매일 아침식사를 하는 것이 좋겠다.

금지를 나타내는 표현

- You'd better not take pictures at the museum. 박물관에서는 사진을 찍지 않는 것이 좋겠어.

  = You should not take pictures at the museum.

  = You must not take pictures at the museum.

  = Don't[Do not] take pictures at the museum.

  = You can't take pictures at the museum.

  = You're not supposed[allowed/permitted] to take pictures at the museum.

핵심 Check

2. 다음 우리말과 일치하도록 빈칸에 알맞은 말을 쓰시오.

(1) A: I _____ I've got a _____. (나 감기에 걸린 것 같아.)

　　B: You'd _____ _____ _____ cold water. (너는 차가운 물을 마시지 않는 게 좋겠어.)

(2) A: _____ _____ snacks in here. (이 안에서 과자를 드시지 마세요.)

　　B: Oh, I'm sorry. (오, 죄송합니다.)

(3) A: Excuse me. You _____ _____ your cell phone here.

　　(실례합니다. 이곳에서 휴대 전화를 사용하시면 안 됩니다.)

　　B: Oh, I'm _____. (오, 죄송합니다.)

A. Listen & Speak 1 - A - 1

> B: ❶Mom, can I buy some apple juice?
>
> W: Sure, Chris. ❷Don't forget to check the food label.
>
> B: The food label?
>
> W: Yes. ❸Too much sugar is not good for you.
>
> B: Okay, I will check it.

B: 엄마, 사과 주스 좀 사도 돼요?

W: 물론, Chris. 식품 라벨을 확인하는 것을 잊지 마라.

B: 식품 라벨이요?

W: 그래. 너무 많은 설탕은 너에게 좋지 않아.

B: 네, 확인해 볼게요.

❶ Can I ~?: 제가 ~해도 될까요? (허락 요청하기)
❷ Don't forget to+동사원형 ~: ~하는 것을 잊지 마라. (상기시켜 주기)
❸ be good for: ~에 좋다

Check(√) True or False

(1) The boy will buy some apple juice.　　　　　　T ☐ F ☐

(2) The boy forgot to check the food label.　　　　T ☐ F ☐

Conversation B

> Teacher: ❶I told you a few safety rules for earthquakes today. ❷Now, let's practice. Are you ready?
>
> Amy & Jiho: Yes.
>
> Teacher: Everything is shaking. ❸Don't forget to get under the desk and protect your body first.
>
> Jiho: It's so scary.
>
> Amy: You're doing fine, Jiho. ❹Hold on to the leg of the desk.
>
> Jiho: Oh, the shaking stopped for now. ❺Let's get out!
>
> Teacher: Remember! ❻You'd better not use the elevator. Use the stairs.
>
> Amy: Where should we go now?
>
> Teacher: You need to find an open area with no buildings.
>
> Jiho: Then, let's go to the park.

선생님: 오늘 지진에 대한 몇 가지 안전 수칙들을 말했죠. 자, 실습해 봅시다. 준비됐나요?

Amy와 지호: 네.

선생님: 모든 것이 흔들리고 있어요. 책상 밑에 들어가서 먼저 여러분의 몸을 보호하는 것을 잊지 마세요.

지호: 너무 무서워요.

Amy: 너는 잘하고 있어, 지호야. 책상 다리를 꽉 잡아.

지호: 오, 떨림이 잠시 멈췄어. 나가자!

선생님: 기억하세요! 엘리베이터를 이용하면 안 돼요. 계단을 이용하세요.

Amy: 이제 우린 어디로 가야 하죠?

선생님: 건물이 없는 확 트인 곳을 찾아야 해요.

지호: 그럼, 공원에 가자.

❶ a few: 몇 가지 / safety rule: 안전 규칙 / earthquake: 지진
❷ Let's ~: ~하자. / practice: 연습하다
❸ Don't forget to+동사원형 ~: ~하는 것을 잊지 마라.(상기시켜 주기) / get under the desk: 책상 밑에 들어가다
❹ hold on to: ~을 꽉 잡다
❺ get out: 나가다
❻ You'd better not + 동사원형 ~: 너는 ~하지 않는 게 좋겠다.

Check(√) True or False

(3) They learned a few safety rules for earthquakes yesterday.　　　T ☐ F ☐

(4) When the students go out, they should not use the elevator.　　　T ☐ F ☐

Listen & Speak 1 - A - 2

G: Dad, I'm leaving.

M: ❶You need to wear this, Julie. ❷There is a lot of fine dust in the air today.

G: Oh, I didn't know that.

M: ❸It will be bad for your health. ❹So don't forget to wear this mask.

G: ❺All right. Thank you.

❶ need to+동사원형: ~할 필요가 있다 / wear: 쓰다
❷ There is ~: ~이 있다 / fine dust: 미세 먼지
❸ be bad for: ~에 나쁘다
❹ Don't forget to + 동사원형 ~.: ~하는 것을 잊지 마라.

Listen & Speak 2 - A - 1

B: Hi, Amy. ❶What's up?

G: ❷I'm here to buy a shirt. What about you?

B: I have a lunch meeting in this shopping center. ❸Oh, I should go now. I'm late.

G: ❹Okay, but you'd better not run. ❺The sign says the floor is wet.

B: I didn't see it. Thanks.

❶ What's up?: 왠일이야?
❷ to buy: to부정사의 부사적 용법 중 목적(~하기 위하여)
❸ I should + 동사원형 ~: 나는 ~해야겠다.
❹ You'd better not + 동사원형 ~: 너는 ~하지 않는 게 좋겠다.(금지의 표현)
❺ The sign says ~.: 표지판에 ~라고 되어 있어. / wet: 젖은

Listen & Speak 2 - A - 2

G: ❶What does the sign mean?

B: ❷It means that you'd better not look at your smartphone while you are walking.

G: That's interesting, but why?

B: ❸You can bump into people and there are many cars around here. It's so dangerous.

G: Now I see.

❶ What does[do] + 주어 + mean? = ~는 무슨 뜻이야?
❷ It means ~.: 그것은 ~라는 뜻이야. / You'd better not + 동사원형 ~: 너는 ~하지 않는 게 좋겠다.
❸ bump into: ~에 부딪히다 / There are + 복수명사 ~: ~이 있다

Conversation A

B: I was ❶having a good time with my family last night. ❷Suddenly everything started to shake. ❸I couldn't stand still and almost fell down. Dad shouted, "❹Get under the table. ❺ Don't forget to protect your head." Luckily, the shaking soon stopped. ❻It was a scary experience.

❶ have a good time: 좋은 시간을 보내다
❷ suddenly: 갑자기 / shake: 흔들리다
❸ fall down: 넘어지다
❹ get under the table: 책상 밑에 들어가다
❺ Don't forget + 동사원형 ~: ~하는 것을 잊지 마라.(=Remember+동사원형 ~) / protect: 보호하다
❻ scary: 무서운 / experience: 경험

Wrap Up - Listening 1

G: Many people use this almost every day. ❶ People stand in line to enter this. ❷They wait for others to get off before they enter. ❸ They use this to move up and down floors in a building. ❹You'd better not use this in case of a fire.

❶ stand in line: 줄을 서다
❷ wait for: ~을 기다리다 / get off: 내리다
❸ up and down: 위아래로
❹ You'd better not + 동사원형 ~: 너는 ~하지 않는 게 좋겠다. / in case of: ~의 경우에

Wrap Up - Listening 2

B: ❶I'm going to go to Jiri Mountain with my dad tomorrow.

G: It sounds great.

B: ❷I'm excited because we are going to stay there for two days and one night.

G: ❸That'll be great, but don't forget to check the weather.

B: Okay.

❶ be going to: ~할 것이다
❷ excited: 신이 난 / for two days and one night: 1박 2일 동안
❸ Don't forget to+동사원형 ~: ~하는 것을 잊지 마라. / weather: 날씨

다음 우리말과 일치하도록 빈칸에 알맞은 말을 쓰시오.

Listen & Speak 1 - A - 1

B: Mom, _____ I _____ some apple juice?

W: Sure, Chris. Don't _____ _____ check the food label.

B: The _____ _____?

W: Yes. Too much sugar is not good _____ you.

B: Okay, I _____ _____ it.

Listen & Speak 1 - A - 2

G: Dad, I'm _____.

M: You need to _____ this, Julie. There is a lot of _____ _____ in the air today.

G: Oh, I _____ _____ that.

M: It will be _____ _____ your health. So _____ _____ to wear this mask.

G: _____ _____. Thank you.

Listen & Speak 2 - A - 1

B: Hi, Amy. What's _____?

G: I'm here _____ _____ a shirt. What _____ you?

B: I _____ a lunch meeting _____ this shopping center. Oh, I _____ _____ now. I'm _____.

G: Okay, but you'd _____ _____ run. The sign _____ the floor is _____.

B: I _____ see it. Thanks.

Listen & Speak 2 - A - 2

G: What _____ the sign _____?

B: It means that _____ _____ _____ look at your smartphone _____ you are walking.

G: That's interesting, _____ why?

B: You can _____ _____ people and _____ _____ many cars _____ here. It's so _____.

G: Now I _____.

해석

B: 엄마, 사과 주스 좀 사도 돼요?
W: 물론, Chris. 식품 라벨을 확인하는 것을 잊지 마라.
B: 식품 라벨이요?
W: 그래. 너무 많은 설탕은 너에게 좋지 않아.
B: 네, 확인해 볼게요.

G: 아빠, 저 나가요.
M: Julie, 이걸 쓸 필요가 있어. 오늘은 공기 중에 미세먼지가 많아.
G: 오, 전 몰랐어요.
M: 그것은 건강에 나쁠 거야. 그러니 이 마스크 쓰는 걸 잊지 마라.
G: 알겠습니다, 감사합니다.

B: 안녕, Amy. 왠일이야?
G: 셔츠를 사러 왔어. 너는?
B: 이 쇼핑센터에서 점심 모임이 있어. 오, 이만 가 봐야겠어. 늦었어.
G: 그래, 하지만 뛰지 않는 게 좋겠어. 표지판에 바닥이 젖었다고 적혀 있어.
B: 난 못 봤어. 고마워.

G: 그 표지판은 무슨 뜻이니?
B: 걷는 동안 스마트폰을 보지 않는 게 낫다는 뜻이야.
G: 재미있네, 그런데 왜지?
B: 사람들과 부딪힐 수 있고 이 근처에는 차도 많아. 너무 위험해.
G: 이제 알겠어.

Conversation A

B: I was _____ a good time _____ my family last night. Suddenly everything started _____ _____. I _____ stand still and almost _____ _____. Dad shouted, "_____ under the table. _____ _____ to protect your head." _____, the shaking soon stopped. It was a _____ _____.

Conversation B

Teacher: I _____ you _____ _____ safety rules for earthquakes today. Now, _____ practice. Are you _____?

Amy & Jiho: Yes.

Teacher: Everything _____ _____. Don't _____ _____ _____ under the desk and _____ your body first.

Jiho: It's so _____.

Amy: You're doing fine, Jiho. _____ _____ _____ the leg of the desk.

Jiho: Oh, the shaking stopped _____ _____. Let's get _____!

Teacher: Remember! You'd _____ _____ _____ the elevator. _____ the stairs.

Amy: Where _____ we _____ now?

Teacher: You _____ _____ find an open area _____ no buildings.

Jiho: Then, _____ go _____ the park.

Wrap Up - Listening 1

G: Many people use this _____ every day. People _____ _____ _____ to enter this. They _____ _____ others to _____ _____ before they enter. They use this to _____ and _____ floors in a building. _____ _____ not use this _____ _____ a fire.

Wrap Up - Listening 2

B: I'm _____ _____ go to Jiri Mountain _____ my dad tomorrow.

G: It _____ great.

B: I'm excited _____ we are going to stay there _____ two days and _____ _____.

G: That'll be great, but _____ _____ _____ _____ the weather.

B: Okay.

해석

B: 나는 어젯밤에 가족과 즐거운 시간을 보내고 있었다. 갑자기 모든 것이 흔들리기 시작했다. 나는 가만히 있을 수가 없어서 하마터면 넘어질 뻔했다. 아빠는 "테이블 밑으로 들어가. 머리를 보호하는 걸 잊지 마."라고 소리쳤다. 다행히도, 흔들림은 곧 멈추었다. 그것은 무서운 경험이었다.

선생님: 오늘 지진에 대한 몇 가지 안전 수칙들을 말했죠. 자, 실습해 봅시다. 준비됐나요?
Amy와 지호: 네.
선생님: 모든 것이 흔들리고 있어요. 책상 밑에 들어가서 먼저 여러분의 몸을 보호하는 것을 잊지 마세요.
지호: 너무 무서워요.
Amy: 너는 잘하고 있어, 지호야. 책상 다리를 꽉 잡아.
지호: 오, 떨림이 잠시 멈췄어. 나가자!
선생님: 기억하세요! 엘리베이터를 이용하면 안 돼요. 계단을 이용하세요.
Amy: 이제 우린 어디로 가야 하죠?
선생님: 건물이 없는 확 트인 곳을 찾아야 해요.
지호: 그럼, 공원에 가자.

G: 많은 사람들이 거의 매일 이것을 사용한다. 사람들이 이것에 들어가기 위해 줄을 선다. 그들은 다른 사람들이 들어오기 전에 내리기를 기다린다. 그들은 건물의 층을 위아래로 움직이기 위해 이것을 사용한다. 화재가 났을 때는 이것을 사용하면 안 된다.

B: 나는 내일 아빠와 지리산에 갈 거야.
G: 멋진데.
B: 우리는 1박 2일 동안 묵을 예정이어서 신나.
G: 그거 좋겠네. 하지만, 날씨를 확인하는 걸 잊지 마.
B: 알았어.

01 다음 대화의 빈칸에 알맞은 것은?

> A: I have a headache. What should I do?
> B: Take some rest and don't _____ to take a medicine.

take some rest 좀 쉬다

① mind
② awake
③ delay
④ insist
⑤ forget

02 다음 대화의 밑줄 친 부분과 바꾸어 쓸 수 있는 것은?

> A: Peter, you'd better not run when you cross the street.
> B: Okay, I will.

① you may run when you cross the street
② You must run when you cross the street
③ You need to run when you cross the street
④ You would run when you cross the street
⑤ You shouldn't run when you cross the street

[03~04] 다음 대화의 빈칸에 알맞은 것을 고르시오.

03

> A: I'm going to swim at the beach.
> B: Don't forget to _____.

① wear safety gear
② put on hiking shoes
③ wear a helmet
④ wear a life jacket
⑤ turn on the fan

04

> A: It's going to rain. _____
> B: Okay. If it rains, I'll stay inside.

stay 머물다

① You will go outside.
② You shouldn't go outside.
③ You would go outside.
④ You might not go outside.
⑤ You can go outside.

[01~04] 다음 대화를 읽고, 물음에 답하시오.

> G: Dad, I'm leaving.
> M: You need to wear this, Julie. There ⓐ a lot of fine dust in the air today.
> G: Oh, I didn't know that.
> M: It will be bad for your health. ⓑ ⓒdon't forget to wear this mask.
> G: All right. Thank you.

서답형

01 위 대화의 빈칸 ⓐ에 알맞은 말을 쓰시오.

➡ _____

02 위 대화의 빈칸 ⓑ에 알맞은 것은?

① Or   ② But   ③ So
④ And   ⑤ Yet

중요

03 위 대화의 밑줄 친 ⓒ의 의도로 알맞은 것은?

① 확신하기   ② 사과하기
③ 불평하기   ④ 상기시켜 주기
⑤ 허락 구하기

04 위 대화의 내용과 일치하지 <u>않는</u> 것은?

① 오늘은 미세 먼지가 많다.
② 소녀는 미세 먼지가 많은 것을 알지 못했다.
③ 미세 먼지는 건강에 나쁘다.
④ 아빠는 소녀에게 마스크를 쓸 것을 당부하고 있다.
⑤ 소녀는 마스크를 쓰지 않을 것이다.

[05~08] 다음 대화를 읽고, 물음에 답하시오.

> Teacher: I told you ⓐ safety rules for earthquakes today. Now, let's practice. Are you ready?
> Amy & Jiho: Yes.
> Teacher: Everything is shaking. Don't forget to get under the desk and protect your body first.
> Jiho: It's so scary.
> Amy: You're doing fine, Jiho. Hold on ⓑ the leg of the desk.
> Jiho: Oh, the shaking stopped for now. Let's get out!
> Teacher: Remember! ⓒ use the elevator. Use the stairs.

05 위 대화의 빈칸 ⓐ에 알맞은 것은?

① any   ② much
③ little   ④ a few
⑤ a little

06 위 대화의 빈칸 ⓑ에 알맞은 것은?

① to   ② of
③ for   ④ up
⑤ out

중요

07 위 대화의 빈칸 ⓒ에 가장 알맞은 것은?

① You would not
② You'd better not
③ You're supposed to
④ You don't have to
⑤ You're not able to

08 위 대화를 읽고, 다음 질문에 완전한 문장으로 답하시오.

> **Q:** What are Amy and Jiho practicing now?
> **A:** _____

[09~11] 다음 담화문을 읽고, 물음에 답하시오.

> I was having a good time with my family last night. (①) I couldn't stand still and almost fell down. (②) Dad shouted, "Get under the table. (③) Don't forget to protect your head." (④) Luckily, the shaking soon stopped. It was a scary experience. (⑤)

09 위 글의 ①~⑤ 중 다음 문장이 들어갈 알맞은 곳은?

> Suddenly everything started to shake.

①   ②   ③   ④   ⑤

10 위 글의 밑줄 친 부분을 다음과 같이 바꿔 쓸 때 빈칸에 알맞은 말을 쓰시오.

> _____ to protect your head.

11 위 글을 읽고, 답할 수 <u>없는</u> 질문은?

① What is the writer talking about?
② When did the earthquake occur?
③ Were the writer and his/her father in the drawing room?
④ What did the dad shout to the writer?
⑤ Did the shaking stop soon?

[12~15] 다음 대화를 읽고, 물음에 답하시오.

> **G:** What does the sign mean?
> **B:** It means that ⓐyou'd better not look at your smartphone while you are walking.
> **G:** That's interesting, ___ⓑ___ why?
> **B:** You can bump ___ⓒ___ people and there are many cars around here. It's so dangerous.
> **G:** Now I see.

12 위 대화의 밑줄 친 ⓐ와 바꿔 쓸 수 있는 것은? (2개)

① You must not
② You don't have to
③ You shouldn't
④ You're permitted to
⑤ You're allowed to

13 위 대화의 빈칸 ⓑ에 알맞은 것은?

① so   ② or   ③ but
④ and   ⑤ for

14 위 대화의 빈칸 ⓒ에 알맞은 것은?

① at   ② with
③ into   ④ for
⑤ from

15 What does the sign mean? Answer in Korean.

➡ _____

[01~02] 다음 우리말에 맞도록 괄호 안에 주어진 단어를 배열하여 문장을 완성하시오.

01

> 장갑 끼는 것을 잊지 마.
> (wear / gloves / don't / to / forget / your).

➡ _____

02

> 쓰레기를 가져오는 것을 명심해라.
> (back / bring / to / your / make / trash / sure).

➡ _____

03 다음 괄호 안에 주어진 단어들을 배열하여 대화를 완성하시오.

> A: Tony, (play / better / you'd / not) with a ball near the street.
> B: Okay, I see.

➡ _____

04 다음 대화의 순서를 바르게 배열하시오.

> A: I'm going to go to Jiri Mountain with my dad tomorrow.
> (A) Okay.
> (B) It sounds great.
> (C) That'll be great, but don't forget to check the weather.
> (D) I'm excited because we are going to stay there for two days and one night.

➡ _____

05 다음 대화의 밑줄 친 말과 바꿔 쓸 수 있는 표현을 2개 이상 쓰시오.

> A: Jane, <u>you'd better not use</u> your smartphone while you are riding a bike.
> B: Okay, I see.

➡ _____
_____

[06~08] 다음 대화를 읽고, 물음에 답하시오.

> B: Hi, Amy. What's up?
> G: I'm here ⓐ<u>buy</u> a shirt. What about you?
> B: I have a lunch meeting in this shopping center. Oh, I should go now. I'm late.
> G: Okay, but you'd better not run. The sign says the floor is wet.
> B: I didn't see it. Thanks.

06 위 대화의 밑줄 친 ⓐ를 알맞은 형태로 바꿔 쓰시오.

➡ _____

07 Why did the girl come to this shopping center? Answer in English.

➡ _____

08 Why should the boy not run? Answer in English.

➡ _____

Grammar

교과서

① 의문사+to부정사

> • I learned **how to do** CPR. 나는 심폐소생술을 하는 방법을 배웠다.
> • We couldn't decide **what to eat** for dinner. 우리는 저녁으로 무엇을 먹을지 결정할 수 없었다.
> • Can you tell me **where to buy** a life jacket? 구명조끼를 어디서 사는지 말해 줄래?

■ 의문사 뒤에 to부정사를 써서 '~해야 하는지, ~하는 것이 좋을지'라는 의무의 뜻을 나타낼 수 있다. 이때 「의문사+to부정사」는 보통 문장 안에서 동사의 목적어 역할을 한다. 또, 의문사 대신 접속사 whether를 쓸 수도 있다.

• I can't decide **what to do**. 나는 무엇을 할지 결정할 수 없다.

• I don't know **where to buy** notebooks. 나는 공책을 어디서 사야 할지 모른다.

■ 의문사와 to부정사 사이에 명사가 오면 의문사와 함께 하나의 의문사(구)를 형성한다.

• I wanted to know **what time to** start. 나는 몇 시에 출발해야 하는지 알고 싶었다.

의문사+to부정사		의문사+명사+to부정사	
what to do where to go when to start which to choose how to swim	무엇을 해야 하는지 어디에 가야 하는지 언제 출발해야 하는지 어느 것을 골라야 할지 어떻게 수영해야 할지	what book to read which way to go what time to get up how many books to read	어떤 책을 읽어야 할지 어느 길로 가야 할지 몇 시에 일어나야 할지 얼마나 많은 책을 읽어야 할지

■ 「의문사+to부정사」는 의무를 나타내므로 should를 써서 「의문사+주어+should+동사 원형」 구문으로 바꿔 쓸 수 있다.

• I don't know **what to make** next. 다음에 무엇을 만들어야 할지 모르겠다.

→ I don't know **what I should make** next.

핵심 Check

1. 다음 괄호 안에서 알맞은 것을 고르시오.

(1) She doesn't know (which / how) to play chess.

(2) I asked her (which / where) book to buy.

(3) Please tell him (why / where) to buy the doll.

(4) The doctor told me (what / when) to take medicine.

(5) I want to travel this summer, but I don't know (where / what) to go.

② as + 형용사/부사의 원급 + as

- I was **as** scared **as** the others. 나는 다른 사람들 만큼 무서웠다.
- My shoes are **not as** big **as** yours. 내 신발은 너의 신발만큼 크지 않다.
- Teri studies **as** hard **as** her twin sister. Teri는 그녀의 쌍둥이 여동생만큼 열심히 공부한다.

■ **동등비교**
둘을 비교하여 두 대상의 정도가 같음을 비교하는 표현으로 「as+형용사[부사]의 원급+as」의 형태로 '~만큼 …한[하게]'라는 의미이다.
- I am **as** tall **as** Sam. 나는 Sam만큼 키가 크다.

■ **동등 비교의 부정**
'not as[so]+형용사[부사]의 원급+as'의 형태로 '~만큼 …하지 못한'의 의미이다. 비교급으로 바꿔 쓸 수도 있다.
- Jane is **not as** tall **as** Tony.
  = Tony is **taller than** Jane. Tony는 Jane보다 더 키가 크다.

■ **as+원급+as+사람+can[could]**
'가능한 한 ~하게'의 뜻으로 「as ~ as …」 구문의 관용적인 표현이다. 같은 뜻으로 'as+원급+as possible'의 구문을 쓰기도 한다.
- He swam **as** fast **as he could**. 그는 가능한 한 빨리 수영을 했다.
  = He swam **as** fast **as possible**.

■ **배수 표현**
'…의 몇 배만큼 ~한'이라고 배수 표현을 나타낼 경우 「숫자+times+as+형용사/부사+as」 또는 「배수사+as+형용사/부사+as」의 표현을 사용한다.
- Their house is about **twice as** big **as** ours. 그들의 집은 우리 집보다 두 배 정도 크다.

핵심 Check

2. 다음 괄호 안의 말을 알맞은 순서로 배열하시오.

(1) Sally runs (fast / as / Bora / as).
➡ Sally runs ＿＿＿＿＿＿＿＿＿＿＿.

(2) Is your camera (as, mine, new, as)?
➡ Is your camera ＿＿＿＿＿＿＿＿＿＿?

(3) The red pencil is (the, as, not, yellow, as, long, one).
➡ The red pencil is ＿＿＿＿＿＿＿＿＿＿.

01 다음 우리말과 일치하도록 빈칸에 알맞은 말을 쓰시오.

(1) Julie는 어디로 가야 할지 모른다.

➡ Julie doesn't know ＿＿＿＿ ＿＿＿＿ ＿＿＿＿.

(2) 그는 김치 만드는 법을 알고 싶어 한다.

➡ He wants to know ＿＿＿＿ ＿＿＿＿ ＿＿＿＿ kimchi.

(3) 우리는 중국 식당에서 무엇을 먹을지 얘기하고 있다.

➡ We're talking about ＿＿＿＿ ＿＿＿＿ ＿＿＿＿ at the Chinese restaurant.

(4) 그 문을 언제 열어야 할지 너의 엄마에게 물어 보아라.

➡ Ask your mother ＿＿＿＿ ＿＿＿＿ ＿＿＿＿ the door.

> make kimchi 김치를 만들다
> restaurant 식당

02 다음 밑줄 친 부분을 바르게 고쳐 쓰시오.

(1) Your bag is as heavy as me.

➡ ＿＿＿＿＿＿＿＿＿＿＿＿＿＿＿＿

(2) I can as run fast as my father.

➡ ＿＿＿＿＿＿＿＿＿＿＿＿＿＿＿＿

(3) Tokyo's population is as large as Seoul.

➡ ＿＿＿＿＿＿＿＿＿＿＿＿＿＿＿＿

(4) This is as not delicious as it looks.

➡ ＿＿＿＿＿＿＿＿＿＿＿＿＿＿＿＿

(5) The second question was more difficult as the first question.

➡ ＿＿＿＿＿＿＿＿＿＿＿＿＿＿＿＿

> delicious 맛있는

03 다음 두 문장의 의미가 같도록 빈칸에 알맞은 말을 쓰시오.

(1) I want to know where to park my car.

= I want to know ＿＿＿＿ ＿＿＿＿ ＿＿＿＿ ＿＿＿＿ my car.

(2) They learned how to use the computer.

= They learned ＿＿＿＿＿＿＿ ＿＿＿＿ ＿＿＿＿
＿＿＿＿.

01 다음 문장의 빈칸에 알맞은 것은?

> Jake is _____ old as my big brother.

① as ② so
③ than ④ very
⑤ much

02 다음 두 문장의 빈칸에 공통으로 알맞은 것은?

> • Can you show me how _____ do it?
> • They knew what _____ buy at the mall.

① on ② to
③ for ④ must
⑤ should

03 다음 주어진 문장에 맞도록 빈칸에 알맞은 것은?

> • Tom is 175 centimeters tall.
> • John is 175 centimeters tall, too.
> ➡ John is _____ Tom.

① shorter than ② as tall as
③ taller than ④ not as tall as
⑤ not taller than

04 다음 문장의 빈칸에 알맞은 것으로 짝지어진 것은?

> • She didn't decide _____ to wear that morning.
> • Can you tell me _____ to cook it?

① what – why ② how – who
③ what – how ④ when – which
⑤ where – what

05 다음 문장의 빈칸에 알맞은 것은?

> I don't know what to say about it.
> = I don't know what I _____ say about it.

① can ② should
③ would ④ may
⑤ could

서답형
06 다음 문장의 빈칸에 알맞은 말을 쓰시오.

	Ted	Minho	Eric
height	175cm	172cm	175cm

➡ Eric is _____ _____ _____.

07 다음 우리말을 영어로 바르게 옮긴 것은?

> 나는 동생에게 중국어 책 읽는 법을 가르쳤다.

① I taught my brother how to read Chinese books.
② I taught my brother where to read Chinese books.
③ I taught my brother why to read Chinese books.
④ I taught my brother what to read Chinese books.
⑤ I taught my brother how he could read Chinese books.

서답형
08 다음 두 문장의 뜻이 같도록 빈칸에 알맞은 말을 쓰시오.

> We could not agree as to where we should go during the holidays.
> = We could not agree as to _____ _____ _____ during the holidays.

서답형

09 다음 두 문장의 뜻이 같도록 빈칸에 알맞은 말을 쓰시오.

> I don't have _____ much money _____ you.
> ➡ I have less money than you.

중요

10 다음 중 어법상 어색한 문장은?

① Can you tell me what to do first?
② She decided what to eat lunch.
③ They showed him how to make it.
④ I didn't know where to find her.
⑤ Jack explains them how to finish it quickly.

11 다음 글에서 가장 빨리 달리는 사람은?

> • Eric runs very fast.
> • Junho cannot run as fast as Eric.
> • Mina and Mike are faster than Eric.
> • Mina is slower than Mike.

① Junho   ② Mike
③ Mina   ④ Eric
⑤ Mina and Mike

12 다음 밑줄 친 부분의 문장 성분이 다른 하나는?

① He told me where to go.
② The important thing is what to read.
③ I don't know which book to buy.
④ I didn't know whether to take this bus or not.
⑤ I have no idea about how to solve this problem.

서답형

13 다음 문장과 뜻이 같도록 빈칸에 알맞은 말을 쓰시오.

> He didn't tell them what to read.
> ➡ He didn't tell them what _____ _____ read.

서답형

14 다음 두 문장의 의미가 같도록 빈칸에 알맞은 말을 쓰시오.

> The desk is cheaper than the table.
> ➡ The table is _____ _____ _____ _____ the desk.

중요

15 다음 밑줄 친 부분이 어색한 것은?

① Can you show me how to cook it?
② I didn't know what to wear.
③ They decided where to go first.
④ Jack explained them how to make next.
⑤ She told me when to start it.

서답형

16 다음 두 문장이 같은 뜻이 되도록 빈칸에 알맞은 말을 쓰시오.

(1) February is colder than March.
　➡ March isn't as _____ as Februay.
(2) It wasn't as hot in Pusan as in Taegu.
　➡ It was _____ in Taegu _____ in Pusan.

17 다음 중 어법상 <u>잘못된</u> 것은?

① I am as pretty as you.

② You're as tall as me.

③ They are not as scary as lions.

④ English is easier than math.

⑤ Minsu can speak Chinese as good as I do.

18 다음 중 어법상 <u>어색한</u> 문장은?

① Does she know when to start?

② I don't know how use this camera.

③ We don't know which bus to get on.

④ They had no idea where to go.

⑤ I'm wondering what to buy for my mother's birthday.

서답형

19 다음 괄호 안에 주어진 단어를 이용하여 우리말을 영어로 옮기시오.

> 그녀는 너만큼 인기 있지 않다. (as, popular)

➡ _____

20 다음 빈칸에 들어갈 말로 바르게 짝지어진 것은?

> • You may eat as much _____ you like.
> • This picture is _____ beautiful than mine.

① as – much　　② as – more

③ so – few　　④ as – little

⑤ so – much

21 다음 두 문장의 뜻이 같도록 빈칸에 알맞은 것은?

> Seoul is bigger than Incheon.
> = Incheon is _____ Seoul.

① as big as　　② larger than

③ bigger than　　④ not so big as

⑤ not smaller than

서답형

22 다음 우리말과 같도록 괄호 안의 단어들을 이용하여 문장을 쓰시오.

> 카메라 사용법 좀 가르쳐 주실래요?
> (can / show / how)

➡ _____

23 다음 중 어법상 <u>틀린</u> 문장은?

① Can you tell me when to get up?

② They told me where to go.

③ Jack decided what to eat in the morning.

④ Will you tell me who to invite Jack?

⑤ I learned how to make lemonade.

24 다음 빈칸에 들어갈 말이 나머지 넷과 <u>다른</u> 것은?

① What _____ learn in youth is very important.

② I want you to decide where _____ go first.

③ We discussed who _____ take the responsibility.

④ She completely forgot how _____ make a paper crane.

⑤ I will tell you what _____ see in London.

01 다음 빈칸에 알맞은 말을 〈보기〉에서 골라 쓰시오. (중복 사용 금지)

┌─── 보기 ───┐
what   where   which   how

(1) Jim learned _____ to ride a bike.
(2) I wanted to know _____ time to start.
(3) I asked her _____ book to read.
(4) Can I ask you _____ to write my name?

02 다음 표를 보고, 빈칸에 알맞은 말을 고르시오.

	Kevin	Junho	Brian
height(cm)	172	178	172
age(years old)	15	16	16

(1) Brian is (taller than / as tall as) Kevin.
(2) Junho is (taller than / as tall as) Kevin.
(3) Brian is (older than / as old as) Junho.
(4) Kevin is (as old as / not as old as) Junho and Brain.

03 다음 문장에서 어색한 부분을 찾아 바르게 고쳐 쓰시오.

(1) I can't decide what will buy for my mother's birthday.

➡ _____

_____

(2) Bill didn't tell us where to staying.

➡ _____

04 다음 문장을 as ~ as 구문으로 고쳐 쓰시오.

(1) Jimin is shorter than Taemin.

➡ _____

(2) Jane is less heavy than Kirk.

➡ _____

05 주어진 단어를 순서에 맞게 배열하여 문장을 완성하시오.

(1) You don't know about history _____
_____. (I, as, do, much, as)
(2) I got here _____.
(as, could, fast, I, as)
(3) This bed is _____.
(that, not, as, bed, comfortable, as)

06 다음 문장을 should를 써서 같은 의미의 문장으로 바꿔 쓰시오.

(1) My brother doesn't know where to go.

➡ _____

(2) Alice doesn't know what to cook.

➡ _____

(3) Please tell me when to help you.

➡ _____

(4) The problem is how to escape from here.

➡ _____

07 다음 우리말과 의미가 같도록 문장을 완성하시오.

(1) 어디서 노래 연습을 해야 할지 선생님에게 여쭤 보자.
➡ Let's ask our teacher _____ _____
_____ singing songs.

(2) 나는 언제 서울을 방문해야 할지 결정하지 못했다.
➡ I didn't decide _____ _____
_____ Seoul.

(3) 너는 누구와 그곳에 가야 하는지 아니?
➡ Do you know _____ _____
_____ there with?

(4) 나는 무엇을 사야 할지 몰랐다.
➡ I didn't know _____ _____
_____.

(5) 그녀는 어느 꽃을 살지 정했다.
➡ She decided _____ flower _____
_____.

08 다음 두 문장을 as ~ as를 써서 〈보기〉와 같이 한 문장으로 나타내시오.

┌─ 보기 ┐
Jack has six dogs. Kate also has six dogs.
➡ Jack has as many dogs as Kate has.
└────┘

(1) Ella has nine hats. I also have nine hats.
➡ _____

(2) This new tool is useful. That old one is useful, too.
➡ _____

(3) Tom drank much wine. He also drank much water.
➡ _____

09 다음 문장에서 어법상 <u>어색한</u> 곳을 찾아 바르게 고쳐 쓰시오.

┌────────────────────┐
Mary didn't know which way she to take.
└────────────────────┘

_____ ➡ _____

10 다음 두 문장을 한 문장으로 만들 때, 괄호 안의 말을 이용해 빈칸에 알맞은 말을 쓰시오.

┌────────────────────┐
Amy scored 100 on the test. Junsu scored 90 on it. (well)
➡ Amy scored _____ than Junsu did.
➡ Junsu didn't score _____ _____
_____ Amy did.
└────────────────────┘

11 다음 주어진 단어를 바르게 배열하여 문장을 완성하시오.

(1) (didn't / leave / I / to / when / know).
➡ _____

(2) (do / how / know / the guitar / play / to / you)?
➡ _____

(3) (to / I / her / where / meet / know / don't).
➡ _____

12 다음 빈칸에 알맞은 말을 〈보기〉에서 골라 쓰시오.

┌─ 보기 ┐
early   wise   twice   just
└────┘

(1) This cat is _____ as pretty as that one.

(2) He's not as _____ as he used to be.

(3) This box is _____ as large as that one.

(4) He doesn't get up as _____ as Ann.

CPR Saves Lives

Announcer: Yesterday, a teenager saved the life of an old man. The brave student is in the studio with us today. Please introduce yourself.

Sejin: My name is Kim Sejin. I'm in the second grade at Hanguk Middle School.

Announcer: Could you tell us your experience?

Sejin: Sure. I was waiting for the bus with my friend, Jinho. A man suddenly fell in front of us. Nobody knew what to do. I was as scared as the others at first. Then, I ran to him and tapped him on the shoulder. He wasn't moving or breathing. I said to Jinho, "Call 119," and started CPR.

CPR 심폐소생술
save 구하다
announcer 아나운서
teenager 십대
brave 용감한
introduce 소개하다
grade 학년
experience 경험
suddenly 갑자기
fall 넘어[쓰러]지다
scared 무서워하는, 겁먹은
tap (가볍게) 톡톡 두드리다[치다]
shoulder 어깨
breathe 숨을 쉬다, 호흡하다

확인문제

● 다음 문장이 본문의 내용과 일치하면 T, 일치하지 않으면 F를 쓰시오.

1 Sejin is in the studio now. ☐

2 Sejin saved the life of an old man today. ☐

3 Sejin is in the second grade at Hanguk Middle School. ☐

4 Sejin wasn't scared when a man fell down. ☐

5 Sejin told Jinho to call 119 before he started CPR. ☐

Announcer: That's impressive. When did you learn such an important skill?

such a/an+형+명=so+형+a/an+명

Sejin: We had Safety Training Day at school last week. I learned how to do CPR and had a chance to practice.

지난주   how+to부정사: ~하는 방법

to부정사의 형용사적 용법(~할)

Announcer: Can you show the audience how to perform CPR?

how+to부정사: 어떻게 행하는지

Sejin: Yes. Keep your arms straight. Your arms and the other person's chest must be at a 90 degree angle. Push down in the center of the chest hard and fast until an ambulance comes.

keep+목적어+목적격보어: ~을 …하게 유지하다

~해야 한다   ~을 누르다

(부) 세게   (접) ~할 때까지

Announcer: Are there any other things to remember?

Are there + 복수명사 ~?: ~이 있니?   to부정사의 형용사적 용법(~할)

Sejin: Yes. You need to remember the four minutes of "Golden Time." It means that you should start CPR within four minutes after someone's heart stops. To begin CPR later than that will greatly lower the chances of saving someone's life.

~할 필요가 있다

= the four minutes of "Golden Time"   ~ 이내에[안에]   (접) ~한 후에

= Beginning   ~보다 늦게

전치사+동명사

Announcer: Timing is as important as doing CPR. Thank you for joining us.

as+원급+as: ~만큼 …한   ~해서 고맙다

Sejin: My pleasure.

- impressive 인상적인
- important 중요한
- skill 기술
- safety 안전
- training 훈련
- chance 기회, 가능성
- practice 연습하다
- audience 청중, 시청자
- perform 행하다, 실시하다
- chest 가슴
- degree (각도의 단위인) 도
- angle 각도
- hard 세게, 힘껏
- ambulance 구급차
- remember 기억하다
- heart 심장
- greatly 대단히, 크게
- lower 낮추다, 낮아지다
- join 함께하다

📎 **확인문제**

● 다음 문장이 본문의 내용과 일치하면 T, 일치하지 <u>않으면</u> F를 쓰시오.

1 Sejin learned how to do CPR yesterday. ☐

2 Sejin showed the audience how to perform CPR. ☐

3 Your arms and the other person's chest must be at a 45 degree angle. ☐

4 We push down in the center of the chest when we perform CPR. ☐

5 You should start CPR within four minutes after someone's heart stops. ☐

● 우리말을 참고하여 빈칸에 알맞은 말을 쓰시오.

1 Announcer: Yesterday, a teenager _____ the _____ of an old man.

2 The _____ student is in the studio _____ _____ today.

3 Please introduce _____.

4 Sejin: _____ name _____ Kim Sejin.

5 I'm _____ the _____ grade _____ Hanguk Middle School.

6 Announcer: Could you _____ _____ your _____?

7 Sejin: Sure. I was _____ _____ the bus _____ my friend, Jinho.

8 A man suddenly fell _____ _____ _____ us.

9 Nobody knew _____ _____ _____.

10 I was _____ scared _____ the others _____ first.

11 Then, I _____ to him and _____ him _____ the shoulder.

12 He _____ moving or _____.

13 I _____ _____ Jinho, "Call 119," and started _____.

14 Announcer: That's _____.

1 아나운서: 어제, 한 십대가 어떤 노인의 생명을 구했습니다.

2 그 용감한 학생이 오늘 우리와 함께 스튜디오에 있습니다.

3 자기소개를 해 보세요.

4 세진: 제 이름은 김세진입니다.

5 저는 한국중학교 2학년입니다.

6 아나운서: 당신의 경험을 우리에게 말해 줄 수 있나요?

7 세진: 물론이죠. 저는 친구 진호와 버스를 기다리고 있었어요.

8 갑자기 한 남자가 우리 앞에 쓰러졌어요.

9 아무도 무엇을 해야 할지 몰랐어요.

10 저는 처음엔 다른 사람들처럼 겁이 났어요.

11 그리고 나서, 저는 그에게 달려가서 그의 어깨를 두드렸어요.

12 그는 움직이지도 숨을 쉬지도 않았어요.

13 저는 진호에게 "119에 전화해."라고 말하고 심폐소생술을 시작했습니다.

14 아나운서: 인상적이네요.

15 When _____ you learn _____ _____ important skill?

16 Sejin: We had _____ _____ Day _____ school last week.

17 I learned _____ _____ _____ CPR and had a chance _____ _____.

18 Announcer: Can you _____ the audience _____ _____ perform CPR?

19 Sejin: Yes. _____ your arms _____.

20 Your arms and the _____ person's chest _____ be _____ a 90 degree _____.

21 _____ _____ in the center of the chest _____ and fast _____ an ambulance comes.

22 Announcer: _____ _____ any other things _____ _____?

23 Sejin: Yes. You _____ _____ remember the four _____ of "Golden Time."

24 It means _____ you _____ start CPR _____ four minutes _____ someone's heart _____.

25 _____ _____ CPR _____ _____ that will greatly lower the chances of _____ someone's life.

26 Announcer: Timing is _____ _____ _____ doing CPR.

27 Thank you _____ _____ us.

28 Sejin: My _____.

---

15 언제 그런 중요한 기술을 배웠나요?

16 세진: 지난주에 학교에서 '안전 교육의 날'이 있었어요.

17 저는 심폐소생술을 하는 방법을 배웠고 연습할 기회도 가졌어요.

18 아나운서: 청중들에게 심폐소생술을 어떻게 하는지 보여줄 수 있나요?

19 세진: 네. 팔을 쭉 펴세요.

20 당신의 팔과 다른 사람의 가슴은 90도 각도여야 합니다.

21 구급차가 올 때까지 가슴 중앙을 세게 그리고 빨리 누르세요.

22 아나운서: 기억해야 할 다른 것이 있나요?

23 세진: 네. "골든타임" 4분을 기억해야 합니다.

24 그것은 여러분이 누군가의 심장이 멈춘 후 4분 안에 심폐소생술을 시작해야 한다는 것을 의미합니다.

25 그보다 늦게 심폐소생술을 시작하는 것은 누군가의 생명을 구할 가능성을 크게 낮출 것입니다.

26 아나운서: 타이밍은 심폐소생술을 하는 것만큼이나 중요하군요.

27 저희와 함께 해 주셔서 감사합니다.

28 세진: 제가 더 고맙습니다.

● 우리말을 참고하여 본문을 영작하시오.

1 아나운서: 어제, 한 십대가 어떤 노인의 생명을 구했습니다.

➡ _____

2 그 용감한 학생이 오늘 우리와 함께 스튜디오에 있습니다.

➡ _____

3 자기소개를 해 보세요.

➡ _____

4 세진: 제 이름은 김세진입니다.

➡ _____

5 저는 한국중학교 2학년입니다.

➡ _____

6 아나운서: 당신의 경험을 우리에게 말해 줄 수 있나요?

➡ _____

7 세진: 물론이죠. 저는 친구 진호와 버스를 기다리고 있었어요.

➡ _____

8 갑자기 한 남자가 우리 앞에 쓰러졌어요.

➡ _____

9 아무도 무엇을 해야 할지 몰랐어요.

➡ _____

10 저는 처음엔 다른 사람들처럼 겁이 났어요.

➡ _____

11 그러고 나서, 저는 그에게 달려가서 그의 어깨를 두드렸어요.

➡ _____

12 그는 움직이지도 숨을 쉬지도 않았어요.

➡ _____

13 저는 진호에게 "119에 전화해."라고 말하고 심폐소생술을 시작했습니다.

➡ _____

14 아나운서: 인상적이네요.

➡ _____

15 언제 그런 중요한 기술을 배웠나요?

➡️ _____

16 세진: 우리는 지난주에 학교에서 '안전 교육의 날'이 있었어요.

➡️ _____

17 저는 심폐소생술을 하는 방법을 배웠고 연습할 기회를 가졌어요.

➡️ _____

18 아나운서: 청중들에게 심폐소생술을 어떻게 하는지 보여줄 수 있나요?

➡️ _____

19 세진: 네. 팔을 쭉 펴세요.

➡️ _____

20 당신의 팔과 다른 사람의 가슴은 90도 각도여야 합니다.

➡️ _____

21 구급차가 올 때까지 가슴 중앙을 세게 그리고 빨리 누르세요.

➡️ _____

22 아나운서: 기억해야 할 다른 것이 있나요?

➡️ _____

23 세진: 네. "골든타임" 4분을 기억해야 합니다.

➡️ _____

24 그것은 여러분이 누군가의 심장이 멈춘 후 4분 안에 심폐소생술을 시작해야 한다는 것을 의미합니다.

➡️ _____

25 그보다 늦게 심폐소생술을 시작하는 것은 누군가의 생명을 구할 가능성을 크게 낮출 것입니다.

➡️ _____

26 아나운서: 타이밍은 심폐소생술을 하는 것만큼이나 중요하군요.

➡️ _____

27 저희와 함께 해 주셔서 감사합니다.

➡️ _____

28 세진: 제가 더 고맙습니다.

➡️ _____

[01~05] 다음 글을 읽고, 물음에 답하시오.

Announcer: Yesterday, a teenager saved the life of an old man. The brave student is in the studio with us today. Please introduce ⓐ .

Sejin: My name is Kim Sejin. I'm ⓑ the second grade at Hanguk Middle School.

Announcer: Could you tell us your experience?

Sejin: Sure. I was waiting for the bus with my friend, Jinho. A man ⓒsuddenly fell in front of us. ⓓ아무도 무엇을 해야 할지 몰랐다. I was as scared as the others at first. Then, I ran to him and tapped him on the shoulder. He wasn't moving or breathe. I said to Jinho, "Call 119," and started CPR.

01 위 글의 빈칸 ⓐ에 알맞은 것은?

① him
② you
③ itself
④ yourself
⑤ himself

 서답형

02 위 글의 빈칸 ⓑ에 알맞은 말을 쓰시오.

➡ _____

03 위 글의 밑줄 친 ⓒ와 뜻이 같은 것은?

① specially
② exactly
③ actually
④ certainly
⑤ unexpectedly

서답형

04 위 글의 밑줄 친 ⓓ의 우리말을 주어진 단어를 이용하여 5 단어로 영작하시오.

(nobody / what)

➡ _____

05 위 글을 읽고, 답할 수 없는 질문은?

① Whose life did Sejin save?
② Where is Sejin now?
③ Who was Sejin waiting for the bus with?
④ What does the old man do for a living?
⑤ How did Sejin feel when a man fell in front of her?

[06~09] 다음 글을 읽고, 물음에 답하시오.

Announcer: Are there any other things ⓐ remember?

Sejin: Yes. You need to remember the four minutes of "Golden Time." ⓑIt means that you should start CPR within four minutes after someone's heart ⓒ . ⓓBegin CPR later than that will greatly ⓔ the chances of saving someone's life.

 위 글의 밑줄 친 ⓐ와 ⓓ의 알맞은 형태로 짝지어진 것은?

① remember – Begin
② to remember – Begin
③ remembering – To begin
④ remembering – Beginning
⑤ to remember – To begin

07 위 글의 밑줄 친 ⓑ가 가리키는 것을 영어로 쓰시오.

➡ _____

08 위 글의 빈칸 ⓒ에 문맥상 알맞은 것은?

① hurts   ② begins

③ beats   ④ pounds

⑤ stops

09 위 글의 빈칸 ⓔ에 다음 영영풀이에 해당하는 단어를 주어진 철자로 시작하여 쓰시오.

> to reduce something in amount, degree, strength etc, or to become less

➡ l_____

[10~14] 다음 글을 읽고, 물음에 답하시오.

Announcer: When did you learn ⓐ(skill / such / important / an)?

Sejin: We had Safety Training Day at school last week. I learned how ___ⓑ___ do CPR and had a chance ⓒto practice.

Announcer: Can you show the audience how to perform CPR?

Sejin: Yes. Keep your arms straight. Your arms and the other person's chest must be at a 90 degree angle. Push down in the center of the chest hard and fast until an ambulance comes.

10 위 글의 괄호 ⓐ 안의 단어들을 순서대로 배열하시오.

➡ _____

11 위 글의 빈칸 ⓑ에 알맞은 말을 쓰시오.

➡ _____

12 위 글의 밑줄 친 ⓒ와 쓰임이 같은 것은?

① I got up early to see her.

② Watch your step not to slip.

③ I have so many friends to help me.

④ You can spend money to help poor people.

⑤ He did his best to solve the problem.

13 위 글에서 다음 영영풀이에 해당하는 단어를 찾아 쓰시오.

> to do an action or activity that usually requires training or skill

➡ _____

14 위 글을 읽고, 다음 질문에 완전한 문장으로 답하시오.

> Q: When we perform CPR, at how many degree angle must our arms and the other person's chest be?
>
> A: _____
>
> _____

[15~20] 다음 글을 읽고, 물음에 답하시오.

Sejin: I was waiting for the bus with my friend, Jinho. A man suddenly fell in front of us. Nobody knew what to do. I was as ⓐ＿＿ as the others at first. Then, I ran to ⓑhim and tapped him ⓒ＿＿ the shoulder. ⓓHe wasn't moving or breathe. I said to Jinho, "Call 119," and started ⓔ＿＿ .

15 문맥상 위 글의 빈칸 ⓐ에 알맞은 것은?

① tired   ② scared
③ bored   ④ busy
⑤ excited

16 위 글의 밑줄 친 ⓑ가 가리키는 말을 찾아 쓰시오.

➡ ＿＿＿＿＿＿＿＿＿＿＿＿

17 위 글의 빈칸 ⓒ에 알맞은 것은?

① at   ② in
③ on   ④ up
⑤ over

18 위 글의 밑줄 친 ⓓ에서 어법상 틀린 부분을 찾아 바르게 고쳐 쓰시오.

➡ ＿＿＿＿＿＿＿＿＿＿＿＿

19 위 글의 빈칸 ⓔ에 다음 영영풀이에 해당하는 단어를 세 글자로 쓰시오.

a way of trying to save the life of someone who has stopped breathing and whose heart has stopped beating

➡ ＿＿＿＿＿＿＿＿＿＿＿＿

20 위 글을 읽고, 다음 질문에 완전한 문장으로 답하시오.

Q: What was Sejin doing when a man fell in front of her?
A: ＿＿＿＿＿＿＿＿＿＿＿＿

[21~26] 다음 글을 읽고, 물음에 답하시오.

Announcer: ⓐIs there any other things to remember?
Sejin: Yes. You need to remember the four minutes of "Golden Time." It means that you should start CPR ⓑ＿＿ four minutes after someone's heart stops. To begin CPR later than ⓒthat will greatly lower the chances ⓓ＿＿ saving someone's life.
Announcer: Timing is as ⓔ＿＿ as doing CPR. Thank you for ⓕjoin us.
Sejin: My pleasure.

21 위 글의 밑줄 친 ⓐ에서 어법상 틀린 부분을 찾아 바르게 고쳐 쓰시오.

＿＿＿＿＿ ➡ ＿＿＿＿＿

22 위 글의 빈칸 ⓑ에 알맞은 것은?

① with　　　　② for
③ within　　　④ during
⑤ between

서답형
23 위 글의 밑줄 친 ⓒthat이 가리키는 것을 우리말로 쓰시오.

➡ _____

중요
24 위 글의 빈칸 ⓓ에 알맞은 것은?

① by　　　　② of
③ to　　　　④ on
⑤ for

25 위 글의 빈칸 ⓔ에 문맥상 가장 알맞은 것은?

① easy　　　　② popular
③ difficult　　④ creative
⑤ important

서답형
26 위 글의 밑줄 친 ⓕ를 알맞은 형태로 고쳐 쓰시오.

➡ _____

[27~30] 다음 글을 읽고, 물음에 답하시오.

Announcer: Can you show the audience
_____ⓐ_____ ?
Sejin: Yes. Keep your arms straight. Your
arms and the other person's ___ⓑ___ must
be ___ⓒ___ a 90 degree angle. ___ⓓ___ in
the center of the chest hard and fast until an
ambulance comes.

중요
27 위 글의 빈칸 ⓐ에 알맞은 것은?

① how to call 119
② how to perform CPR
③ how to stand straight
④ how to do safety training
⑤ how to breathe

서답형
28 위 글의 빈칸 ⓑ에 다음 영영풀이에 해당하는 단어를 찾아 쓰시오.

the front part of the body between the
neck and the stomach

➡ _____

서답형
29 위 글의 빈칸 ⓒ에 알맞은 전치사를 쓰시오.

➡ _____

30 위 글의 빈칸 ⓓ에 문맥상 알맞은 것은?

① Put down　　② Push out
③ Push down　④ Pull up
⑤ Put off

[01~06] 다음 글을 읽고, 물음에 답하시오.

Sejin: My name is Kim Sejin. I'm in the second grade at Hanguk Middle School.

Announcer: ⓐCould you tell us your experience?

Sejin: Sure. I was waiting for the bus with my friend, Jinho. A man suddenly fell ⓑ~ 앞에서 us. Nobody knew what to do. ⓒ저는 처음엔 다른 사람들처럼 겁이 났어요. Then, I ran to him and tapped him ⓓ the shoulder. He wasn't moving or breathing. I said to Jinho, "Call 119," and started CPR.

01 What grade is Sejin in? Answer in English.

➡ _____

02 위 글의 밑줄 친 ⓐ의 4형식 문장을 3형식 문장으로 바르게 전환하시오.

➡ _____

03 위 글의 밑줄 친 ⓑ의 우리말에 맞게 세 단어로 쓰시오.

➡ _____

04 위 글의 밑줄 친 ⓒ의 우리말에 맞도록 주어진 어구를 순서대로 배열하시오.

(the others / as / I / first / scared / was / as / at)

➡ _____

05 위 글의 빈칸 ⓓ에 알맞은 전치사를 쓰시오.

➡ _____

06 What did Sejin say to Jinho before starting CPR?

➡ _____

[07~11] 다음 글을 읽고, 물음에 답하시오.

Announcer: Are there any other things ⓐ remember?

Sejin: Yes. You need to remember the four minutes of "Golden Time." It means ⓑ _____ you should start CPR within four minutes after someone's heart stops. To begin CPR later than that will greatly lower the ⓒ _____ of saving someone's life.

Announcer: Timing is ⓓ(CPR / as / doing / as / important). Thank you for joining us.

Sejin: My pleasure.

07 위 글의 밑줄 친 ⓐ를 알맞은 형태로 고치시오.

➡ _____

08 위 글의 빈칸 ⓑ에 알맞은 것을 쓰시오.

➡ _____

09 What does the four minutes of "Golden Time" mean? Answer in Korean.

➡ _____

_____

10 ⭐중요 위 글의 빈칸 ⓒ에 다음 영영풀이에 해당하는 단어를 주어진 철자로 시작하여 쓰시오. (복수형으로 쓸 것)

| the possibility that something will happen |

➡ c_____

11 위 글의 괄호 ⓓ 안의 단어들을 알맞은 순서로 바르게 배열하시오.

➡ _____

[12~17] 다음 글을 읽고, 물음에 답하시오.

Announcer: When did you learn ⓐsuch an important skill?

Sejin: We had Safety Training Day at school last week. ⓑ나는 심폐소생술을 하는 방법을 배웠다 and had a chance to practice.

Announcer: Can you show the ___ⓒ___ how to perform CPR?

Sejin: Yes. Keep your arms straight. Your arms and the other person's chest must be at a 90 degree angle. ⓓPush down in the center of the chest hard and fast until an ambulance will come.

12 위 글의 밑줄 친 ⓐ를 다음과 같이 바꿔 쓸 때 빈칸에 알맞은 것을 쓰시오.

| _____ important a skill |

13 When and where did Sejin have Safety Training Day? Answer in English.

➡ _____

14 ⭐중요 위 글의 밑줄 친 ⓑ의 우리말에 맞도록 주어진 단어를 바르게 배열하시오.

| (to / CPR / I / do / learned / how) |

➡ _____

15 위 글의 빈칸 ⓒ에 다음 영영풀이에 해당하는 단어를 쓰시오.

| the group of people who have gathered to watch or listen to something (a play, concert, someone speaking, etc.) |

➡ _____

16 ⭐중요 위 글의 밑줄 친 ⓓ에서 어법상 틀린 부분을 찾아 바르게 고쳐 쓰시오.

_____ ➡ _____

17 위 글을 읽고, 심폐소생술을 하는 과정을 우리말로 쓰시오.

➡ _____

_____

My Writing B

Save Your Life from a Fire

Do you know what to do when there is a fire? You should shout, "Fire!" You

what+to부정사: 무엇을 ~해야 할지   there is + 단수명사: ~이 있다   ~해야 한다

need to cover your face and body with a wet towel. You have to stay as low

~으로   ~해야 한다(=must)

as possible and get out. Also, you need to call 119 as soon as you can. Don't

as ~ as possible: 가능한 한 ~하게   가능한 한 빨리(=as soon as possible)

forget to use the stairs, not the elevator.

Don't forget to+동사원형 ~: ~하는 것을 잊지 마라

구문해설 • shout: 외치다 • cover: 덮다 • wet: 젖은 • also: 또한 • stair: 계단

해석

화재로부터 여러분의 생명을 구하라

불이 나면 여러분은 무엇을 해야 하는지 아는가? 여러분은 "불이야!"라고 외쳐야 한다. 여러분은 젖은 수건으로 얼굴과 몸을 가려야 한다. 가능한 한 낮은 자세로 밖으로 나가야 한다. 또한, 가능한 한 빨리 119에 전화해야 한다. 엘리베이터가 아니라 계단을 이용하는 것을 잊지 마라.

Wrap Up

Safety Training Day

Today we had Safety Training Day at school. Teachers taught us what to do

수여동사(teach)+간접목적어+직접목적어

when an earthquake hits. We learned how to protect our heads and bodies. We

how+to부정사: ~하는 방법

also learned where to go when the shaking stops.

where+to부정사: 어디로 ~할지

구문해설 • safety: 안전 • training: 교육, 훈련 • earthquake: 지진 • protect: 보호하다

• shaking: 흔들림

안전 교육의 날

오늘은 학교에서 안전 교육의 날이었다. 선생님들은 우리에게 지진이 일어났을 때 무엇을 해야 하는지 가르쳐 주셨다. 우리는 머리와 몸을 보호하는 법을 배웠다. 우리는 또한 흔들림이 멈추었을 때 어디로 가야 하는지 배웠다.

Project - Step 3

We'll tell you what to do for safety in the science room. First, don't forget to

수여동사(tell)+간접목적어+직접목적어   Don't forget to+동사원형 ~: ~하는 것을 잊지 마라

use safety glasses. Second, you'd better not run around.

보안경   You'd better not + 동사원형 ~: ~하면 안 된다

구문해설 • science room: 과학실 • use: 사용하다 • run around: 뛰어다니다

과학실에서 안전을 위해 무엇을 해야 하는지 알려드리겠습니다. 첫째, 보안경을 쓰는 것을 잊지 마세요. 둘째, 뛰어다니면 안 됩니다.

영역별 핵심문제

01 다음 중 짝지어진 단어의 관계가 나머지 넷과 <u>다른</u> 것은?

① late : early
② heavy : light
③ cheap : expensive
④ wet : dry
⑤ brave : fearless

02 다음 빈칸에 공통으로 알맞은 것은? (대·소문자 무시)

• There is a church _____ front of the school.
• _____ case of fire, ring the alarm bell.

① on
② at
③ from
④ in
⑤ with

03 다음 우리말과 같도록 빈칸에 알맞은 말을 쓰시오.

넘어져서 발목을 다치지 않도록 조심하라.
➡ Be careful not to _____ _____ and hurt your ankle.

04 다음 우리말과 같도록 빈칸에 알맞은 말을 주어진 철자로 시작하여 쓰시오.

가장 인상적인 것은 사람들이 매우 친절했다는 거야.
➡ The most _____ thing was the people were very kind.

05 다음 빈칸에 들어갈 말로 적절하지 <u>않은</u> 것은?

• You should _____, "Fire!"
• What does the sign _____?
• Don't forget to _____ the weather.
• You need to _____ your face and body with a wet towel.

① cover
② check
③ pick
④ mean
⑤ shout

06 다음 영영풀이에 해당하는 단어로 알맞은 것은?

to do an action or activity that usually requires training or skill

① exercise
② perform
③ achieve
④ experience
⑤ protect

07 다음 대화의 빈칸에 들어갈 말로 알맞은 것은?

A: I'm going to go to a taekwondo lesson.
B: Don't _____ to wear a uniform.
A: Okay, thanks.

① remember
② forget
③ take
④ bring
⑤ sell

08 다음 대화의 빈칸에 알맞은 것을 <u>모두</u> 고르면? (3개)

> A: I'm going to visit France.
> B: _____ learn some French.

① Don't forget to
② Make sure to
③ He doesn't want you to
④ Remember to
⑤ Are you interested in

09 다음 대화의 밑줄 친 부분과 바꿔 쓸 수 있는 것은?

> A: Is it okay to eat chocolate?
> B: Sure, but <u>don't eat too much.</u>

① you can eat too much
② you don't have to eat too much
③ you won't eat too much
④ you should eat too much
⑤ you'd better not eat too much

10 다음 대화의 빈칸에 알맞은 것은?

> A: Don't forget to take your umbrella.
> B: _____

① No, I'm not.   ② Okay, I see.
③ You're welcome.   ④ Sorry, but I can't.
⑤ I'm sorry to hear that.

[11~14] 다음 대화를 읽고, 물음에 답하시오.

> B: Mom, can I buy some apple juice?
> W: ⓐSure, Chris. ⓑ식품 라벨을 확인하는 것을 잊지 마라.
> B: The food label?
> W: Yes. Too much sugar is not good ⓒ_____ you.
> B: Okay, I will check ⓓit.

11 위 대화의 밑줄 친 ⓐ와 바꿔 쓸 수 있는 것은?

① Of course.
② Of course not.
③ That's the problem.
④ Sorry, but I can't.
⑤ I'm afraid I can't.

12 위 대화의 밑줄 친 ⓑ의 우리말에 맞도록 주어진 단어들을 바르게 배열하시오.

> (check / label / forget / the / to / don't / food)

➡ _____

13 위 대화의 빈칸 ⓒ에 알맞은 것은?

① at   ② in
③ of   ④ for
⑤ about

14 위 대화의 밑줄 친 ⓓ가 가리키는 것을 찾아 쓰시오.

➡ _____

15 다음 표의 내용과 일치하도록 빈칸에 알맞은 말을 쓰시오.

	weight(kg)
Insu	65
Kevin	60
Minho	70

➡ Kevin is not _____ heavy _____ Minho.

16 다음 문장의 빈칸에 공통으로 알맞은 말을 쓰시오

- I can't decide what _____ do.
- Can you show me how _____ use this washing machine?

17 다음 중 어법상 어색한 문장은?

① My house is not so large as yours.
② Jenny's mother ran as fast as she could.
③ He is as a great statesman as ever lived.
④ Are you as good at English as her?
⑤ The air is polluted as badly as the rivers.

18 다음 밑줄 친 ①~⑤ 중 어법상 어색한 것은?

①Before winter comes, many different ②kinds of birds ③head south. How do they know ④when to migrate? How do they know ⑤where should go?

①   ②   ③   ④   ⑤

19 다음 주어진 단어를 이용하여 우리말을 영어로 옮기시오.

그는 Tom만큼 테니스를 잘 친다. (as ~ as)

➡ _____

20 다음 두 문장이 같은 의미가 되도록 빈칸에 알맞은 말을 써 넣으시오.

The teacher told us when to begin the test.
= The teacher told us when we _____ _____ the test.

21 다음 중 어법상 어색한 것은?

① It is not as easy as you think.
② John doesn't work as hard as George do.
③ I don't have so much money as you do.
④ Let me have your answer as soon as possible.
⑤ I don't have as many friends as you do.

22 다음 중 어법상 올바른 문장을 모두 고른 것은?

ⓐ Please show me how to solve this problem.
ⓑ They decided what to do after school.
ⓒ We want to know where to go next time.
ⓓ Do you know who to tell me about it?
ⓔ Let me tell you when to move yesterday.

① ⓐ   ② ⓐ, ⓑ
③ ⓐ, ⓑ, ⓒ   ④ ⓐ, ⓑ, ⓒ, ⓓ
⑤ ⓐ, ⓑ, ⓒ, ⓔ

23 다음 중 밑줄 친 부분의 쓰임이 나머지 넷과 <u>다른</u> 것은?

① They were <u>as</u> busy as bees.
② Tom is not <u>as</u> honest as John.
③ Please come home <u>as</u> quickly as possible.
④ This house is twice <u>as</u> large as that.
⑤ He came up <u>as</u> she was speaking.

24 다음 두 문장의 의미가 같도록 빈칸에 알맞은 말을 쓰시오.

> Sarah is more diligent than Jane.
> = Jane is _____ _____ _____
> _____ Sarah.

25 다음 문장의 밑줄 친 부분과 의미가 같은 것은?

> I don't know <u>what to write</u> in the letter.

① what I write in the letter
② what I can write in the letter
③ how should I write in the letter
④ what I should write in the letter
⑤ how might I write in the letter

26 다음 두 문장의 의미가 같도록 할 때 빈칸에 알맞은 것은?

> This room is just the same size _____
> that one.
> = This room is as large as that one.

① as   ② so
③ from   ④ for
⑤ with

[27~32] 다음 글을 읽고, 물음에 답하시오.

Announcer: Yesterday, a teenager saved the life of an old man. The brave student is in the studio with us today. Please introduce ⓐ<u>you</u>.

Sejin: My name is Kim Sejin. I'm in the second grade at Hanguk Middle School.

Announcer: ⓑ<u>Could you tell us your experience?</u>

Sejin: Sure. I was waiting ⓒ the bus with my friend, Jinho. A man suddenly fell ⓓ front of us. ⓔ<u>아무도 무엇을 해야 할지 몰랐다.</u> I was ⓕ scared as the others at first. Then, I ran to him and tapped him on the shoulder. He wasn't moving or breathing. I said to Jinho, "Call 119," and started CPR.

27 위 글의 밑줄 친 ⓐ를 바르게 고쳐 쓰시오.

➡ _____

28 위 글의 밑줄 친 ⓑ의 4형식 문장을 3형식 문장으로 쓰시오.

➡ _____

29 위 글의 빈칸 ⓒ와 ⓓ에 알맞은 말이 바르게 짝지어진 것은?

① at – in   ② by – on
③ for – in   ④ over – on
⑤ into – at

30 위 글의 밑줄 친 ⓔ의 우리말에 맞게 주어진 단어를 바르게 배열하시오.

> (to / nobody / what / knew / do)

➡ _____

31 위 글의 빈칸 ①에 알맞은 것은?

① as   ② so

③ than   ④ very

⑤ much

32 위 글을 읽고, 답할 수 없는 질문은?

① Where is Sejin now?

② What school does Sejin attend?

③ Where was the old man going?

④ How did Sejin feel when a man fell in front of her?

⑤ What did Sejin say to Jinho before starting CPR?

[33~37] 다음 글을 읽고, 물음에 답하시오.

> Save Your Life from a Fire
> ⓐDo you know what to do when there are a fire? You should shout, "Fire!" You need to cover your face and body __ⓑ__ a wet towel. ⓒYou have to stay as low as possible and get out. Also, you need to call 119 as soon as you can. ⓓDon't forget to use the stairs, not the elevator.

33 위 글의 밑줄 친 ⓐ에서 어법상 틀린 부분을 찾아 바르게 고쳐 쓰시오.

_____ ➡ _____

34 위 글의 빈칸 ⓑ에 알맞은 것은?

① to   ② by

③ for   ④ from

⑤ with

35 위 글의 밑줄 친 ⓒ를 다음과 같이 바꿔 쓸 때 빈칸에 알맞은 말을 쓰시오.

> You have to stay _____ _____
> _____ _____ _____

36 위 글의 밑줄 친 ⓓ를 다음과 같이 바꿔 쓸 때 빈칸에 알맞은 말을 쓰시오.

> _____ to use the stairs

37 위 글을 읽고, 화재 발생 시 대처법으로 옳지 않은 것은?

① "불이야!"라고 외쳐야 한다.

② 젖은 수건으로 얼굴과 몸을 가려야 한다.

③ 가능한 한 몸을 낮게 유지하고 밖으로 나간다.

④ 가능한 한 빨리 119를 불러야 한다.

⑤ 엘리베이터를 이용해야 한다.

✏️ 출제율 95%

01 다음 중 〈보기〉와 같은 형태로 변화하는 단어는?

┌─ 보기 ┤
impress : impressive

① change ② act
③ admire ④ train
⑤ practice

✏️ 출제율 100%

02 다음 밑줄 친 반의어를 두 단어로 쓰시오.

The man is taking off his hat.

➡ _____

✏️ 출제율 90%

03 다음 중 영영풀이가 <u>잘못된</u> 것은?

① wet: not yet dry
② scary: causing fear
③ brave: feeling or showing no fear
④ line: a unit for measuring the size of an angle
⑤ tap: to hit someone or something quickly and lightly

✏️ 출제율 85%

04 다음 우리말과 같도록 빈칸에 알맞은 단어를 주어진 철자로 시작하여 쓰시오.

그는 깨끗한 공기를 마실 수 있는 곳에서 살고 싶어 한다.
➡ He wants to live where he can b_____ clean air.

✏️ 출제율 90%

05 다음 빈칸에 공통으로 알맞은 것은? (대·소문자 무시)

• _____ first, Kate didn't like Korean food, but now she loves it.
• This seatbelt protects the dogs _____ case of an accident.

① at – for ② in – on
③ in – with ④ at – in
⑤ of – in

✏️ 출제율 90%

06 다음 짝지어진 단어의 관계가 같도록 빈칸에 알맞은 말을 쓰시오.

floor : ceiling = _____ : safe

✏️ 출제율 100%

07 다음 대화에서 밑줄 친 부분의 의도로 알맞은 것은?

A: Can you take a picture of me?
B: Sure.
A: <u>You'd better not use the flash here, David.</u> The baby animals will wake up.
B: I see.

① 질문하기 ② 요청하기
③ 금지하기 ④ 행동 묘사하기
⑤ 미래의 계획 말하기

08 다음 대화의 밑줄 친 부분과 의미가 같은 것은?

> A: I can't find my seat.
>
> B: Your seat is right here. <u>Don't forget to turn off your smartphone, please.</u>
>
> A: OK, I won't.

① You can take off your smartphone.

② Make sure to use your smartphone.

③ Be sure to turn on your smartphone.

④ You should turn on your smartphone.

⑤ Remember to turn off your smartphone.

[09~10] 다음 대화를 읽고, 물음에 답하시오.

> B: Hi, Amy. What's up?
>
> G: I'm here to buy a shirt. What about you?
>
> B: I have a lunch meeting in this shopping center. Oh, I should go now. I'm late.
>
> G: Okay, but ⓐ너는 뛰지 않는 게 좋을 거야. The sign says the floor is wet.
>
> B: I didn't see ⓑit. Thanks.

09 위 대화의 밑줄 친 ⓐ의 우리말을 주어진 단어를 이용하여 영어로 옮기시오. (4단어)

> better

➡ _____

10 위 대화의 밑줄 친 ⓑ가 가리키는 것을 영어로 쓰시오.

➡ _____

11 다음 문장의 빈칸에 알맞은 것은?

> Books must be chosen as _____ as friends are.

① care

② caring

③ cared

④ careful

⑤ carefully

12 다음 문장에서 어법상 어색한 부분을 찾아 바르게 고쳐 쓰시오.

> Let's decide what to buys for Mina's birthday.

_____ ➡ _____

13 다음 빈칸에 들어갈 말이 나머지와 다른 하나는?

① Can you tell me what _____ buy at the mall?

② They didn't know where _____ go.

③ Let me know how _____ cook bulgogi.

④ He is _____ short to touch the ceiling.

⑤ I can't decide what _____ wear today.

14 다음 주어진 말을 이용하여 우리말에 맞게 문장을 완성하시오.

> 나는 너만큼 예쁘지 않다. (pretty)

➡ _____

출제율 90%

15 다음 두 문장의 뜻이 같도록 빈칸에 알맞은 말을 쓰시오.

> I want to learn cooking.
> = I want to learn _____ _____
> _____.

출제율 85%

16 다음 중 어법상 알맞지 않은 것은?

① Kate doesn't speak Korean as well as Mike do.
② The movie is not as interesting as you think.
③ I don't work so hard as you do.
④ Let me have your answer as soon as possible.
⑤ I don't have as much money as my brother does.

출제율 95%

17 다음 중 밑줄 친 부분이 어색한 것은?

① I'm thinking about what to show you.
② Do you know how to make a kite?
③ She wants to know when turn off the oven.
④ Rachel wants to know where to buy a bike.
⑤ Please tell me which to choose.

출제율 85%

18 다음 우리말과 일치하도록 주어진 단어를 바르게 배열하시오.

> 그는 예전만큼 많이 그녀를 미워하지 않는다.
> He doesn't hate her (as / used / he / as / much / to).

➡ _____

[19~23] 다음 글을 읽고, 물음에 답하시오.

> Announcer: When did you learn such an important skill?
> Sejin: We had Safety Training Day at school last week. I learned ___ⓐ___ to do CPR and ⓑ연습할 기회가 있었어요.
> Announcer: Can you show the audience ___ⓒ___ to perform CPR?
> Sejin: Yes. ⓓ(your / keep / straight / arms). Your arms and the other person's chest must be at a 90 degree angle. Push down in the center of the chest hard and fast ___ⓔ___ an ambulance comes.

출제율 95%

19 위 글의 빈칸 ⓐ와 ⓒ에 공통으로 알맞은 것은?

① what   ② how
③ where   ④ why
⑤ when

출제율 90%

20 위 글의 밑줄 친 ⓑ의 우리말에 맞도록 주어진 단어에 한 단어를 추가하여 바르게 배열하시오.

> (practice / a / had / chance)

➡ _____

출제율 90%

21 위 글의 괄호 ⓓ 안의 단어들을 바르게 배열한 것은?

① Straight your arms keep
② Keep straight your arms
③ Your arms straight keep
④ Your arms keep straight
⑤ Keep your arms straight

22 출제율 95%

위 글의 빈칸 ⓔ에 알맞은 것은?

① as　　　　　② because
③ since　　　　④ until
⑤ after

23 출제율 100%

위 글을 읽고, 다음 질문에 영어로 답하시오.

> Q: What did Sejin learn on Safety Training Day?
>
> A: _____

[24~28] 다음 글을 읽고, 물음에 답하시오.

Announcer: Are there any other things ⓐto remember?

Sejin: Yes. You need to remember the four minutes of "Golden Time." ⓑIt means that you should start CPR within four minutes ⓒ_____ someone's heart stops. ⓓBegin CPR later than that will greatly lower the chances of save someone's life.

Announcer: ⓔ_____ is as important as doing CPR. Thank you for joining us.

Sejin: My pleasure.

24 출제율 100%

위 글의 밑줄 친 ⓐ와 쓰임이 다른 것은?

① Give me something to drink.
② We need a house to live in.
③ I want a chair to sit on.
④ I sat down to take a break.
⑤ He has no friends to help him.

25 출제율 85%

위 글의 밑줄 친 ⓑ가 가리키는 것을 우리말로 쓰시오.

➡ _____

26 출제율 95%

위 글의 빈칸 ⓒ에 알맞은 것은?

① though　　　② before
③ after　　　　④ until
⑤ because

27 출제율 95%

위 글의 밑줄 친 ⓓ에서 어법상 틀린 부분을 두 군데 찾아 바르게 고쳐 쓰시오.

(1) _____ ➡ _____
(2) _____ ➡ _____

28 출제율 90%

위 글의 빈칸 ⓔ에 다음 영영풀이에 해당하는 단어를 쓰시오.

> the time when something happens or is done especially when it is thought of as having a good or bad effect on the result

➡ _____

01 다음 두 문장이 같은 뜻이 되도록 빈칸에 알맞은 말을 쓰시오.

> Make sure to wash your hands.
> = _____ to wash your hands.

➡ _____

02 다음 대화의 밑줄 친 부분과 바꿔 쓸 수 있는 말을 3개 쓰시오.

> A: Is it okay to eat chocolate?
> B: Sure, but you'd better not eat too much.

➡ _____

03 다음 괄호 안의 단어를 바르게 배열하여 대화를 완성하시오.

> A: I'm going to ride a bike.
> B: (gear / wear / don't / safety / to / forget)

➡ _____

04 자연스러운 대화가 되도록 (A)~(E)의 순서를 바르게 배열하시오.

> (A) The food label?
> (B) Okay, I will check it.
> (C) Mom, can I buy some apple juice?
> (D) Yes. Too much sugar is not good for you.
> (E) Sure, Chris. Don't forget to check the food label.

➡ _____

05 다음 〈조건〉에 맞게 괄호 안의 단어를 이용하여 우리말을 영어로 옮기시오.

> ┤ 조건 ├
> 1. 주어진 단어를 모두 이용할 것.
> 2. 필요시 어형 변화를 할 것.
> 3. as ~ as ...를 쓸 것.
> 4. 대·소문자 및 구두점에 유의할 것.

(1) Meg는 너만큼 노래를 잘 부른다. (sing, well)

➡ _____

(2) 이 거리는 저 거리와 아주 똑같은 넓이이다.
(street, just, wide, that one)

➡ _____

(3) 서울 타워는 이 탑보다 약 세 배 높다.
(Seoul Tower, about, time, as)

➡ _____

(4) 나는 나의 언니만큼 요리를 잘하지 못한다.
(can, cook, well, my sister)

➡ _____

06 다음 〈조건〉에 맞게 괄호 안의 단어를 이용하여 우리말을 영어로 옮기시오.

> ┤ 조건 ├
> 1. 주어진 단어를 모두 이용할 것.
> 2. 필요시 어형을 바꾸거나 단어를 추가할 것.
> 3. '의문사+to부정사'를 이용할 것.
> 4. 대·소문자 및 구두점에 유의할 것.

(1) 나는 어느 것을 골라야 할지 결정할 수 없었다.
(make / which / mind / choose / can / my / up)

➡ _____

(2) 그는 언제 공부하고 언제 놀아야 할지 알지 못한다. (when / play / and / he / know / does / study)

➡ _____
➡ _____

[07~10] 다음 글을 읽고, 물음에 답하시오.

Save Your Life from a Fire

Do you know what to do ⓐ불이 나면? You should shout, "Fire!" You need to cover your face and body ___ⓑ___ a wet towel. You have to stay as low as possible and get out. Also, you need to call 119 as soon as you can. Don't forget to use the stairs, not the elevator.

07 위 글의 밑줄 친 ⓐ의 우리말에 맞도록 주어진 단어들을 바르게 배열하시오.

(a / when / is / fire / there)

➡ _____

08 위 글의 빈칸 ⓑ에 알맞은 말을 쓰시오.

➡ _____

09 위 글에서 다음 영영풀이에 해당하는 단어를 찾아 쓰시오.

not dry

➡ _____

10 Should we use the elevator instead of the stairs in case of fire? Answer in English.

➡ _____

[11~13] 다음 글을 읽고, 물음에 답하시오.

Announcer: When did you learn such an important skill?

Sejin: We had Safety Training Day at school last week. I learned how ___ⓐ___ do CPR and had a chance ___ⓑ___ practice.

Announcer: Can you show the audience how to perform CPR?

Sejin: Yes. ⓒ당신의 팔을 똑바로 펴세요. Your arms and the other person's chest must be at a 90 degree angle. Push down in the center of the chest hard and fast until an ambulance comes.

11 위 글의 빈칸 ⓐ와 ⓑ에 공통으로 알맞은 것을 쓰시오.

➡ _____

12 위 글의 밑줄 친 ⓒ의 우리말에 맞도록 주어진 단어를 바르게 배열하시오.

(your / keep / straight / arms)

➡ _____

13 Where on the body do we push down when we perform CPR? Answer in English.

➡ _____

➡ _____

창의사고력 서술형 문제

01 다음 표를 참고하여 허락을 구하는 표현과 당부하는 표현을 넣어 대화를 완성하시오.

May I ~?	Don't forget to ~
• use this computer • borrow this book • ride my bike • use my cell phone here • eat here	• return it • turn it off • talk quietly • ride slowly • pick up any trash

A: Excuse me. May I _____?
B: Yes, you may. But don't forget to _____.
A: All right.

02 다음 〈보기〉와 같이 동등비교 구문(as ~ as / not as ~ as)을 이용하여 자신의 입장에서 문장을 만드시오. (4 문장)

보기
I am as tall as Minho.

(1) _____
(2) _____
(3) _____
(4) _____

03 「의문사 + to부정사」 구문을 활용하여 〈보기〉와 같이 자신의 입장에서 문장을 만드시오.

보기
I know how to swim.

(1) _____
(2) _____
(3) _____
(4) _____

단원별 모의고사

01 다음 중 짝지어진 단어의 관계가 <u>다른</u> 것은?

① wet : dry ② late : early
③ hard : soft ④ brave : fearless
⑤ dangerous : safe

02 다음 빈칸에 알맞은 말이 바르게 짝지어진 것은?

- She held on _____ his arm for support.
- I bumped _____ a big boy and fell on the ice.

① at – over ② about – to
③ with – in ④ to – into
⑤ of – over

03 다음 영영풀이에 해당하는 단어를 쓰시오.

a person whose job is to take care of animals, especially in a zoo

➡ _____

04 다음 빈칸에 들어갈 말로 적절하지 <u>않은</u> 것은?

- You should _____ a swimming cap.
- You'd better not _____ the animals.
- You should _____ plants and eat them.
- You'd better not play with a ball when you _____ the street.

① pick ② touch
③ cross ④ wear
⑤ shake

[05~06] 다음 우리말에 맞도록 빈칸에 알맞은 말을 쓰시오.

05

나는 버스 정류장에서 너를 기다릴게.
➡ I'll _____ _____ you at the bus stop.

06

가능한 한 빨리 오세요.
➡ Please come _____ soon _____ .

07 다음 대화의 빈칸에 알맞은 것은?

A: Don't forget to take your cellphone.
B: _____

① Don't forget me.
② OK, I won't.
③ I have my cellphone.
④ Thank you for your help.
⑤ I don't remember anything.

08 다음 대화의 밑줄 친 부분과 바꿔 쓸 수 있는 것은?

A: <u>You'd better not to</u> pick flowers here.
B: Oh, I'm sorry. I didn't know that.

① You should
② You don't want to
③ You would like to
④ You're not permitted to
⑤ You might want to

09 다음 대화의 빈칸에 들어갈 말로 알맞은 것은?

> A: What's the weather like there in winter?
> B: It's rainy. _____ take your umbrella.

① Forget to
② Don't forget
③ Don't forget to
④ I would like to
⑤ Don't remember to

[10~11] 다음 대화를 읽고, 물음에 답하시오.

> A: I'm going to make fried eggs.
> B: ⓐDon't forget to turn on the fan.
> A: ⓑOkay, I see.

10 위 대화의 밑줄 친 ⓐ와 바꿔 쓸 수 있는 것은?

① You don't need to turn on the fan.
② Remember to turn on the fan.
③ You can turn on the fan.
④ Make sure to turn on the fan.
⑤ Don't learn to turn on the fan.

11 위 대화의 밑줄 친 ⓑ와 바꿔 쓸 수 있는 <u>모두</u> 고르면?

① No, I won't.
② Sorry, I can't.
③ Thank you for reminding me.
④ You're welcome.
⑤ I'm happy to meet you.

12 다음 대화의 빈칸에 들어갈 말로 알맞은 것은?

> A: You must not _____.
> B: Oh, I'm sorry. I won't do that again.

① walk to school
② recycle plastics
③ reuse gift boxes
④ leave computers on
⑤ take a short shower

13 다음 빈칸에 알맞은 말이 바르게 짝지어진 것은?

> • Can you tell us _____ to play this game?
> • Do you know _____ to get to the ABC shopping mall?

① where – how   ② what – where
③ how – what   ④ what – how
⑤ when – where

14 다음 중 어법상 <u>틀린</u> 것은?

① Bungee jumping is as exciting as skydiving.
② This apple is as red as a rose.
③ Kevin is twice as old as Brian.
④ Jane is as heavier as Tom.
⑤ My sister can run as fast as my brother.

15 다음 두 문장이 같도록 빈칸에 알맞은 말을 쓰시오. (3 단어)

> He didn't know what he should say.
> = He didn't know _____.

16 다음 중 어법상 어색한 것은?

① You're as brave as I am.
② I'm not as pretty as the actress.
③ She is twice as popular as you.
④ It's not so expensive as your computer.
⑤ Get out of the building so quickly as possible.

17 다음 문장의 잘못된 부분을 고칠 때 빈칸에 알맞은 말을 쓰시오.

The question is why to go there.
➡ The question is why we _____
_____ _____ .

18 다음 문장에서 어법상 틀린 부분을 찾아 바르게 고쳐 쓰시오.

I study as harder as you do.

_____ ➡ _____

19 다음 중 어법상 어색한 것은?

① Let's decide where to go.
② I can't decide what to wear.
③ Please tell me which bus to take.
④ Can you tell me what to read a book?
⑤ Can you show me how to use the computer?

20 다음 두 문장을 한 문장으로 만들 때 빈칸에 알맞은 말을 쓰시오.

He runs fast. I can run fast, too.
➡ He runs fast, but I can run _____
_____ _____ he does.

[21~24] 다음 글을 읽고, 물음에 답하시오.

Announcer: Yesterday, a teenager saved the life of an old man. The brave student is in the studio with us today. Please introduce yourself.

Sejin: My name is Kim Sejin. I'm _____ⓐ_____ the second grade at Hanguk Middle School.

Announcer: Could you tell us your experience?

Sejin: Sure. I was waiting for the bus with my friend, Jinho. A man suddenly fell in front of us. Nobody knew ⓑ무엇을 해야 할지. I was as _____ⓒ_____ as the others at first. Then, I ran to him and tapped him _____ⓓ_____ the shoulder. He wasn't moving or breathing. I said to Jinho, "Call 119," and started CPR.

21 위 글의 빈칸 ⓐ와 ⓓ에 알맞은 말이 바르게 짝지어진 것은?

① at – over ② on – to
③ to – by ④ of – from
⑤ in – on

22 위 글의 밑줄 친 ⓑ의 우리말에 맞도록 세 단어로 쓰시오.

➡ _____

23 위 글의 빈칸 ⓒ에 다음 영영풀이에 해당하는 단어를 주어진 철자로 시작하여 쓰시오.

frightened of something or afraid that something bad night happen

➡ s_____

24 위 글의 내용과 일치하지 <u>않는</u> 것은?

① 세진이는 어제 노인의 생명을 구했다.

② 세진이는 지금 방송국의 스튜디오에 있다.

③ 세진이는 노인을 구한 경험을 이야기하고 있다.

④ 갑자기 노인이 세진이 앞에서 쓰러졌다.

⑤ 세진이는 노인이 움직이지 않고 있다는 것을 몰랐다.

[25~27] 다음 글을 읽고, 물음에 답하시오.

Announcer: When did you learn (A)[so /such] an important skill?

Sejin: We had Safety Training Day at school last week. I learned how to do CPR and had a chance to practice.

Announcer: Can you show the audience how to perform CPR?

Sejin: Yes. Keep your arms (B)[straight straightly]. Your arms and the other person's chest must be at a 90 degree angle. Push down in the center of the chest hard and fast until an ambulance comes.

Announcer: Are there any other things (C) [remembering / to remember]?

Sejin: Yes. You need to remember the four minutes of "Golden Time." @It means that you should start CPR within four minutes after someone's heart stops. To begin CPR later than that will greatly lower the chances of saving someone's life.

25 위 글의 괄호 (A)~(C)에서 알맞은 것이 바르게 짝지어진 것은?

① so – straight – remembering

② so – straightly – remembering

③ such – straight – to remember

④ such – straight – remembering

⑤ such – straightly – to remember

26 위 글의 밑줄 친 @가 가리키는 것을 찾아 영어로 쓰시오.

➡ _____

27 위 글의 내용과 일치하지 <u>않는</u> 것은?

① Sejin learned how to do CPR on Safety Training Day.

② Sejin had a chance to practice CPR on Safety Training Day.

③ Sejin is showing how to perform CPR to the audience.

④ We should push down in the center of the chest when we perform CPR.

⑤ Beginning CPR later than the four minutes increases the chances of saving someone's life.

[28~29] 다음 글을 읽고, 물음에 답하시오.

Today we had Safety Training Day at school. Teachers taught us what to do when an earthquake hits. We learned how to protect our heads and bodies. We also learned ___@___ to go when the shaking stops.

28 위 글의 빈칸 @에 알맞은 의문사를 쓰시오.

➡ _____

29 What did the teachers teach us on the Safety Training? Answer in English.

➡ _____

_____

Lesson 3

Living a Healthy Life

 의사소통 기능

- 능력 여부 묻기

  Do you know how to ride a longboard?

- 좋아하는 것 표현하기

  I enjoy riding my longboard because it reduces my stress.

 언어 형식

- 사역동사

  It will **make** your eyes **feel** more comfortable.

- 조건을 나타내는 접속사 if

  If you massage yourself and stretch every day, you will feel healthier.

Words & Expressions

교과서

Key Words

- **activity**[æktívəti] 명 활동
- **advice**[ædváis] 명 조언, 충고(= tip)
- **already**[ɔ:lrédi] 부 벌써, 이미
- **back**[bæk] 명 뒤쪽, 뒷부분
- **backward**[bǽkwərd] 부 뒤로(↔ forward)
- **behind**[biháind] 전 ~ 뒤에
- **bend**[bend] 동 구부리다
- **both**[bouθ] 대 둘 다
- **bowl**[boul] 명 그릇
- **comfortable**[kʌ́mfərtəbl] 형 편안한(↔ uncomfortable)
- **count**[kaunt] 동 세다
- **difficult**[dífikʌlt] 형 어려운(↔ easy)
- **download**[dáunlòud] 동 다운로드하다
- **exercise**[éksərsàiz] 동 운동하다
- **face**[feis] 동 ~을 마주보다[향하다] 명 얼굴
- **fall**[fɔ:l] 동 넘어지다
- **fishing**[fíʃiŋ] 명 낚시
- **fresh**[freʃ] 형 신선한
- **habit**[hǽbit] 명 습관
- **healthy**[hélθi] 형 건강한, 건강에 좋은
- **hold**[hould] 동 유지하다
- **however**[hauévər] 부 그러나
- **life**[laif] 명 삶
- **light**[lait] 명 빛
- **like**[laik] 전 ~와 같은, ~처럼
- **lower**[lóuər] 동 ~을 낮추다, ~을 낮게 하다
- **massage**[məsá:ʒ] 명 마사지 동 마사지를 하다
- **move**[mu:v] 동 움직이다
- **nature**[néitʃər] 명 자연
- **neck**[nek] 명 목
- **place**[pleis] 동 놓다, 두다
- **position**[pəzíʃən] 명 자세
- **pour**[pɔ:r] 동 붓다
- **pull**[pul] 동 당기다, 끌다
- **push**[puʃ] 동 밀다
- **put**[put] 동 놓다, 두다
- **reduce**[ridjú:s] 동 줄이다(↔ increase)
- **relax**[rilǽks] 동 (근육 등의) 긴장이 풀리다, 긴장을 풀다
- **second**[sékənd] 명 (시간 단위인) 초
- **shoulder**[ʃóuldər] 명 어깨
- **show**[ʃou] 동 보여[가르쳐] 주다
- **simple**[símpl] 형 간단한, 단순한(↔ complicated)
- **softly**[sɔ́:ftli] 부 부드럽게
- **step**[step] 명 걸음
- **stress**[stres] 동 스트레스를 받다[주다]
- **stretch**[stretʃ] 동 스트레칭하다
- **switch**[switʃ] 동 바꾸다(= change)
- **understand**[ʌndərstǽnd] 동 이해하다, 알다
- **usually**[jú:ʒuəli] 부 보통, 대개
- **waist**[weist] 명 허리
- **warm**[wɔ:rm] 형 따뜻한(↔ cool)
- **way**[wei] 명 길

Key Expressions

- **a little bit** 조금
- **at the same speed** 같은 속도로
- **be good for** ~에 좋다
- **be worried about** ~에 대해 걱정하다
- **block out** (빛을) 가리다[차단하다]
- **each other** 서로
- **from top to bottom** 위에서 아래까지
- **focus on** ~에 집중하다
- **for a few seconds** 몇 초 동안
- **get over** 회복[극복]하다
- **have a cold** 감기에 걸리다
- **loosen up** 몸을 풀어 주다
- **more than** ~ 이상
- **prepare for** ~을 준비하다
- **straighten up** 똑바로 하다
- **take a walk** 산책하다
- **team up with** ~와 협력하다, ~와 한 팀이 되다
- **three times a week** 일주일에 세 번
- **warm up** 준비 운동을 하다
- **what kind of** 어떤 종류의

Word Power

※ 동사에 접미사 -able를 붙여 형용사가 되는 단어

□ **comfort → comfortable** (편안한)

□ **change → changeable** (바뀔 수 있는)

□ **use → usable** (사용 가능한)

□ **move → movable** (움직이는)

□ **respect → respectable** (존경할 만한)

□ **desire → desirable** (바람직한)

※ 접두사 un-은 형용사 · 부사 · 명사 앞에 붙어 부정이나 반대의 의미를 나타낸다.

□ **comfortable** (편안한) → **uncomfortable** (불편한)

□ **easy** (편한) → **uneasy** (불편한)

□ **fair** (공평한) → **unfair** (불공평한)

□ **friendly** (친절한) → **unfriendly** (불친절한)

□ **happy** (행복한) → **unhappy** (행복하지 않은)

□ **known** (알려진) → **unknown** (알려지지 않은)

English Dictionary

□ **advice** 조언
→ an opinion or suggestion about what someone should do
누군가에게 어떻게 하라고 알려 주는 말이나 제안

□ **bend** 구부리다
→ to move your body so that it is not straight
몸을 움직여 구부리다

□ **comfortable** 편안한
→ making you feel physically relaxed
당신을 신체적으로 편안함을 느끼게 하는

□ **count** 세다
→ to say numbers in order
숫자를 순서대로 말하다

□ **habit** 습관
→ something that a person does often in a regular and repeated way
사람이 규칙적으로 또는 반복적으로 자주 하는 행동

□ **massage** 마사지
→ the action of rubbing and pressing a person's body with the hands to reduce pain in the muscles and joints
근육과 관절의 통증을 줄이기 위해 손으로 사람의 몸을 문지르고 누르는 행동

□ **neck** 목
→ the part of the body between the head and the shoulders
머리와 어깨 사이의 신체 부위

□ **position** 자세
→ the way someone stands, sits, or lies down
어떤 사람이 서거나 앉거나 눕는 방식

□ **pull** 당기다
→ to hold something firmly and use force in order to move it or try to move it toward yourself
뭔가를 단단히 잡고 힘을 사용하여 움직이거나 자신을 향해 움직이려고 하다

□ **reduce** 줄이다
→ to make something smaller in size, amount, number, etc.
어떤 것의 크기, 양, 수 등이 작아지게 하다

□ **relax** (근육 등의) 긴장을 풀다
→ to cause something to become less tense, tight, or stiff
어떤 것이 긴장, 팽팽함 또는 경직성이 줄어들게 하다

□ **simple** 간단한
→ not hard to understand or do
이해하거나 하기가 어렵지 않은

□ **stretch** 스트레칭하다
→ to put your arms, legs, etc., in positions that make the muscles long and tight
근육이 길고 팽팽해지게 하는 자세로 팔, 다리 등을 뻗다

□ **switch** 바꾸다
→ to change or replace something with another thing
어떤 것을 다른 것으로 바꾸다

□ **warm up** 준비 운동을 하다
→ to do gentle physical exercises to prepare your body for a sport or other activity
운동이나 다른 활동을 위해 당신의 몸을 준비하기 위해 가벼운 신체 운동을 하다

01 다음 중 〈보기〉와 같이 변화하는 단어가 <u>아닌</u> 것은?

┌─ 보기 ┐
move – movable

① use
② change
③ respect
④ impress
⑤ comfort

02 다음 빈칸에 알맞은 말이 바르게 짝지어진 것은?

• Fruits are good _____ your health.
• You can focus _____ your studies better.

① at – in
② for – on
③ on – at
④ from – in
⑤ about – on

서답형
03 다음 짝지어진 단어의 관계가 같도록 빈칸에 알맞은 말을 쓰시오.

strong : weak = cool : _____

04 다음 영영풀이에 해당하는 단어로 알맞은 것은?

making you feel physically relaxed

① simple
② comfortable
③ pleasure
④ serious
⑤ popular

서답형
05 다음 우리말에 맞게 빈칸에 알맞은 말을 쓰시오.

너희 둘 다 어린애들 같구나.
➡ _____ _____ you are acting like children.

서답형
06 다음 영영풀이에 해당하는 단어를 쓰시오.

to do gentle physical exercises to prepare your body for a sport or other activity

➡ _____

07 다음 문장의 빈칸에 알맞은 것은?

I hope you will get _____ your cold soon.

① from
② over
③ off
④ up
⑤ through

서답형
08 다음 빈칸에 공통으로 알맞은 말을 쓰시오.

• He runs 100 meters in 13 _____s.
• He is a _____ year in middle school.

01 다음 짝지어진 두 단어의 관계가 같도록 빈칸에 알맞은 말을 쓰시오.

(1) before : after = backward : _____

(2) wrong : right = reduce : _____

(3) delicious : tasty = tip : _____

(4) appear : disappear = comfortable : _____

02 다음 우리말에 맞도록 빈칸에 알맞은 말을 쓰시오.

(1) 그들은 서로 쳐다보고 웃었다.
➡ They looked at _____ _____ and laughed.

(2) 나는 일주일에 세 번 이상 운동을 한다.
➡ I exercise _____ _____ three times a week.

(3) 그 문제는 조금 어렵다.
➡ The problem is _____ _____ _____ difficult.

03 다음 빈칸에 들어갈 알맞은 말을 〈보기〉에서 골라 쓰시오.

┌── 보기 ──┐
download   count   reduce   ride

(1) I _____ my longboard when I'm stressed.

(2) The beautiful pictures _____ my stress.

(3) Tom, _____ to ten and open your eyes.

(4) Users can _____ the full image.

04 다음 괄호 안의 단어를 문맥에 맞게 고쳐 쓰시오.

(1) I want to eat something _____. (health)

(2) My bike is very old, but it is still _____. (move)

(3) We should wear _____ shoes for walking for a long time. (comfort)

05 다음 빈칸에 알맞은 말을 〈보기〉에서 골라 쓰시오.

┌── 보기 ──┐
am worried about / prepare for / get over

(1) Do you know how to _____ a cold?

(2) I will _____ the English speech contest.

(3) I _____ the math quiz on Monday.

06 다음 영영풀이에 해당하는 단어를 주어진 철자로 시작하여 쓰시오.

(1) s_____ : to put your arms, legs, etc., in positions that make the muscles long and tight

(2) h_____ : something that a person does often in a regular and repeated way

(3) s_____ : to change or replace something with another thing

(4) r_____ : to cause something to become less tense, tight, or stiff

Conversation

① 능력 여부 묻기

> **A** Do you know how to play basketball? 너는 농구를 어떻게 하는지 아니?
> **B** Yes, I do. / No, I don't. 응, 알아. / 아니, 몰라.

- Do you know how to+동사원형 ~?은 '너는 ~를 어떻게 하는지 아니?'라는 뜻으로, 어떤 일을 할 수 있는지 물을 때 사용하는 표현이다.
  - A: Do you know how to do rock climbing? 너는 암벽 등반을 어떻게 하는지 아니?
  - B: Yes, I do. 응, 알아.

상대방의 능력 여부를 묻는 표현

- Do you know how to + 동사원형 ~? 너는 ~하는 방법을 아니?
- Can you + 동사원형 ~? 너는 ~할 수 있니?
- Are you able to + 동사원형 ~? 너는 ~할 수 있니?
- Are you good at ~? 너는 ~를 잘하니?

능력을 나타내는 표현

- I know how to + 동사원형 ~. 나는 ~하는 방법을 알아.
- I can + 동사원형 ~. 나는 ~할 수 있어.
- I'm able to + 동사원형 ~. 나는 ~할 수 있어.
- I'm good at ~. 나는 ~을 잘해.

능력 여부에 답하기

〈긍정〉 Yes, I do. / Yes, I can. / I'm good at ~. / Yes, I know how to + 동사원형 ~. / Sure. / Of course.

〈부정〉 No, I don't. / No, I can't. / I'm not good at ~. / No, I don't know how to + 동사원형 ~. / No, I'm poor at ~.

핵심 Check

1. 다음 우리말과 일치하도록 빈칸에 알맞은 말을 쓰시오.

 (1) **A:** Do you know _____ _____ fix a computer? (컴퓨터를 어떻게 고치는지 아니?)

 B: I'm _____ _____ _____ fixing machines. (난 기계 고치는 일을 잘 못해.)

 (2) **A:** Do you know how to make potato salad? (너는 감자 샐러드를 어떻게 만드는지 아니?)

 B: No, I don't know _____ _____ _____ it. (아니, 나는 그것을 만드는 방법을 몰라.)

2 좋아하는 것 표현하기

> **A** Kate, what do you enjoy doing to be healthy?
> Kate, 너는 건강해지기 위해 무엇을 하는 걸 즐기니?
>
> **B** I enjoy riding a bike. 나는 자전거 타는 것을 즐겨.

■ I enjoy ~(very much).는 '나는 ~하는 것을 (매우) 즐겨.'라는 뜻으로, 자신이 좋아하는 것을 말하는 표현이다.

- A: Amy, what do you enjoy doing to be healthy? Amy, 너는 건강해지기 위해 무엇을 하는 걸 즐기니?
  B: I enjoy growing vegetables. 나는 채소 기르는 것을 즐겨.

좋아하는 것 말하는 표현

- I enjoy -ing ~. 나는 ~하는 것을 즐겨.
- I love ~. 나는 ~하는 것을 정말 좋아해.
- I like ~. 나는 ~하는 것을 좋아해.
- I feel great when I ~. 나는 ~할 때 기분이 좋아.

관심을 나타내는 표현

- Sounds cool. / That's great. / That's interesting! / How interesting!

- A: I enjoy watching birds. 나는 새를 관찰하는 것을 즐겨.
  B: How interesting! 정말 흥미롭구나!

핵심 Check

2. 다음 우리말과 일치하도록 빈칸에 알맞은 말을 쓰시오.

(1) A: _____ do you _____ _____ do after school? (넌 방과 후에 무엇 하기를 좋아하니?)

   B: I enjoy _____ a bike. (난 자전거 타는 것을 즐겨.)

(2) A: David, _____ do you _____ _____ to be healthy?

   (David, 너는 건강해지기 위해 무엇을 하는 것을 즐기니?)

   B: I enjoy _____. (나는 낚시를 즐겨.)

(3) A: What _____ _____ _____ in your free time? (너는 여가 시간에 무엇을 하니?)

   B: I _____ _____ cartoons. I post them on the Internet.

   (나는 만화 그리는 것을 즐겨. 나는 그것들을 인터넷에 게시하지.)

   A: _____ interesting! (정말 흥미롭구나!)

🎤 A. Listen & Speak 1 - A - 1

B: ❶I want to eat something healthy. Do you have any advice?

G: I often eat fresh salad. ❷It makes me feel good.

B: Really? ❸Do you know how to make it?

G: Yes, it's quite simple. ❹First, cut many vegetables into small pieces. ❺Next, put them into a bowl. Then, pour some lemon juice on them. Finally, mix everything together.

B: That's it? I should try it.

B: 나는 건강에 좋은 것을 먹고 싶어. 말해 줄 조언이 있니?

G: 나는 신선한 샐러드를 자주 먹어. 그것은 나를 기분 좋게 만들어.

B: 정말? 그것을 어떻게 만드는지 아니?

G: 응. 아주 간단해. 먼저, 많은 채소들을 작은 조각으로 잘라. 다음으로 그것들을 그릇에 담아. 그런 다음, 레몬주스를 조금 부어. 마지막으로 모든 것을 함께 섞어.

B: 그게 다야? 한번 해 봐야겠다.

❶ -thing으로 끝나는 부정대명사는 형용사가 뒤에서 수식한다.
❷ It=fresh salad / make me feel good: 나를 기분 좋게 만들다
❸ Do you know how to+동사원형 ~?: ~하는 방법을 아니?(능력 여부 묻기)
❹ cut A into B: A를 B로 자르다
❺ put A into B: A를 B에 넣다 / them: small pieces

Check(√) True or False

(1) The girl knows how to make fresh salad.   T ☐ F ☐

(2) The first step in making fresh salad is to put vegetables into a bowl.   T ☐ F ☐

🎤 **Conversation B**

Karl: Hana, ❶what's the matter?

Hana: Well, ❷I'm stressed about the test next week.

Karl: I understand. I ride my longboard when I'm stressed. ❸Do you know how to ride a longboard?

Hana: No, I don't.

Karl: Let's go out! I can teach you. Put one foot on the board and push hard with the other.

Hana: Like this? Wow! This is fun. ❹I feel better already.

Karl: See? ❺I enjoy riding my longboard because it reduces my stress.

Hana: That's great!

Karl: 하나야. 무슨 일 있니?

하나: 음. 다음 주에 있을 시험 때문에 스트레스를 받아.

Karl: 난 이해돼. 나는 스트레스를 받을 때 롱보드를 타. 넌 롱보드를 어떻게 타는지 아니?

하나: 아니, 몰라.

Karl: 나가자! 내가 가르쳐 줄 수 있어. 한 발을 보드 위에 올려놓고 다른 한 발로 세게 밀어.

하나: 이렇게? 와! 이거 재밌다. 벌써 기분이 좋아졌어.

Karl: 봤지? 나는 롱보드를 타는 것이 나의 스트레스를 줄여 주기 때문에 즐겨.

하나: 정말 멋진데!

❶ What's the matter?: 슬픔, 불만족, 실망의 원인에 대해 묻기
❷ be stressed about: ~에 대해 스트레스를 받다
❸ Do you know how to + 동사원형 ~? = Can you + 동사원형 ~?
❹ feel better: 기분이 더 좋아지다
❺ I enjoy + (동)명사 ~: 나는 ~하는 것을 즐긴다.(좋아하는 것 말하기) / it=riding my longboard / reduce: 줄이다

Check(√) True or False

(3) Hana doesn't know how to ride a longboard.   T ☐ F ☐

(4) Karl listens to music to reduce his stress.   T ☐ F ☐

Listen & Speak 1 - A - 2

B: ❶People say that we should walk more than 10,000 steps every day to be healthy. I can't count the number of my steps easily.

G: You can use this smartphone app. ❷Do you know how to use it?

B: No. ❸Can you show me?

G: Sure. First, download the app. Then, walk with your smartphone. Later, you can check the number of steps you took.

B: Thank you. ❹I will start using it today.

❶ more than: ~ 이상 / to be: to부정사의 부사적 용법 중 목적 ❷ Do you know how to + 동사원형 ~?: 너는 ~하는 방법을 아니? (능력 여부 묻기) ❸ Can you + 동사원형 ~?: ~해 줄래? ❹ it = a smartphone app

Listen & Speak 2 - A - 1

G: ❶What do you enjoy doing after school?

B: ❷I enjoy cooking healthy food.

G: ❸Sounds cool. What can you make?

B: I can make salad, Bibimbap, and vegetable juice.

❶ What do you enjoy -ing?: 너는 무엇을 ~하기를 즐기니? (좋아하는 것 묻기) / after school: 방과 후에 ❷ I enjoy -ing ~.: 나는 ~하는 것을 즐긴다. (좋아하는 것 말하기) / healthy: 건강에 좋은 ❸ Sounds cool.: 관심을 나타내는 표현이다.

Listen & Speak 2 - A - 2

B: ❶What do you do on weekends?

G: I take pictures.

B: ❷What kind of pictures do you usually take?

G: ❸I enjoy taking pictures of nature, like trees and flowers. ❹The beautiful pictures reduce my stress.

❶ on weekends: 주말에 ❷ What kind of: 어떤 종류의 ❸ I enjoy -ing ~: 나는 ~하는 것을 즐긴다 / take a picture: 사진을 찍다 / like: ~같은 ❹ reduce one's stress: 스트레스를 줄이다

Listen & Speak 2 - A - 3

G: Do you have a puppy?

B: Yes. Her name is Coco. I really like her.

G: ❶What do you do with her?

B: I enjoy ❷taking a walk with her. ❸It makes me healthy.

❶ with: ~와 함께 / her = Coco ❷ take a walk: 산책하다 ❸ It = taking a walk with her / make + 목적어 + 형용사: ~을 …하게 만들다 / healthy: 건강한

Conversation A

B: Tomorrow, I have an English speaking contest. ❶I started preparing for the contest two weeks ago. ❷I enjoy speaking in English, but I am worried about the contest. I cannot sleep well.

❶ start+to부정사[동명사]: ~하기 시작하다 / prepare for: ~을 준비하다 / two weeks ago: 2주 전 ❷ enjoy+동명사: ~하는 것을 즐기다 / be worried about: ~에 대해 걱정하다

Wrap Up - ❶

B: ❶You look sick. ❷What's the matter?

G: ❸Well, I have a cold.

B: ❹Did you see a doctor?

G: Not yet. ❺Do you know how to get over a cold?

B: Well, I usually drink warm water when I have a cold. It makes me feel better.

G: Sounds good. I will try it.

❶ look+형용사: ~하게 보이다 ❷ What's the matter? = What's wrong? = What's the problem? = What happened? ❸ have a cold: 감기에 걸리다 (=catch[get/take] a cold) ❹ see a doctor: 병원에 가 보다 ❺ get over: 회복하다

Wrap Up - ❷

B: My family enjoys many activities. My dad enjoys fishing. ❶Early in the morning, he goes to the lake and comes back with some fish. ❷ My mom enjoys drawing pictures. ❸She likes to draw beautiful mountains and lakes. My brother and I enjoy playing soccer.

❶ early in the morning: 이른 아침 / come back: 돌아오다 ❷ draw a picture: 그림을 그리다 ❸ lake: 호수

다음 우리말과 일치하도록 빈칸에 알맞은 말을 쓰시오.

Listen & Speak 1-A-1

B: I want to eat _____ _____. Do you _____ any _____?

G: I _____ _____ fresh salad. It _____ me feel _____.

B: Really? Do you know _____ _____ make it?

G: Yes, it's quite simple. First, _____ many vegetables _____ small pieces. Next, _____ them _____ a bowl. Then, _____ some lemon juice on them. Finally, _____ everything together.

B: That's it? I _____ _____ it.

B: 나는 건강에 좋은 것을 먹고 싶어. 말해 줄 조언이 있니?
G: 나는 신선한 샐러드를 자주 먹어. 그것은 나를 기분 좋게 만들어.
B: 정말? 그것을 어떻게 만드는지 아니?
G: 응. 아주 간단해. 먼저, 많은 채소들을 작은 조각으로 잘라. 다음으로 그것들을 그릇에 담아. 그런 다음, 레몬 주스를 조금 부어. 마지막으로 모든 것을 함께 섞어.
B: 그게 다야? 한번 해 봐야겠다.

Listen & Speak 1-A-2

B: People say that we should walk _____ _____ 10,000 steps every day _____ _____ healthy. I can't _____ the number of my _____ easily.

G: You _____ _____ this smartphone app. Do you know _____ _____ _____ it?

B: No. _____ you _____ me?

G: Sure. First, _____ the app. Then, walk _____ your smartphone. Later, you can _____ the number of steps you took.

B: Thank you. I _____ start _____ it today.

B: 사람들은 우리가 건강해지기 위해서 매일 10,000 걸음 이상을 걸어야 한다고 말해. 나는 내 걸음 수를 쉽게 셀 수 없어.
G: 너는 이 스마트폰 앱을 사용할 수 있어. 어떻게 사용하는지 아니?
B: 아니. 내게 보여줄 수 있니?
G: 물론. 먼저 앱을 다운로드해. 그런 다음 스마트폰을 가지고 걸어. 나중에 네가 걸은 걸음 수를 확인할 수 있어.
B: 고마워. 오늘부터 그것을 쓰기 시작해야겠어.

Listen & Speak 2 - A - 1

G: _____ do you enjoy _____ after school?

B: I _____ _____ healthy food.

G: _____ cool. What _____ you make?

B: I _____ _____ salad, Bibimbap, and vegetable juice.

G: 너는 방과 후에 뭐 하는 걸 즐기니?
B: 나는 건강에 좋은 음식을 요리하는 것을 즐겨.
G: 멋지구나. 너는 무엇을 만들 수 있니?
B: 나는 샐러드, 비빔밥 그리고 야채 주스를 만들 수 있어.

Listen & Speak 1-A-1

B: What do you do _____ _____?

G: I _____ pictures.

B: _____ _____ of pictures do you usually _____?

G: I enjoy _____ pictures _____ nature, _____ trees and flowers. The beautiful pictures _____ my stress.

B: 너는 주말에 무엇을 하니?
G: 나는 사진을 찍어.
B: 너는 보통 어떤 종류의 사진을 찍니?
G: 나는 나무와 꽃 같은 자연의 사진을 찍는 것을 좋아해. 그 아름다운 사진들은 내 스트레스를 줄여주거든.

Listen & Speak 2-A-3

G: Do you have a _____?

B: Yes. _____ name is Coco. I _____ like her.

G: What do you do _____ her?

B: I _____ _____ a walk with her. It _____ me _____.

Conversation A

B: Tomorrow, I _____ an English _____ contest. I started _____ _____ the contest two weeks _____. I enjoy _____ _____ English, but I am worried _____ the contest. I _____ _____ well.

Conversation B

Karl: Hana, what's the _____?

Hana: Well, I'm _____ _____ the test next week.

Karl: I understand. I _____ my longboard _____ I'm stressed. Do you know _____ _____ _____ a longboard?

Hana: No, I don't.

Karl: Let's _____ _____! I _____ teach you. _____ one foot _____ the board and _____ hard _____ the other.

Hana: _____ this? Wow! This is fun. I _____ _____ already.

Karl: See? I enjoy _____ my longboard _____ it reduces my stress.

Hana: That's great!

Wrap Up 1

B: You look _____. _____ the matter?

G: Well, I have a _____.

B: Did you _____ a doctor?

G: Not _____. Do you know how to _____ _____ a cold?

B: Well, I usually drink _____ water _____ I have a cold. It _____ me _____ better.

G: Sounds good. I _____ _____ it.

Wrap Up 2

B: My family _____ many activities. My dad enjoys _____. _____ in the morning, he goes to the lake and _____ _____ with some fish. My mom _____ _____ pictures. She likes _____ _____ beautiful mountains and lakes. My brother and I _____ _____ soccer.

해석

G: 너는 강아지를 기르고 있니?

B: 응. 그녀의 이름은 코코야. 난 코코를 아주 좋아해.

G: 너는 코코와 함께 무엇을 하니?

B: 난 코코와 산책하는 걸 즐겨. 그것은 나를 건강하게 만들어.

B: 내일 영어 말하기 대회가 있어. 나는 2주 전에 대회를 준비하기 시작했어. 나는 영어로 말하는 것을 즐기지만, 난 그 대회가 걱정돼. 나는 잠을 잘 못 자.

Karl: 하나야, 무슨 일 있니?

하나: 음. 다음 주에 있을 시험 때문에 스트레스를 받아.

Karl: 난 이해돼. 나는 스트레스를 받을 때 롱보드를 타. 넌 롱보드를 어떻게 타는지 아니?

하나: 아니, 몰라.

Karl: 나가자! 내가 가르쳐 줄 수 있어. 한 발을 보드 위에 올려놓고 다른 한 발로 세게 밀어.

하나: 이렇게? 와! 이거 재밌다. 벌써 기분이 좋아졌어.

Karl: 봤지? 나는 롱보드를 타는 것이 나의 스트레스를 줄여주기 때문에 즐겨.

하나: 정말 멋진데!

B: 너 아파 보여. 무슨 일 있니?

G: 음, 감기에 걸렸어.

B: 병원에 가봤니?

G: 아직. 넌 감기가 나아지는 방법을 아니?

B: 음, 나는 감기에 걸렸을 때 보통 따뜻한 물을 마셔. 그것은 내 기분을 좋아지게 해.

G: 좋아. 한번 해 볼게.

B: 우리 가족은 많은 활동을 즐겨. 우리 아빠는 낚시를 즐기셔. 이른 아침, 그는 호수에 가셔서 약간의 물고기를 가지고 돌아오셔. 우리 엄마는 그림 그리기를 즐기셔. 그녀는 아름다운 산과 호수를 그리는 것을 좋아하셔. 나의 형과 나는 축구를 즐겨.

01 다음 대화의 빈칸에 알맞은 것은?

> A: Do you know _____ healthy juice?
> B: Yes, I do.

① when to make
② how to make
③ what to make
④ where to make
⑤ how to do

healthy 건강한

02 다음 대화의 빈칸에 들어갈 말로 적절하지 <u>않은</u> 것은?

> A: Kate, what do you enjoy doing to be healthy?
> B: I enjoy _____.

① fishing
② jogging
③ playing catch
④ riding a bike
⑤ playing computer games

03 다음 문장과 바꿔 쓸 수 있는 것은?

> Do you know how to fix the watering can?

① Are you fixing the watering can?
② Can you fix the watering can?
③ Can I fix the watering can?
④ May I fix the watering can?
⑤ Did you fix the watering can?

04 다음 대화의 ⓐ~ⓓ를 자연스러운 대화가 되도록 바르게 배열하시오.

take a walk 산책하다

> ⓐ What do you do with her?
> ⓑ Yes. Her name is Coco. I really like her.
> ⓒ Do you have a puppy?
> ⓓ I enjoy taking a walk with her. It makes me healthy.

➡ _____

[01~05] 다음 대화를 읽고, 물음에 답하시오.

Karl: Hana, what's the matter?

Hana: Well, I'm stressed ___ⓐ___ the test next week. (①)

Karl: I understand. I ride my longboard when I'm stressed. Do you know how ⓑride a longboard?

Hana: No, I don't. (②)

Karl: Let's go out! I can teach you. (③) Put one foot on the board and push hard ___ⓒ___ the other. (④)

Hana: Like this? Wow! This is fun. (⑤)

Karl: See? I enjoy ⓓride my longboard because ⓔit reduces my stress.

Hana: That's great!

01 위 대화의 ①~⑤ 중 다음 문장이 들어갈 알맞은 곳은?

I feel better already.

①   ②   ③   ④   ⑤

중요

02 위 대화의 빈칸 ⓐ와 ⓒ에 알맞은 말이 바르게 짝지어진 것은?

① for – to
② of – with
③ on – from
④ from – into
⑤ about – with

03 위 대화의 밑줄 친 ⓑ와 ⓓ를 알맞은 형태로 각각 고쳐 쓰시오.

ⓑ _____   ⓓ _____

서답형
04 위 대화의 밑줄 친 ⓔ가 가리키는 것을 영어로 쓰시오.

➡ _____

05 위 대화를 읽고, 답할 수 없는 질문은?

① Why is Hana stressed?
② What does Hana do when she's stressed?
③ Did Hana know how to ride a longboard?
④ Does Karl teach Hana how to ride a longboard?
⑤ Why does Karl enjoy riding his longboard?

[06~08] 다음 대화를 읽고, 물음에 답하시오.

B: You look sick. ⓐWhat's the matter?

G: Well, I have a cold.

B: Did you see a doctor?

G: Not yet. ⓑDo you know how to get over a cold?

B: Well, I usually drink warm water when I have a cold. ⓒIt makes me feel better.

G: Sounds good. I will try it.

06 위 대화의 밑줄 친 ⓐ와 바꿔 쓸 수 없는 것은?

① What's wrong?
② What happened?
③ How have you been?
④ What's the problem?
⑤ Is there something wrong?

07 위 대화의 밑줄 친 ⓑ의 의도로 알맞은 것은?

① 제안하기   ② 주제 정하기
③ 능력 여부 묻기   ④ 위로하기
⑤ 반문하기

서답형

08 위 대화의 밑줄 친 ⓒ가 의미하는 것을 우리말로 쓰시오.

➡ _____

[09~11] 다음 대화를 읽고, 물음에 답하시오.

> B: ⓐI want to eat healthy something. Do you have any advice?
> G: I often eat fresh salad. ⓑIt makes me feel good.
> B: Really? ⓒDo you know how to make it?
> G: Yes, it's quite simple. First, cut many vegetables into small pieces. Next, put them into a bowl. Then, pour some lemon juice on them. Finally, mix everything together.
> B: That's it? I should try it.

서답형

09 위 대화의 밑줄 친 ⓐ에서 어법상 어색한 부분을 고쳐 문장을 다시 쓰시오.

➡ _____

서답형

10 위 대화의 밑줄 친 ⓑ가 의미하는 것을 영어로 쓰시오.

➡ _____

중요

11 위 대화의 밑줄 친 ⓒ와 의미가 같은 문장은? (2개)

① Can you make it?
② Why don't you make it?
③ Are you good at making it?
④ When did you make it?
⑤ Are you interested in cooking?

[12~14] 다음 글을 읽고, 물음에 답하시오.

> B: Tomorrow, I have an English speaking contest. I started preparing _____ⓐ_____ the contest two weeks ago. I enjoy speaking in English, _____ⓑ_____ I am worried _____ⓒ_____ the contest. I cannot sleep well.

중요

12 위 글의 빈칸 ⓐ와 ⓒ에 알맞은 말이 바르게 짝지어진 것은?

① at – of   ② for – about
③ with – for   ④ of – at
⑤ from – over

13 위 글의 빈칸 ⓑ에 알맞은 것은?

① so   ② but
③ and   ④ for
⑤ or

14 위 글의 글쓴이의 심경으로 알맞은 것은?

① bored   ② excited
③ stressed   ④ pleased
⑤ happy

[01~04] 다음 대화를 읽고, 물음에 답하시오.

> B: People say that we should walk more than 10,000 steps every day to be healthy. I can't count the number of my steps easily.
>
> G: You can use this smartphone ⓐ . ⓑDo you know how to use it?
>
> B: No. Can you show me?
>
> G: Sure. First, download the ⓒ . Then, walk with your smartphone. Later, you can check the number of steps you took.

01 How many steps do people say we should walk every day to be healthy? Answer in English.

➡ _____

02 위 대화의 밑줄 친 ⓑ를 해석하고, 이와 바꿔 쓸 수 있는 표현을 2개 쓰시오.

(1) 해석: _____

(2) 같은 표현: _____

_____

03 위 대화의 빈칸 ⓐ와 ⓒ에 공통으로 들어갈 단어를 다음 영영풀이를 참조하여 쓰시오. (세 글자)

> a computer program designed to do a particular job, especially one that you can use on a smartphone

➡ _____

04 What is the first step in using the smartphone app? Answer in English.

➡ _____

[05~08] 다음 대화를 읽고, 물음에 답하시오.

> B: What do you do on weekends?
>
> G: I take pictures.
>
> B: What kind of pictures do you usually take?
>
> G: I enjoy ⓐtake pictures of nature, ⓑlike trees and flowers. The beautiful pictures ⓒ my stress.

05 위 대화의 밑줄 친 ⓐ를 알맞은 형태로 고쳐 쓰시오.

➡ _____

06 What does the girl enjoy doing? Answer in English.

➡ _____

07 위 대화의 밑줄 친 ⓑ를 두 단어로 바꿔 쓰시오.

➡ _____

08 위 대화의 빈칸 ⓒ에 다음 영영풀이에 해당하는 단어를 주어진 글자로 시작하여 쓰시오

> to make something smaller in size, amount, number, etc.

➡ r_____

Grammar

① 사역동사

- It will **make** your eyes **feel** more comfortable. 그것은 너의 눈을 더 편안하게 할 것이다.
- I will **let** you **ride** my new longboard. 나는 네가 나의 새 롱보드를 타게 해 줄게.
- The massage will **help** you **(to) feel** better. 마사지는 너의 기분이 좋아지도록 도울 것이다.

■ 사역동사 make, have, let은 「사역동사+목적어+목적격 보어(동사원형)」의 형태로 '(목적어)에게 ~하게 하다'라는 의미로 목적어의 행동을 설명한다.

① let: ~ 하도록 허락하다 / I will **let** you **go**. 네가 가도록 허락해 줄게.

② have: ~ 하도록 하다 / I will **have** my brother **clean** my room. 나는 내 남동생이 내 방을 치우도록 할 것이다.

③ make: ~ 하게 시키다 / My mom **makes** me **do** the dishes. 엄마는 내가 설거지를 하도록 시킨다.

■ help는 목적격 보어로 동사원형이나 to부정사 둘 다 사용할 수 있다.

- I **helped** Julia **(to) cook** breakfast for the family. 나는 Julia가 가족을 위해 아침식사를 요리하는 것을 도왔다.

■ get은 목적격 보어로 to부정사를 사용한다.

- He **got** our dreams **to come** true. 그는 우리의 꿈이 실현되게 했다.

■ have는 목적어와 목적격 보어가 능동 관계이면 동사원형을, 수동 관계이면 과거분사형을 쓴다.

- I **had** him **repair** my computer. 나는 그에게 내 컴퓨터를 고치게 했다.
- I **had** my computer **repaired**. 나는 내 컴퓨터를 수리시켰다.

핵심 Check

1. 다음 괄호 안에서 알맞은 것을 고르시오.

(1) The heat makes the ice (melt / to melt).

(2) Parents often don't let their children (doing / do) what they want.

(3) The secretary had the phone (rings / ring) at lunchtime.

(4) He got her (come / to come) to the meeting.

---

2 조건을 나타내는 접속사 if

> - **If** you massage yourself and stretch every day, you will feel healthier.
>   매일 마사지를 하고 스트레칭을 하면, 너는 더 건강하게 느껴질 것이다.
>
> - **If** it is sunny tomorrow, we can go for a bike ride.
>   내일 날씨가 맑으면, 우리는 자전거를 타러 갈 수 있다.
>
> - He will get sick **if** he doesn't stop eating fast food.
>   패스트푸드 먹는 것을 멈추지 않으면, 그는 병에 걸릴 것이다.

■ 접속사 if는 두 개의 절을 연결하는 접속사이며, '만약 ~하면'이라는 의미로 조건을 나타낸다. if가 이끄는 종속절은 주절의 앞이나 뒤에 올 수 있다.

- **If** we take a taxi, we can get there in ten minutes.
  만약 우리가 택시를 타면, 우리는 그곳에 10분 후에 도착할 수 있다.

- You can win the contest **if** you practice hard. 만약 네가 열심히 연습한다면, 너는 대회에서 우승을 할 수 있다.

■ 조건을 나타내는 접속사 if가 이끄는 절에서는 미래의 일을 나타내는 경우에도 동사는 현재시제를 쓴다.

- **If** it will be sunny tomorrow, we will play soccer. (X)
- **If** it **is** sunny tomorrow, we will play soccer. (○) 만약 내일 날씨가 맑으면, 우리는 축구를 할 것이다.

■ '만약 ~하지 않는다면'이라는 의미의 「if+주어+don't[doesn't]+동사원형 ~」은 「unless+주어+동사의 현재형 ~」으로 바꿔 쓸 수 있다.

- **If** he doesn't study hard, he can't get a high score.
  = **Unless** he studies hard, he can't get a high score.
  만일 그가 열심히 공부하지 않는다면, 그는 높은 점수를 얻을 수 없다.

핵심 Check

2. 다음 괄호 안에서 알맞은 것을 고르시오.

(1) If I see her, I (give / will give) it to her.

(2) (If / Because) you arrive early, you will get a good seat.

(3) If she (takes / will take) the subway, she will be there on time.

(4) Unless you (drink / don't drink) some water, you will feel very thirsty.

Grammar 시험대비 기본평가

go to a movie 영화 보러 가다

01 다음 우리말과 같도록 주어진 단어들을 바르게 배열하시오.

(1) 프랑스에 간다면, 나는 에펠탑을 방문할 거야. (France / I / to / if / go)

➡ _____, I will visit the Eiffel Tower.

(2) 내일 비가 오면 난 영화 보러 갈 거야. (rains, if, tomorrow, it)

➡ _____, I will go to a movie.

02 다음 문장에서 어법상 <u>어색한</u> 부분을 찾아 바르게 고쳐 쓰시오.

(1) The dress makes her to look slim.

_____ ➡ _____

(2) She had her son to write the teacher a letter.

_____ ➡ _____

(3) She won't let me to go there.

_____ ➡ _____

03 다음 두 문장이 같은 뜻이 되도록 빈칸에 알맞은 말을 쓰시오.

leave 떠나다, 출발하다
miss 놓치다

(1) If you don't leave now, you will miss the school bus.

= _____ _____ _____ now, you will miss the school bus.

(2) Unless it rains tomorrow, I will go camping.

= _____ _____ _____ _____ tomorrow, I will go camping.

04 다음 주어진 문장을 〈보기〉와 같이 바꾸어 쓸 때, 빈칸에 알맞은 말을 쓰시오.

┤ 보기 ├

I cleaned my hands.

➡ My teacher made me clean my hands.

(1) I went out after dinner.

➡ My mother let _____.

(2) The children played outside.

➡ He had _____.

(3) The bear stood on the ball.

➡ Mr. Brown made _____.

01 다음 문장의 빈칸에 알맞은 것은?

> She had me _____ my work.

① to do   ② starting
③ finish   ④ done
⑤ be finished

02 다음 빈칸에 공통으로 알맞은 것은?

> • I'm not going to work tomorrow _____ I don't feel well.
> • I'm not sure _____ he will enter the speech contest.

① if   ② so
③ that   ④ since
⑤ whether

03 다음 문장의 빈칸에 알맞지 <u>않은</u> 것은?

> Eating chocolate can make you _____.

① fat   ② happy
③ smile   ④ feel better
⑤ feeling good

04 다음 문장의 빈칸에 알맞은 것은?

> If you pass the test, you _____ study more.

① has to   ② don't
③ had to   ④ were to
⑤ won't have to

05 서답형 다음 문장에서 어법상 <u>어색한</u> 부분을 찾아 바르게 고쳐 쓰시오.

> Lisa makes me to do her homework.

_____ ➡ _____

06 다음 문장의 빈칸에 알맞은 것은?

> If you _____ straight two blocks, you will find our school.

① will go   ② were
③ go   ④ must be
⑤ went

07 서답형 다음 주어진 어구를 이용하여 우리말을 영어로 옮기시오. (필요시 어형 변경할 것)

> 나는 엄마가 설거지하시는 것을 도와 드렸다.
> (do the dishes)

➡ _____

08 중요 다음 우리말과 같도록 할 때, 빈칸에 알맞은 것은?

> 만약 내일 그가 오지 않으면, 나는 매우 슬플 것이다.
> = _____, I will feel very sad.

① If he comes tomorrow
② If he won't come tomorrow
③ If he doesn't come tomorrow
④ Unless he won't come tomorrow
⑤ Unless he doesn't come tomorrow

09 다음 문장의 빈칸에 알맞지 <u>않은</u> 것은?

> My mother _____ me clean the room.

① let
② had
③ wanted
④ made
⑤ helped

10 다음 두 문장의 의미가 같도록 빈칸에 알맞은 것은?

> If you don't eat breakfast, you can't focus on your studies.
> = _____ you eat breakfast, you can't focus on your studies.

① When
② While
③ Because
④ Unless
⑤ Although

11 다음 중 밑줄 친 부분의 쓰임이 나머지와 <u>다른</u> 하나는?

① I <u>made</u> him wash the dishes.
② Please <u>make</u> me laugh.
③ I <u>made</u> him carry the box.
④ My mom <u>made</u> me some snacks.
⑤ His advice <u>made</u> me do the work.

서답형

12 다음 문장에서 어법상 어색한 부분을 찾아 바르게 고쳐 쓰시오.

> If it will rain tomorrow, I will not go there, either.

_____ ➡ _____

13 다음 문장의 빈칸에 알맞은 것은?

> If it _____, we'll play soccer outside.

① won't rain
② don't rain
③ doesn't rain
④ didn't rain
⑤ hadn't rained

서답형

14 다음 우리말과 일치하도록 주어진 표현을 이용하여 영작하시오.

> 그의 미소는 항상 나를 미소 짓게 만든다.
> (make)

➡ _____

15 다음 빈칸에 공통으로 알맞은 것은?

> • I'll _____ him to see a doctor.
> • How can I _____ him to help me?

① let
② make
③ get
④ have
⑤ help

16 다음 세 문장의 뜻이 같도록 빈칸에 들어갈 말을 순서대로 짝지은 것은?

> Be careful, or you'll be in danger.
> = _____ you are careful, you'll be in danger.
> = _____ you are careful, you won't be in danger.

① If − If
② If − Unless
③ Unless − If
④ As − If
⑤ Unless − As

17 다음 빈칸에 알맞은 말이 바르게 짝지어진 것은?

> Her mother _____ the girl _____ care of her little sister.

① let – to take   ② had – take

③ helped – taking   ④ had – to take

⑤ made – taking

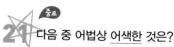

18 다음 두 문장이 같은 뜻이 되도록 빈칸에 알맞은 말을 쓰시오.

> If you don't stop shouting, they will call the police.
> = Unless _____ _____ shouting, they will call the police.

19 다음 밑줄 친 부분 중 어법상 어색한 것은?

① She made me <u>come</u> early.

② My sister let me <u>to go</u> home early.

③ Sumi asked me <u>to call</u> her right now.

④ I will make her <u>go</u> to the party.

⑤ My mother helped me <u>do</u> my homework.

20 다음 우리말과 같도록 주어진 단어를 바르게 배열하여 문장을 완성하시오.

> Judy는 남동생에게 수학 공부를 하도록 시킨다.
> (makes / brother / study / her / math / Judy)

➡ _____

21 다음 중 어법상 <u>어색한</u> 것은?

① If he helps me, I can carry this easily.

② If you don't have breakfast, you will feel hungry soon.

③ If you will leave now, you can get there on time.

④ If she makes a lot of money, she will buy a car.

⑤ If school finishes early today, we'll go to the movies.

22 다음 두 문장의 의미가 같도록 빈칸에 알맞은 말을 쓰시오.

> If you don't like the food, you don't have to pay.
> = _____, you don't have to pay.

23 다음 우리말과 일치하도록 주어진 어구를 바르게 배열하시오.

> 아버지는 내가 무거운 가방 드는 것을 도와 주셨다.
> (me / heavy / my father / bag / carry / helped / the)

➡ _____

24 다음 대화의 밑줄 친 부분과 쓰임이 같은 것은?

> A: Why do you like bright colors?
> B: Because they <u>make</u> me feel happy.

① He <u>made</u> me a toy boat.

② She <u>made</u> us coffee.

③ Wine is <u>made</u> from grapes.

④ She <u>makes</u> her own clothes.

⑤ My mom <u>made</u> me stop playing games.

01 다음 빈칸에 알맞은 말을 〈보기〉에서 골라 쓰시오. (필요시 어형을 바꿀 것)

> ┤ 보기 ├
> help   get   carry   show

(1) He helped me _____ the heavy bag.

(2) I couldn't _____ the car to start this morning.

(3) Please let me _____ you with your homework.

(4) I have lots of pictures _____ _____ you.

02 다음 빈칸에 알맞은 말을 〈보기〉에서 골라 쓰시오. (문장의 앞에 오는 경우 대문자로 쓰시오.)

> ┤ 보기 ├
> when   if   unless

(1) _____ you don't leave now, you will miss the last train.

(2) We had a big party _____ Sarah came home.

(3) _____ you start now, you'll be late for the meeting.

03 다음 문장에서 어법상 <u>어색한</u> 부분을 찾아 바르게 고쳐 쓰시오.

(1) I let Tom to explain why he was late.

_____ ➡ _____

(2) The hot milk will make you fell asleep easily.

_____ ➡ _____

(3) The teacher had his students played outside.

_____ ➡ _____

04 접속사 if를 사용하여 다음 두 문장을 한 문장으로 고쳐 쓰시오. (단, 종속절이 주절의 앞에 오는 문장으로 바꿀 것)

(1) I am late for class. My teacher gets very angry.

➡ _____

(2) The weather is nice. I always walk to school.

➡ _____

(3) It rains on weekends. We watch TV.

➡ _____

[05~06] 다음 주어진 말을 이용하여 우리말을 영작하시오.

05
> 엄마는 내가 밤에 밖에 나가는 것을 허락하지 않으신다. (let, night)

➡ _____

06
> 나는 남동생에게 TV를 끄도록 했다.
> (make, turn)

➡ _____

07 다음 우리말과 일치하도록 빈칸에 알맞은 말을 넣어 문장을 완성하시오.

(1) 네가 만일 열심히 공부한다면, 너는 그 시험에 합격할 거야.

➡ _____, you'll pass the exam.

(2) 만일 내일 비가 오면 우리는 집에 있을 것이다.

➡ _____ tomorrow, we'll stay home.

중요

08 다음 문장에서 어법상 어색한 부분을 찾아 바르게 고쳐 문장을 다시 쓰시오.

(1) Finally, the police let the thief goes.

➡ _____

(2) Love makes people to do unusual things.

➡ _____

(3) I got my dog wear strange glasses.

➡ _____

(4) My English teacher helps us writing a diary every day.

➡ _____

09 다음 문장에서 어법상 어색한 것을 찾아 바르게 고쳐 쓰시오.

(1) You'll be happy if you'll pass the exam.

_____ ➡ _____

(2) If I won't be free tomorrow, I'll see you on Saturday.

_____ ➡ _____

10 다음 〈보기〉와 같이 문장을 바꿔 쓰시오. (단, make, let을 사용할 것)

┌─── 보기 ───┐
My mom: Clean your room.
➡ My mom made me clean my room.
└───────────┘

(1) My parents: Play computer games every Friday.

➡ _____

(2) My teacher: Wash your hands.

➡ _____

(3) My mom: Don't go out.

➡ _____

11 다음 문장에서 어법상 어색한 부분을 바르게 고쳐서 문장을 다시 쓰시오.

(1) If it will rain tomorrow, we won't go hiking.

➡ _____

(2) Unless you don't hurry, you will miss the train.

➡ _____

중요

12 다음 우리말과 일치하도록 주어진 어구를 바르게 배열하시오.

(1) Eddie는 남동생에게 그의 장난감을 갖고 놀게 한다. (lets / play / his toys / Eddie / his brother / with)

➡ _____

(2) 그녀는 아이들에게 영어 공부를 시킨다.
(English / makes / she / children / study / her)

➡ _____

(3) 아빠는 우리에게 일요일마다 아침을 요리하게 한다. (breakfast / Dad / us / Sundays / cook / on / has)

➡ _____

13 다음 주어진 단어를 바르게 배열하여 문장을 완성하시오.

┌─────────────────────────────┐
(she / will / if / study / the exam / , / she / fail / doesn't / hard)
└─────────────────────────────┘

➡ _____

Reading

Loosen Up!

At school you sit for many hours. Do you get tired? Why don't you
오랜 시간 동안   피곤하다 Why don't you ~?: ~하는 게 어때?(권유)

massage yourself and stretch?
재귀대명사(재귀 용법)

Let's begin with the eyes. Close your eyes and massage them softly
~하자   명령문: 동사원형 ~(~해라)   = your eyes

with your fingers. It will relax your eyes. When you finish, cover your
~으로   = Massaging your eyes softly with your fingers   접 ~하면

eyes with your hands to block out the light. It will make your eyes feel
목적을 나타내는 to부정사의 부사적 용법 / (빛을) 차단하다   사역동사 make+목적어+목적격보어(동사원형)

more comfortable.

Next, massage your neck. Put your fingers on the back of your neck.
명령문: 동사원형 ~(~해라)

Draw small circles with your fingers to massage your neck. Massage
~으로   to부정사의 부사적 용법(목적)

from top to bottom. The massage will help you feel better.
위에서 아래로   help+목적어+목적격보어(동사원형/to부정사)

---

loosen up 몸을 풀어 주다

massage 마사지하다

stretch 스트레칭하다

softly 부드럽게

finger 손가락

relax 편안하게 하다

finish 끝나다

cover 가리다

comfortable 편안한

neck 목

back 뒤쪽, 뒷부분

draw 그리다

circle 원

확인문제

● 다음 문장이 본문의 내용과 일치하면 T, 일치하지 않으면 F를 쓰시오.

1 To massage your eyes softly with your fingers will relax your eyes. ☐

2 We cover our eyes with our arms to block out the light. ☐

3 We draw small circles with our fingers to massage our neck. ☐

4 The neck massage will help you feel better. ☐

Let's work on your waist. Team up with a friend. Stand close to each other and face your partner. Hold each other's wrists. Slowly stretch your head and body backward. Hold that position for three seconds. Then, slowly pull each other to a standing position. You and your partner should move at the same speed. If you don't, both of you will fall!

Place the top of your right foot on the desk behind you. Then, slowly bend your left leg and lower yourself. Hold it for a few seconds and slowly straighten up. This position will loosen up your right leg. Switch your legs and repeat the exercise.

How do you feel now? If you massage yourself and stretch every day, you will feel healthier. Also, you can focus on your studies better.

waist 허리
close 가까이
face ~을 마주보다
slowly 천천히
wrist 손목
position 자세
pull 끌어당기다
fall 넘어지다
behind ~ 뒤에
bend 구부리다
lower 낮추다
hold 유지하다
switch 바꾸다
repeat 반복하다
exercise 운동
healthy 건강한
study 공부

확인문제

● 다음 문장이 본문의 내용과 일치하면 T, 일치하지 <u>않으면</u> F를 쓰시오.

1 To work on your waist, you have to team up with a friend. ☐

2 If two people move at the same speed, they will fall. ☐

3 After we place the top of our right foot on the desk behind us, we slowly bend our right leg and lower ourselves. ☐

4 If you massage yourself and stretch every day, you can focus on your studies better. ☐

● 우리말을 참고하여 빈칸에 알맞은 말을 쓰시오.

1 _____ school you sit _____ many hours.

2 Do you _____ _____?

3 _____ _____ you massage _____ and stretch?

4 _____ begin _____ the eyes.

5 _____ your eyes and _____ them softly _____ your fingers.

6 It _____ _____ your eyes.

7 _____ you finish, _____ your eyes _____ your hands to _____ _____ the light.

8 It will _____ your eyes _____ more _____ .

9 Next, _____ your neck.

10 _____ your fingers _____ the back of your neck.

11 _____ small circles _____ your fingers _____ massage your neck.

12 Massage _____ top _____ bottom.

13 The massage will _____ you _____ better.

14 _____ work on your _____ .

15 _____ _____ with a friend.

1	학교에서 너는 오랜 시간에 걸쳐 앉아 있다.
2	여러분은 피곤한가?
3	마사지와 스트레칭을 하는 게 어떤가?
4	눈부터 시작하자.
5	눈을 감고 손가락으로 눈을 부드럽게 마사지해라.
6	그것은 여러분의 눈을 편안하게 해줄 것이다.
7	끝나면, 빛을 차단하기 위해 손으로 눈을 가려라.
8	그것은 여러분의 눈을 더 편안하게 해줄 것이다.
9	다음으로, 여러분의 목을 마사지해라.
10	여러분의 목 뒤에 손가락을 대라.
11	여러분의 목을 마사지하기 위해 손가락으로 작은 원을 그려라.
12	위에서 아래로 마사지해라.
13	마사지는 여러분의 기분이 좋아지도록 도울 것이다.
14	허리 운동을 하자.
15	친구와 짝을 이루어라.

16 Stand close to _____ _____ and _____ your partner.

17 _____ each other's wrists.

18 Slowly _____ your head and body _____.

19 _____ that position _____ three seconds.

20 Then, slowly _____ each other _____ a standing position.

21 You and _____ partner should move _____ the same speed.

22 _____ you don't, _____ _____ you will fall!

23 _____ the top of your right foot _____ the desk _____ you.

24 Then, slowly _____ your left leg and _____ yourself.

25 _____ it for _____ _____ seconds and slowly straighten _____.

26 This position will _____ _____ your right leg.

27 _____ your legs and _____ the exercise.

28 _____ do you _____ now?

29 If you _____ yourself and _____ every day, you will _____ _____.

30 Also, you can _____ _____ your studies _____.

16 서로 가까이 서서 여러분의 파트너를 마주 보아라.

17 서로의 손목을 잡아라.

18 천천히 여러분의 머리와 몸을 뒤로 뻗어라.

19 3초 동안 그 자세를 유지해라.

20 그리고 나서, 천천히 서로 선 자세로 끌어 당겨라.

21 너와 너의 파트너는 같은 속도로 움직여야 한다.

22 그렇지 않으면, 너희 둘 다 넘어질 것이다!

23 여러분의 뒤에 있는 책상 위에 오른쪽 발등을 올려놓아라.

24 그리고 나서, 천천히 왼쪽 다리를 구부리고 몸을 낮추어라.

25 몇 초 동안 그 자세를 유지하다가 천천히 몸을 펴라.

26 이 자세는 여러분의 오른쪽 다리를 풀어 줄 것이다.

27 다리를 바꿔서 운동을 반복해라.

28 지금 기분이 어떤가?

29 매일 마사지와 스트레칭을 하면, 여러분은 더 건강해지는 것을 느낄 것이다.

30 또한, 여러분은 공부에 더 집중할 수 있을 것이다.

● 우리말을 참고하여 본문을 영작하시오.

1 ▶ 학교에서 여러분은 오랜 시간에 걸쳐 앉아 있다.

➡ _____

2 ▶ 여러분은 피곤한가?

➡ _____

3 ▶ 마사지와 스트레칭을 하는 게 어떤가?

➡ _____

4 ▶ 눈부터 시작하자.

➡ _____

5 ▶ 눈을 감고 손가락으로 눈을 부드럽게 마사지해라.

➡ _____

6 ▶ 그것은 여러분의 눈을 편안하게 해줄 것이다.

➡ _____

7 ▶ 끝나면, 빛을 차단하기 위해 손으로 눈을 가려라.

➡ _____

8 ▶ 그것은 여러분의 눈을 더 편안하게 해줄 것이다.

➡ _____

9 ▶ 다음으로, 여러분의 목을 마사지해라.

➡ _____

10 ▶ 여러분의 목 뒤에 손가락을 대라.

➡ _____

11 ▶ 여러분의 목을 마사지하기 위해 손가락으로 작은 원을 그려라.

➡ _____

12 ▶ 위에서 아래로 마사지해라.

➡ _____

13 ▶ 마사지는 여러분의 기분이 좋아지도록 도울 것이다.

➡ _____

14 ▶ 허리 운동을 하자.

➡ _____

15 ▶ 친구와 짝을 이루어라.

➡ _____

16 서로 가까이 서서 여러분의 파트너를 마주 보아라.

➡ _____

17 서로의 손목을 잡아라.

➡ _____

18 천천히 여러분의 머리와 몸을 뒤로 뻗어라.

➡ _____

19 3초 동안 그 자세를 유지해라.

➡ _____

20 그러고 나서, 천천히 서로 선 자세로 끌어 당겨라.

➡ _____

21 너와 너의 파트너는 같은 속도로 움직여야 한다.

➡ _____

22 그렇지 않으면, 너희 둘 다 넘어질 것이다!

➡ _____

23 여러분의 뒤에 있는 책상 위에 오른쪽 발등을 올려놓아라.

➡ _____

24 그러고 나서, 천천히 왼쪽 다리를 구부리고 몸을 낮추어라.

➡ _____

25 몇 초 동안 그 자세를 유지하다가 천천히 몸을 펴라.

➡ _____

26 이 자세는 여러분의 오른쪽 다리를 풀어 줄 것이다.

➡ _____

27 다리를 바꿔서 운동을 반복해라.

➡ _____

28 지금 기분이 어떤가?

➡ _____

29 매일 마사지와 스트레칭을 하면, 여러분은 더 건강해지는 것을 느낄 것이다.

➡ _____

30 또한, 여러분은 공부에 더 집중할 수 있을 것이다.

➡ _____

[01~05] 다음 글을 읽고, 물음에 답하시오.

At school you sit ____ⓐ____ many hours. Do you ____ⓑ____ tired? Why don't you massage yourself and stretch?

Let's begin with the eyes. Close your eyes and massage ⓒthem softly with your fingers. It will relax your eyes. When you finish, cover your eyes with your hands to block ____ⓓ____ the light. ⓔIt will make your eyes feel more comfortable.

01 위 글의 빈칸 ⓐ와 ⓓ에 알맞은 말이 바르게 짝지어진 것은?

① in – up   ② by – off
③ for – out   ④ over – into
⑤ during – over

02 위 글의 빈칸 ⓑ에 알맞은 것은?

① go   ② get   ③ put
④ take   ⑤ have

서답형

03 위 글의 밑줄 친 ⓒ가 가리키는 것을 찾아 영어로 쓰시오.

➡ _____

서답형

04 위 글에서 다음 영영풀이에 해당하는 단어를 찾아 쓰시오.

to put your arms, legs, etc., in positions that make the muscles long and tight

➡ _____

05 위 글의 밑줄 친 ⓔIt이 의미하는 것은?

① 스트레칭을 하는 것
② 눈을 감는 것
③ 손으로 눈을 비비는 것
④ 손가락으로 눈을 마사지하는 것
⑤ 빛을 차단하기 위해 손으로 눈을 가리는 것

[06~10] 다음 글을 읽고, 물음에 답하시오.

Let's work on your waist. Team up with a friend. Stand close to each other and ⓐface your partner. Hold each other's wrists. Slowly stretch your head and body backward. Hold that position ____ⓑ____ three seconds. Then, slowly pull each other to a standing ____ⓒ____. You and your partner should move at the same speed. ____ⓓ____ you don't, both ____ⓔ____ you will fall!

06 위 글의 밑줄 친 ⓐ와 쓰임이 같은 것은?

① She looks thin in the face.
② She'll face with a difficult decision.
③ I turned the chair to face him.
④ The man is wiping his face.
⑤ The birds build their nests in the rock face.

서답형

07 위 글의 빈칸 ⓑ와 ⓔ에 알맞은 말을 쓰시오.

ⓑ _____ ⓔ _____

서답형

08 위 글의 빈칸 ⓒ에 다음 영영풀이에 해당하는 단어를 쓰시오.

> the way someone stands, sits, or lies down

➡ _____

09 위 글의 빈칸 ⓓ에 알맞은 것은?

① As　　　　② If
③ That　　　④ While
⑤ When

10 위 글의 내용과 일치하지 <u>않는</u> 것은?

① 친구와 함께 협력한다.
② 서로 가까이 서서 파트너를 마주 본다.
③ 서로의 손목을 잡는다.
④ 천천히 머리와 몸을 뒤로 뻗는다.
⑤ 두 사람이 같은 속도로 움직이면 둘 다 넘어진다.

[11~15] 다음 글을 읽고, 물음에 답하시오.

①<u>Place</u> the top of your right foot on the desk behind you. Then, ②<u>slowly</u> ⓐ<u>bend</u> your left leg and lower ③<u>itself</u>. Hold it ④ <u>for</u> a few seconds and ⓑ<u>slow</u> straighten ____ⓒ____. This position will loosen ____ⓓ____ your right leg. Switch your legs and ⑤<u>repeat</u> the exercise.

11 위 글의 밑줄 친 ①~⑤ 중 어법상 틀린 것은?

①　　②　　③　　④　　⑤

12 위 글의 밑줄 친 ⓐ의 영영풀이로 알맞은 것은?

① to add something to something else
② to change or replace something with another thing
③ to move your body so that it is not straight
④ to put something or someone in a particular place or position
⑤ to extend your arm, leg, etc., in order to reach something

서답형

13 위 글의 밑줄 친 ⓑ를 알맞은 형태로 고쳐 쓰시오.

➡ _____

14 위 글의 빈칸 ⓒ와 ⓓ에 공통으로 알맞은 것은?

① on　　　　② out
③ off　　　　④ up
⑤ over

서답형

15 위 글의 다리를 풀어 주는 방법을 순서대로 배열하시오.

> ⓐ 다리를 구부리고 몸을 낮춘 상태로 몇 초 동안 유지한다.
> ⓑ 뒤에 있는 책상 위에 오른쪽 발의 윗부분을 올려놓는다.
> ⓒ 천천히 왼쪽 다리를 구부리고 몸을 낮춘다.

➡ _____

[16~20] 다음 글을 읽고, 물음에 답하시오.

> Let's begin with the eyes. Close your eyes and massage them ⓐsoft with your fingers. ⓑIt will relax your eyes. When you finish, ____ⓒ____ your eyes with your hands ⓓblock out the light. ⓔ그것은 너의 눈을 더 편안하게 해줄 것이다.

16 위 글의 밑줄 친 ⓐ를 알맞은 형태로 고쳐 쓰시오.

➡ _____

17 위 글의 밑줄 친 ⓑIt이 가리키는 것을 우리말로 쓰시오.

➡ _____

18 문맥상 위 글의 빈칸 ⓒ에 알맞은 것은?

① open   ② rub
③ cover   ④ close
⑤ massage

19 위 글의 밑줄 친 ⓓ의 형태로 알맞은 것은?

① block   ② blocks
③ blocking   ④ to block
⑤ to blocking

20 위 글의 밑줄 친 ⓔ의 우리말에 맞게 주어진 어구를 이용하여 문장을 완성하시오.

It will _____.

[21~23] 다음 글을 읽고, 물음에 답하시오.

> Next, massage your neck. ____ⓐ____ your fingers on the back of your neck. ____ⓑ____ small circles with your fingers ⓒto massage your neck. ____ⓓ____ from top to bottom. ⓔThe massage will help you feeling better.

21 위 글의 빈칸 ⓐ, ⓑ, ⓓ에 알맞은 말이 바르게 짝지어진 것은?

① Draw – Massage – Put
② Put – Draw – Massage
③ Massage – Put – Draw
④ Draw – Put – Massage
⑤ Put – Massage – Draw

22 위 글의 밑줄 친 ⓒ와 쓰임이 같은 것은?

① The boy wants to drink juice.
② He loves to play outside.
③ She dressed up to meet her boyfriend.
④ To swim in this river is dangerous.
⑤ My plan is to travel around Thailand.

23 위 글의 밑줄 친 ⓔ에서 어법상 틀린 부분을 찾아 바르게 고쳐 쓰시오.

_____ ➡ _____

[24~27] 다음 글을 읽고, 물음에 답하시오.

Let's work on your ⓐ＿＿＿. Team up with a friend. ①Stand close to each other and face your partner. ②Hold each other's wrists. Slowly stretch your head and body ③forward. ④Hold that position for three ⓑseconds. Then, slowly ⑤pull each other to a standing position. You and your partner ⓒ＿＿＿ move at the same speed. If you don't, both of you ⓓ＿＿＿ fall!

서답형

24 위 글의 빈칸 ⓐ에 다음 영영풀이에 해당하는 단어를 쓰시오.

the area around the middle of the body between the ribs and the hips

➡ ＿＿＿＿＿＿＿＿＿＿＿

25 위 글의 밑줄 친 ①~⑤ 중 문맥상 단어의 쓰임이 어색한 것은?

① ② ③ ④ ⑤

26 위 글의 밑줄 친 ⓑ와 쓰임이 같은 것은?

① I agreed to speak second.
② The light flashes every 5 seconds.
③ He was the second to arrive.
④ Milan is Italy's second largest city.
⑤ Fill the second bowl with warm water.

중요
27 위 글의 빈칸 ⓒ와 ⓓ에 알맞은 말이 바르게 짝지어진 것은?

① might – will　　② would – can
③ must – may　　④ could – will
⑤ should – will

[28~31] 다음 글을 읽고, 물음에 답하시오.

(①) Place the top of your right foot on the desk behind you. (②) Then, slowly bend your left leg and lower ⓐyou. (③) This position will ⓑ＿＿＿ your right leg. (④) Switch your legs and repeat the exercise. (⑤)

중요
28 위 글의 ①~⑤ 중 다음 문장이 들어갈 알맞은 곳은?

Hold it for a few seconds and slowly straighten up.

① ② ③ ④ ⑤

서답형
29 위 글의 밑줄 친 ⓐ를 알맞은 형태로 고쳐 쓰시오.

➡ ＿＿＿＿＿＿＿＿＿＿＿

서답형
30 위 글에서 다음 영영풀이에 해당하는 단어를 찾아 쓰시오.

to make a change from one thing to another

➡ ＿＿＿＿＿＿＿＿＿＿＿

31 위 글의 빈칸 ⓑ에 알맞은 것은?

① get over　　② put on
③ block out　　④ focus on
⑤ loosen up

[01~04] 다음 글을 읽고, 물음에 답하시오.

At school you sit for many hours. Do you get tired? ⓐ(you / why / massage / don't) yourself and stretch?

Let's begin with the eyes. Close your eyes and massage them softly with your fingers. It will relax your eyes. When you finish, cover your eyes with your hands to block out the light. ⓑIt will make your eyes feel more comfortably.

01 위 글의 빈칸 ⓐ 안의 단어들을 바르게 배열하시오.

➡ _____

02 위 글에서 다음 영영풀이에 해당하는 단어를 찾아 쓰시오.

to rub or press someone's body in a way that helps muscles to relax or reduces pain in muscles and joints

➡ _____

03 위 글의 밑줄 친 ⓑ에서 어법상 틀린 부분을 찾아 바르게 고쳐 쓰시오.

_____ ➡ _____

04 What can we do to block out the light? Answer in English.

➡ _____

[05~08] 다음 글을 읽고, 물음에 답하시오.

Next, massage your neck. Put your fingers on the back of your neck. Draw small circles with your fingers ⓐmassage your neck. Massage ___ⓑ___ top to bottom. ⓒ마사지는 여러분의 기분이 나아지도록 도울 것이다.

05 위 글의 밑줄 친 ⓐ를 알맞은 형태로 고쳐 쓰시오.

➡ _____

06 위 글의 빈칸 ⓑ에 알맞은 말을 쓰시오.

➡ _____

07 위 글의 밑줄 친 ⓒ의 우리말에 맞도록 주어진 어구를 바르게 배열하시오.

(you / will / the massage / help / better / feel)

➡ _____

08 목을 마사지하는 방법을 순서대로 배열하시오.

ⓐ 목을 마사지하기 위해 손가락으로 작은 원을 그린다.
ⓑ 위에서부터 아래로 마사지한다.
ⓒ 목 뒷부분에 손가락을 댄다.

➡ _____

[09~12] 다음 글을 읽고, 물음에 답하시오.

Place the top of your right foot on the desk behind you. Then, slowly bend your left leg and ___ⓐ___ yourself. Hold ⓑit for a few seconds and slowly straighten ___ⓒ___. ⓓThis position will loosen up your right leg. Switch your legs and repeat the exercise.

09 위 글의 빈칸 ⓐ에 다음 영영풀이에 해당하는 단어를 주어진 철자로 시작하여 쓰시오.

> to move something down from higher up

➡ l_____

10 위 글의 밑줄 친 ⓑ가 의미하는 것을 우리말로 구체적으로 쓰시오.

➡ _____

11 위 글의 밑줄 친 ⓒ에 '똑바로 하다'라는 의미가 되도록 할 때 빈칸에 알맞은 말을 쓰시오.

➡ _____

12 위 글의 밑줄 친 ⓓ를 우리말로 옮기시오.

➡ _____

[13~16] 다음 글을 읽고, 물음에 답하시오.

Let's work on your waist. Team up with a friend. Stand close to each other and ___ⓐ___ your partner. Hold each other's wrists. Slowly stretch your head and body backward. Hold ⓑthat position for three seconds. ⓒThen, slowly push each other to a standing position. You and your partner should move at the same speed. If you don't, both of you will fall!

13 위 글의 빈칸 ⓐ에 다음 영영풀이에 해당하는 단어를 주어진 철자로 시작하여 쓰시오.

> to stand or sit with your face and body turned toward something or someone

➡ f_____

14 위 글의 밑줄 친 ⓑ가 의미하는 것을 우리말로 구체적으로 쓰시오.

➡ _____

15 위 글의 밑줄 친 ⓒ에서 문맥상 단어의 쓰임이 어색한 것을 찾아 바르게 고쳐 쓰시오.

_____ ➡ _____

16 If two people don't move at the same speed, what will happen?

➡ _____

해석

Enjoy Writing C

My Plan to Be Healthier

Here is my plan to be healthier.
Here is + 단수 명사 ~: 여기 ~이 있다

1. I will exercise more than three times a week.
   ~ 이상   일주일에 세 번

2. I will eat breakfast every day.
   매일

   If I exercise more than three times a week, I will become stronger. Also, if
   조건을 나타내는 접속사 if(~한다면)   become+형용사: ~해지다

   I eat breakfast every day, I will feel better in the morning. I will change my
                                          기분이 좋아지다

   habits, and it will make me live a healthy life.
                          사역동사 make+목적어+목적격 보어(동사원형): ~을 ...하게 하다

구문해설 • healthy: 건강한 • exercise: 운동하다 • change: 바꾸다 • habit: 습관

더 건강해지기 위한 나의 계획
여기 더 건강해지기 위한 나의 계획이 있다.
1. 나는 일주일에 세 번 이상 운동을 할 것이다.
2. 나는 매일 아침을 먹을 것이다. 일주일에 세 번 이상 운동을 하면 더 강해질 것이다. 또한, 매일 아침을 먹으면 아침에 기분이 나아질 것이다. 나는 습관을 바꿀 것이고, 그것은 나를 건강한 삶을 살게 할 것이다.

Project - Step 2

Do you know how to stretch your shoulders? Our stretching exercise is
                how+to부정사: 어떻게 ~하는지   ~라고 불리다

called "Number Stretching." First, make a number "1" with your arm to warm
                                                        목적을 나타내는 to부정사의 부사적 용법(~하기 위해)

up. Then, make a number "2" with your arms. It will stretch your shoulders.
                          ~으로

Now, make a number "3". If you move your arms in a circle, it will feel nice.
                                                              feel+형용사: ~하게 느끼다

Finally, make a number "4". It is a little bit difficult, but it will be good for
                              조금   ~에 좋다

your shoulders.

구문해설 • stretch: 스트레칭하다 • shoulder: 어깨 • warm up: 준비 운동을 하다 • circle: 원
         • finally: 마지막으로 • difficult: 어려운

여러분은 어깨를 어떻게 스트레칭하는지 아는가? 우리의 스트레칭 운동은 "숫자 스트레칭"이라고 부른다. "첫 번째, 준비 운동을 하기 위해 팔로 숫자 "1"를 만들어라. 그런 다음, 팔로 숫자 2를 만들어라. 그것은 여러분의 어깨를 쫙 펴줄 것이다. 이제 숫자 3을 만들어라. 팔을 동그랗게 움직이면 기분이 좋아질 것이다. 마지막으로, 숫자 4를 만들어라. 그것은 조금 어렵긴 하지만, 여러분의 어깨에 좋을 것이다.

Wrap Up - Writing

Sumi: I feel stressed these days. What should I do?
                          요즘

Jiae: When I get stressed, I listen to music. It makes me feel better. If you don't
                  스트레스를 받다   사역동사 make+목적어+목적격 보어(동사원형): ~을 ...하게 하다

know how to download music, I will show you.
      다운로드하는 방법

구문해설 • listen to: ~을 듣다 • feel better: 기분이 더 좋아지다 • show: 보여주다, 가르쳐 주다

수미: 나는 요즘 스트레스를 받고 있어. 어떻게 해야 하지?
지애: 스트레스를 받을 때, 나는 음악을 들어. 그건 내 기분을 좋아지게 해. 음악을 다운로드하는 방법을 모르면, 내가 가르쳐 줄게.

Words & Expressions

01 다음 중 짝지어진 단어의 관계가 <u>다른</u> 것은?

① warm : cool
② difficult : easy
③ heavy : light
④ switch : change
⑤ backward : forward

02 다음 영영풀이에 해당하는 단어는?

> to move your body so that it is not straight

① pull
② bend
③ place
④ push
⑤ stretch

03 다음 우리말과 같도록 빈칸에 알맞은 말을 쓰시오.

> 새로운 과학 프로젝트를 위해, 우리는 친구들과 협력할 필요가 있다.
> ➡ For the new science project, we need to _____ _____ with friends.

04 다음 영영풀이에 해당하는 단어를 쓰시오.

> the action of rubbing and pressing a person's body with the hands to reduce pain in the muscles and joints

➡ _____

05 다음 빈칸에 공통으로 알맞은 것은?

> • What is the best _____ to get to City Hall?
> • I don't know the _____ to the stadium.

① tip
② part
③ way
④ top
⑤ choice

06 다음 빈칸에 알맞은 말이 바르게 짝지어진 것은?

> • You have to loosen _____ your arms and legs before swimming.
> • The trees in the park block _____ a lot of sunlight.

① of – in
② over – at
③ to – off
④ from – on
⑤ up – out

Conversation

07 다음 대화의 빈칸에 알맞지 <u>않은</u> 것은?

> A: What do you enjoy doing after school?
> B: _____

① I like to go hiking.
② I enjoy playing soccer.
③ I enjoy cooking healthy food.
④ I'm interested in science.
⑤ I enjoy listening to music.

08 다음 대화의 빈칸에 알맞은 것은?

> A: How about making paper flowers?
> B: That sounds great. But I don't know
> _____.

① what to make them
② how to make them
③ how to use them
④ where to get there
⑤ what to use them

09 다음 대화의 빈칸에 알맞은 것은?

> A: _____
> B: I enjoy listening to pop music.

① Can you play music?
② Why don't you listen to music?
③ What kind of music do you like?
④ Do you want to listen to music?
⑤ What's your favorite sport?

10 다음 대화의 빈칸에 들어갈 말로 알맞은 것은?

> A: Are you good at solving math problems?
> B: No, I _____ math.

① am going to
② can get
③ am not good at
④ feel so good
⑤ am looking forward to

11 다음 대화의 순서를 바르게 배열하시오.

> (A) I enjoy cooking healthy food.
> (B) I can make salad, Bibimbap, and vegetable juice.
> (C) What do you enjoy doing after school?
> (D) Sounds cool. What can you make?

➡ _____

[12~15] 다음 대화를 읽고, 물음에 답하시오.

> B: I want to eat something healthy. Do you have any advice?
> G: I often eat fresh salad. It makes me ⓐfeel good.
> B: Really? Do you know how ⓑmake it?
> G: Yes, it's quite simple. ___(A)___, cut many vegetables ___ⓒ___ small pieces. ___(B)___, put them into a bowl. Then, pour some lemon juice on them. ___(C)___, mix everything together.
> B: That's it? I should try it.

12 위 대화의 밑줄 친 ⓐ와 ⓑ를 알맞은 형태로 쓰시오.

ⓐ _____ ⓑ _____

13 위 대화의 빈칸 ⓒ에 알맞은 것은?

① by   ② on   ③ for
④ into   ⑤ with

14 위 대화의 빈칸 (A)~(C)에 들어갈 말을 순서대로 나열한 것은?

① Second – Finally – Third
② First – Two – Third
③ First – Then – Finally
④ First – Finally – After then
⑤ Finally – First – End

15 위 대화를 읽고, 다음 물음에 완전한 문장으로 답하시오.

> Q: What is the second step in making fresh salad?
> A: _____
> _____

Grammar

16 다음 빈칸에 공통으로 알맞은 것은?

> • He _____ me cook dinner.
> • Mom _____ me clean up my room.

① gave   ② wanted

③ made   ④ enjoyed

⑤ asked

17 다음 중 〈보기〉의 밑줄 친 부분과 쓰임이 같은 것은?

> ┤ 보기 ├
>
> I want to know if it will rain tomorrow.

① If he comes back, I will tell him about it.

② I won't go there if is cold tomorrow.

③ If you turn right, you can see the building.

④ You may go home early if you don't feel well.

⑤ I doubt if the baby can understand your words.

18 다음 밑줄 친 부분의 쓰임이 나머지와 다른 것은?

① Let me tell you about my teacher.

② I made him do his homework last night.

③ The students have many books to read.

④ I helped my dad wash his car.

⑤ My teacher had the students play outside.

19 다음 문장에서 어법상 어색한 부분을 바르게 고쳐서 문장을 다시 쓰시오.

> What do you do if he visits your home tomorrow?

➡ _____

20 다음 중 어법상 어색한 문장은?

① Mom let me go to bed early.

② Mr. Han told me go home early.

③ He made the children wash his car.

④ Jack will help you find the bicycle.

⑤ It lets you know about the price.

21 다음 빈칸에 공통으로 알맞은 것은?

> • You will get one free _____ you buy this.
> • I wonder _____ she is really a middle school student.

① as   ② if

③ that   ④ since

⑤ whether

22 다음 주어진 어구를 바르게 배열하여 문장을 완성하시오.

> 그녀는 아이들에게 축구를 하게 한다.
> (soccer / she / the children / play / has)

➡ _____

23 다음 〈보기〉의 밑줄 친 부분의 의미와 같은 것은?

> ┤ 보기 ├
>
> He made me do my math homework.

① She made it after all.

② I want to make money to buy the ring.

③ She made pasta for her little son.

④ They make the students do voluntary service at school.

⑤ You have to make an effort to be happy.

24 다음 밑줄 친 부분 중 어법상 어색한 것은?

① Unless he is late, we will start on time.

② Don't open the box until he says it's safe.

③ I'll go swimming if it will be sunny.

④ She will be happy when he sends her some flowers.

⑤ I'll wait here until the concert is over.

25 다음 문장에서 어법상 어색한 부분을 찾아 고쳐 쓰시오.

> Nothing will make me changing my mind.

_____ ➡ _____

26 다음 두 문장을 접속사 if를 써서 한 문장으로 바꿔 쓰시오.

> Jenny does not get up now. She will miss the train.

➡ _____
_____

27 다음 빈칸에 들어갈 말이 나머지 넷과 다른 것은?

① Mike will stay at home _____ it is cold.

② You can stay at home _____ you're tired.

③ She'll watch TV _____ she finishes her work early.

④ He'll buy a necktie for his dad _____ he goes shopping.

⑤ I think _____ Anderson won't come back.

[28~31] 다음 글을 읽고, 물음에 답하시오.

At school you sit (A)[for / during] many hours. Do you get tired? Why don't you massage (B)[itself / yourself] and stretch?
Let's begin ___ⓐ___ the eyes. ①Close your eyes and ②massage them softly ___ⓑ___ your fingers. It will ③relax your eyes. When you finish, ④open your eyes with your hands (C)[blocking / to block] out the light. It will ⓒ(feel / eyes / make / your) more ⑤comfortable.

28 위 글의 괄호 (A)~(C)에서 알맞은 것이 바르게 짝지어진 것은?

① for – itself – blocking

② for – yourself – to block

③ during – itself – blocking

④ during – yourself – blocking

⑤ during – itself – to block

29 위 글의 빈칸 ⓐ와 ⓑ에 공통으로 알맞은 말을 쓰시오.

➡ _____

30 위 글의 밑줄 친 ①~⑤ 중 흐름상 적절하지 않은 것은?

①   ②   ③   ④   ⑤

31 위 글의 괄호 ⓒ 안의 단어들을 순서대로 바르게 배열하시오.

➡ _____

[32~35] 다음 글을 읽고, 물음에 답하시오.

Let's ⓐ<u>work</u> on your waist. Team __(A)__ with a friend. (①) Stand close to each other and ⓑ<u>face</u> your partner. (②) Hold each other's __(B)__ . (③) Slowly ⓒ<u>stretch</u> your head and body backward. (④) Then, ⓓ<u>slowly</u> pull each other to a standing position. (⑤) You and your partner should move at the same speed. If you don't, both of you ⓔ<u>fall</u>!

32 위 글의 빈칸 (A)에 알맞은 것은?

① on   ② in
③ out   ④ up
⑤ down

33 위 글의 빈칸 (B)에 다음 영영풀이에 해당하는 단어를 쓰시오. (복수형으로 쓸 것)

the part of your body where your hand joins your arm

➡ _____

34 위 글의 ①~⑤ 중 다음 문장이 들어갈 알맞은 곳은?

Hold that position for three seconds.

①   ②   ③   ④   ⑤

35 위 글의 밑줄 친 ⓐ~ⓔ 중 어법상 어색한 것은?

① ⓐ   ② ⓑ   ③ ⓒ   ④ ⓓ   ⑤ ⓔ

[36~39] 다음 글을 읽고, 물음에 답하시오.

ⓐ<u>너는 너의 어깨를 스트레칭하는 방법을 아니?</u> Our stretching exercise is called "Number Stretching." __(A)__ , make a number "1" with your arm to warm up. __(B)__ , make a number "2" with your arms. ⓑ<u>It</u> will stretch your shoulders. Now, make a number "3". If you move your arms in a circle, it will feel nice. __(C)__ , make a number "4". It is a little bit difficult, __ⓒ__ it will be good for your shoulders.

36 위 글의 밑줄 친 ⓐ의 우리말과 일치하도록 빈칸에 알맞은 말을 쓰시오.

Do you know _____ _____ _____ your shoulders?

37 위 글의 빈칸 (A)~(C)에 알맞은 말을 <보기>에서 골라 차례대로 쓰시오.

┌─ 보기 ─────────────────┐
│   Finally   First   Then   │
└────────────────────────┘

(A) _____ (B) _____ (C) _____

38 위 글의 밑줄 친 ⓑIt이 가리키는 것을 우리말로 쓰시오.

➡ _____

39 위 글의 빈칸 ⓒ에 알맞은 것은?

① so   ② and
③ for   ④ but
⑤ also

01 다음 〈보기〉와 같이 변화하는 단어는?

> ┌─ 보기 ┐
> use → usable

① create   ② act

③ comfort   ④ attract

⑤ impress

02 다음 짝지어진 단어의 관계가 같도록 빈칸에 알맞은 말을 쓰시오.

> simple : complicated = top : _____

03 다음 빈칸에 알맞은 말이 바르게 짝지어진 것은?

> • I want to focus _____ losing weight.
> • Straighten _____ your shoulders when you walk.

① in – on   ② at – up

③ of – off   ④ into – for

⑤ on – up

04 다음 영영풀이에 해당하는 단어는?

> to become or to cause something to become less tense, tight, or stiff

① bend   ② switch

③ reduce   ④ relax

⑤ prepare

05 다음 우리말에 맞게 빈칸에 알맞은 말을 쓰시오.

(1) 몇 초 동안 수프를 저어라.

➡ Stir the soup for _____ _____ _____.

(2) 나는 항상 저녁 식사 후에 산책을 한다.

➡ I always _____ _____ _____ after dinner.

(3) 너는 보통 어떤 종류의 사진을 찍니?

➡ _____ _____ _____ pictures do you usually take?

06 다음 대화의 밑줄 친 부분의 의도로 알맞은 것은?

> A: Do you know how to make healthy juice?
> B: No, I don't.

① 의견 동의하기   ② 도움 요청하기

③ 능력 여부 묻기   ④ 제안이나 권유하기

⑤ 선호에 대해 묻기

07 다음 대화의 빈칸에 알맞지 <u>않은</u> 것은?

> A: What do you do in your free time?
> B: _____
> A: How interesting!

① I ride a bike in the park.

② I hate to study English and math.

③ I take pictures of animals.

④ I enjoy drawing cartoons.

⑤ I play badminton with my sister.

[08~11] 다음 대화를 읽고, 물음에 답하시오.

B: People say that we should walk more than 10,000 steps every day ⓐbe healthy. I can't count the number of my steps easily.

G: You can use this smartphone app. ⓑ(you / how / do / it / use / know / to)?

B: No. Can you show me?

G: Sure. First, download the app. Then, walk with your smartphone. ⓒLate, you can check the number of steps you took.

B: Thank you. I will start using ⓓit today.

출제율 95%

08 위 대화의 밑줄 친 ⓐ를 알맞은 형태로 고쳐 쓰시오.

➡ _____

출제율 90%

09 위 대화의 괄호 ⓑ 안의 단어들을 바르게 배열하시오.

➡ _____

출제율 100%

10 위 대화의 밑줄 친 ⓒ를 알맞은 형태로 고치시오.

➡ _____

출제율 95%

11 위 대화의 밑줄 친 ⓓ가 가리키는 것을 영어로 쓰시오.

➡ _____

출제율 95%

12 다음 빈칸에 들어갈 말로 알맞은 것은?

| She won't let me _____ home early. |

① to go   ② going
③ went   ④ will go
⑤ go

출제율 100%

13 다음 중 어법상 <u>어색한</u> 것은?

① We can make the robots work better.
② My father made my dog stand up.
③ The house is the biggest in our town.
④ It makes students practicing their English a lot.
⑤ Swimming is the most interesting activity for me.

출제율 95%

14 다음 문장의 빈칸에 알맞은 것은?

| If it _____ tomorrow, we won't go fishing. |

① rain   ② rains
③ rained   ④ will rain
⑤ would rain

출제율 90%

15 다음 글의 밑줄 친 ①~⑤ 중 <u>어색한</u> 것은?

Sanghui ①loves ②repairing machines. She can ③make any broken machine ④working again. And Mr. Han makes children run away by ⑤shouting at them.

①   ②   ③   ④   ⑤

출제율 95%

16 다음 우리말을 영어로 바르게 옮긴 것은?

> 나는 날씨가 좋으면 주말마다 낚시하러 간다.

① I go fishing on weekends because the weather is good.
② The weather is good, so I go fishing on weekends.
③ As the weather is good, I will go fishing on weekends.
④ If the weather will be good, I go fishing on weekends.
⑤ I go fishing on weekends if the weather is good.

출제율 100%

17 다음 빈칸에 들어갈 말이 바르게 짝지어진 것은?

> • I was late _____ the bus broke down.
> • I can finish that work _____ I have three days.

① when – how
② when – where
③ if – because
④ because – that
⑤ because – if

출제율 90%

18 다음 우리말과 같도록 빈칸에 알맞은 말을 써서 문장을 완성하시오.

> 만약 이번 일요일에 날씨가 맑으면, 우리는 소풍을 갈 것이다.
>
> = _____ _____ _____ sunny this Sunday, we _____ _____ on a picnic.

출제율 85%

19 다음 우리말과 같은 뜻이 되도록 빈칸에 알맞은 말을 쓰시오. (필요하면 어형을 바꾸시오.)

> 선생님은 Martin이 반 아이들 앞에서 그 이야기를 읽도록 하셨다. (have)

➡ The teacher _____ the story in front of the class.

[20~23] 다음 글을 읽고, 물음에 답하시오.

> (①) Place the _____ⓐ_____ of your right foot _____ⓑ_____ the desk behind you. (②) Then, slowly bend your left leg and lower yourself. (③) Hold it for _____ⓒ_____ seconds and slowly straighten up. (④) Switch your legs and repeat the exercise. (⑤)

출제율 85%

20 위 글의 빈칸 ⓐ에 다음 영영풀이에 해당하는 단어를 쓰시오.

> an upper surface of something

➡ _____

출제율 95%

21 위 글의 빈칸 ⓑ에 알맞은 것은?

① at
② with
③ in
④ on
⑤ for

출제율 100%

22 위 글의 빈칸 ⓒ에 알맞은 것은?

① few
② little
③ much
④ a little
⑤ a few

출제율 95%

23 위 글의 ①~⑤ 중 다음 문장이 들어갈 알맞은 곳은?

> This position will loosen up your right leg.

①   ②   ③   ④   ⑤

[24~26] 다음 글을 읽고, 물음에 답하시오.

Do you know how ___ⓐ___ stretch your shoulders? Our stretching exercise is called "Number Stretching." First, make a number "1" with your arm ___ⓑ___ warm up. Then, make a number "2" with your arms. It will stretch your shoulders. Now, make a number "3". If you move your arms in a circle, it will feel nice. Finally, make a number "4". It is a little bit difficult, but it will be good ___ⓒ___ your shoulders.

✏️ 출제율 95%

24 위 글의 빈칸 ⓐ와 ⓑ에 공통으로 알맞은 말을 쓰시오.

➡ _____

✏️ 출제율 95%

25 위 글에서 다음 영영풀이에 해당하는 단어를 찾아 쓰시오.

> to do an exercise or set of exercises done to prepare for a sport or other activity

➡ _____

✏️ 출제율 95%

26 위 글의 빈칸 ⓒ에 알맞은 말을 쓰시오.

➡ _____

[27~30] 다음 글을 읽고, 물음에 답하시오.

___ⓐ___ the top of your right foot on the desk behind you. Then, slowly ___ⓑ___ your left leg and lower yourself. ___ⓒ___ it for a few seconds and slowly straighten ___ⓓ___. This position will ___ⓔ___. Switch your legs and repeat the exercise.

How do you feel now? If you massage yourself and stretch every day, you will feel healthier. ___ⓕ___, you can focus ___ⓖ___ your studies better.

✏️ 출제율 95%

27 위 글의 빈칸 ⓐ~ⓒ에 알맞은 말을 〈보기〉에서 골라 쓰시오.

┌─ 보기 ─────────────────┐
│   hold   place   bend   │
└────────────────────────┘

ⓐ _____ ⓑ _____ ⓒ _____

✏️ 출제율 100%

28 위 글의 빈칸 ⓓ와 ⓖ에 알맞은 말이 바르게 짝지어진 것은?

① up – on   ② on – in
③ in – of   ④ off – to
⑤ on – about

✏️ 출제율 90%

29 위 글의 빈칸 ⓔ에 알맞은 것은?

① tighten your right foot
② relax your left leg
③ make your left leg strong
④ straighten up your position
⑤ loosen up your right leg

✏️ 출제율 85%

30 위 글의 빈칸 ⓕ에 알맞은 것은?

① But   ② And
③ Or   ④ Also
⑤ So

[01~02] 괄호 안의 단어를 바르게 배열하여 대화를 완성하시오. (필요하면 어형을 바꿀 것)

01 (중요)

A: (how / do / massage / know / you / to) legs?

B: Yes, I do.

➡ _____

02

A: Kate, what do you enjoy doing to be healthy?

B: (catch / enjoy / I / play).

➡ _____

03 다음 대화의 밑줄 친 말을 주어진 표현을 이용하여 영작하시오.

A: Are you good at solving math problems?

B: No, 나는 수학을 잘 못해. (be good at)

➡ _____

04 (중요) 자연스러운 대화가 되도록 (A)~(D)의 순서를 바르게 배열하시오.

(A) Sounds cool. What can you make?

(B) I can make salad, Bibimbap, and vegetable juice.

(C) I enjoy cooking healthy food.

(D) What do you enjoy doing after school?

➡ _____

05 (중요) 다음 문장에서 어법상 어색한 부분을 고쳐 다시 쓰시오.

(1) I will have my brother cleaned my room.

➡ _____

(2) Inhui made her daughter did the dishes.

➡ _____

(3) My mother let me to watch the TV drama.

➡ _____

06 다음 괄호 안의 어구를 이용하여 우리말을 영어로 옮기시오.

(1) 열이 있으면 너는 의사의 진찰을 받아야 한다.
(have, you, a, fever, should, see, doctor)

➡ _____

(2) 내일 비가 오면 난 영화 보러 갈 거야.
(rains, tomorrow, it, go, a movie)

➡ _____

(3) 파란색에 노란색을 섞으면 초록색이 된다.
(add, to, blue, green, yellow, you, become)

➡ _____

07 다음 주어진 어구를 바르게 배열하시오.

(1) (makes / my / clean / mother / my / me / room)

➡ _____

(2) (librarian / find / the / a / helped / book / me)

➡ _____

(3) (safely / her / they / go / let)

➡ _____

Let's begin with the eyes. Close your eyes and massage them softly with your fingers. It will relax your eyes. When you finish, cover your eyes with your hands to block out the light. ⓐIt will make your eyes feel more comfortable.

Next, massage your neck. Put your fingers on the back of your neck. Draw small circles with your fingers to massage your neck. Massage from top to bottom. ⓑ마사지는 여러분의 기분이 좋아지도록 도울 것이다.

08 How do we massage our eyes with our fingers? Answer in English.

➡ _____

09 위 글의 밑줄 친 ⓐ를 우리말로 옮기시오.

➡ _____

10 What can we do to massage our neck? Answer in English.

➡ _____

11 위 글의 밑줄 친 ⓑ의 우리말에 맞도록 괄호 안의 어구를 순서대로 배열하시오.

(will / the / feel / help / you / better / massage)

➡ _____

[12~15] 다음 글을 읽고, 물음에 답하시오.

ⓐHere are my plan to be healthier.
1. I will exercise more than three times a week.
2. I will eat breakfast every day.
   If I exercise more than three times a week, I will become stronger. Also, if I eat breakfast every day, I will feel better in the morning. I will change my habits, and ⓑit will ⓒ (healthy / live / a / me / make / life).

12 위 글의 밑줄 친 ⓐ에서 어법상 틀린 부분을 찾아 바르게 고쳐 쓰시오.

_____ ➡ _____

13 How many times a week does the writer plan to exercise? Answer in English.

➡ _____
_____

14 위 글의 밑줄 친 ⓑit이 가리키는 것을 우리말로 쓰시오.

➡ _____

15 위 글의 괄호 ⓒ 안의 단어들을 바르게 배열하시오.

➡ _____

창의사고력 서술형 문제

01 다음 주어진 표현을 보고, 자신이 할 수 있는 일에 ∨표 한 후, 〈보기〉와 같이 대화문을 완성하시오.

> • shop on the Internet (　)
> • cook instant noodles (　)

> ┤ 보기 ├
> A: Do you know how to make fresh salad?
> B: Yes, I know how to make fresh salad. / No, I don't know how to make fresh salad.

(1) A: _____
　　B: _____
(2) A: _____
　　B: _____

02 다음과 같은 상황이 벌어진다면 어떨지 상상하여 〈보기〉와 같이 쓰시오.

> • get an A on the math test
> • go to Paris
> • it is sunny tomorrow
> • find an abandoned dog on the street　　　　　* abandoned dog: 유기견

> ┤ 보기 ├
> If I get an A on the math test, I will be very happy.

(1) _____
(2) _____
(3) _____

03 다음 〈보기〉의 사역동사들을 이용하여 문장을 4개 쓰시오. (필요시 형태를 바꿀 것)

> ┤ 보기 ├
> let　　make　　help　　have

(1) _____
(2) _____
(3) _____
(4) _____

단원별 모의고사

01 다음 영영풀이에 해당하는 단어로 알맞은 것은?

> either of the two parts of the body between the top of each arm and the neck

① hip ② waist

③ back ④ chest

⑤ shoulder

02 다음 중 밑줄 친 우리말 뜻이 <u>잘못된</u> 것은?

① Massage <u>from top to bottom</u>.
위에서부터 아래까지

② I think you should <u>see a doctor</u>.
병원에 가다

③ <u>For a few seconds</u> nobody said anything.
오랫동안

④ You and your partner should move <u>at the same speed</u>. 같은 속도로

⑤ <u>Both</u> of my sisters moved even farther away from home. 둘 다

03 다음 빈칸에 공통으로 알맞은 것은?

> • She has a pretty _____.
> • Stand close to each other and _____ your partner.

① step ② store ③ place

④ face ⑤ switch

04 다음 짝지어진 두 단어의 관계가 같도록 빈칸에 알맞은 말을 쓰시오.

> hungry : full = complicated : _____

05 다음 영영풀이에 해당하는 단어를 주어진 철자로 시작하여 쓰시오.

> an opinion or suggestion about what someone should do

➡ a_____

06 다음 대화의 밑줄 친 부분과 의미가 같은 것은?

> **A:** <u>Do you know how to download photos from the Internet?</u>
> **B:** Yes. I do. I'm good at using computers.

① Do you want to download photos?

② Can I download photos from the Internet?

③ May I download photos from the Internet?

④ Would you mind downloading photos from the Internet?

⑤ Can you download photos from the Internet?

07 다음 밑줄 친 말과 바꿔 쓸 수 있는 것을 <u>모두</u> 고르면?

> **A:** What do you enjoy doing to be healthy?
> **B:** <u>I enjoy riding a bike.</u>

① I can ride a bike.

② I like to ride a bike.

③ I want to ride a bike.

④ I will ride a bike.

⑤ I feel great when I ride a bike.

[08~11] 다음 대화를 읽고, 물음에 답하시오.

Karl: Hana, what's the matter?

Hana: Well, I'm stressed about the test next week.

Karl: I understand. I ride my longboard ⓐ I'm stressed. ⓑDo you know how to ride a longboard?

Hana: No, I don't.

Karl: Let's go out! I can teach you. Put one foot on the board and push hard with ⓒ .

Hana: Like this? Wow! This is fun. I feel better already.

Karl: See? I enjoy riding my longboard ⓓ it reduces my stress.

Hana: That's great!

08 위 대화의 빈칸 ⓐ와 ⓓ에 알맞은 말이 바르게 짝지어진 것은?

① if – as
② when – because
③ as – for
④ if – before
⑤ while – because of

09 위 대화의 밑줄 친 ⓑ와 의미가 다른 것을 모두 고르시오.

① Can you ride a longboard?
② Are you riding a longboard?
③ Are you good at riding a longboard?
④ How can I ride a longboard?
⑤ Are you able to ride a longboard?

10 위 대화의 빈칸 ⓒ에 알맞은 것은?

① two
② others
③ the other
④ the second
⑤ the others

11 Explain how to ride the longboard. Answer in Korean.

➡ _____

12 다음 문장의 빈칸에 알맞은 것은?

Why don't you cook some soup _____ you're hungry?

① and
② but
③ if
④ where
⑤ because

13 다음 문장에서 어법상 틀린 부분을 찾아 고쳐 쓰시오.

Brian makes his dad feels comfortable.

_____ ➡ _____

14 다음 문장의 빈칸에 알맞은 것은?

The police officer let the children _____ the road.

① cross
② crossing
③ to cross
④ to crossing
⑤ crossed

15 다음 밑줄 친 ①~⑤ 중 어법상 틀린 것은?

My father will buy me a computer if I
        ①   ②   ③
will get a perfect score in the final exam.
  ④   ⑤

16 다음 괄호 안에 주어진 단어를 이용하여 우리말을 영어로 옮기시오. (필요하면 어형을 바꿀 것)

> 나의 형은 나에게 방을 청소하라고 시켰다.
> (have)

➡ _____

17 다음 두 문장의 뜻이 같도록 빈칸에 알맞은 말을 쓰시오.

> If you don't hurry up, you will miss the bus.
> = _____ you hurry up, you will miss the bus.

18 다음 중 밑줄 친 make의 쓰임이 다른 하나는?

① He made the dog sit down.
② Mom made him some tea.
③ It makes you have more energy.
④ The Reading Club makes you read faster.
⑤ She made us work again.

19 다음 중 어법상 어색한 것은?

① I'll phone you if I'll have time.
② If you don't have a ticket, you can't come in.
③ We can be in Seoul by 10 if we catch the first train.
④ If you don't give me my money, I'm going to the police.
⑤ If it is sunny tomorrow, we'll have the party outside.

[20~21] 다음 글을 읽고, 물음에 답하시오.

> Place the ⓐbottom of your right foot on the desk behind you. Then, slowly ⓑbend your left leg and ⓒlower yourself. ⓓHold it for a few seconds and slowly ⓔstraighten up. This position will _____ your right leg. Switch your legs and repeat the exercise.

20 위 글의 밑줄 친 ⓐ~ⓔ 중 문맥상 어색한 것은?

① ⓐ   ② ⓑ   ③ ⓒ   ④ ⓓ   ⑤ ⓔ

21 위 글의 빈칸에 알맞은 것은?

① block out   ② team up
③ fasten up   ④ loosen up
⑤ get along with

[22~23] 다음 글을 읽고, 물음에 답하시오.

> Next, massage your neck. ⓐ your fingers on the back of your neck. Draw small circles with your fingers to massage your neck. ⓑ위에서 아래로 마사지해라. The massage will help you feel better.

22 문맥상 위 글의 빈칸 ⓐ에 알맞은 것은?

① Put   ② Pull
③ Bend   ④ Move
⑤ Cover

23 위 글의 밑줄 친 ⓑ의 우리말에 맞게 주어진 단어를 바르게 배열하시오.

> (bottom / to / massage / top / from)

➡ _____

[24~27] 다음 글을 읽고, 물음에 답하시오.

Let's work on your waist. Team up with a friend. Stand close to each other and __(A)__ your partner. Hold each other's wrists. Slowly __(B)__ your head and body backward. Hold that position __ⓐ__ three seconds. Then, slowly __(C)__ each other to a standing position. You and your partner should move __ⓑ__ the same speed. ⓒIf you won't, both of you will fall!

24 위 글의 빈칸 (A)~(C)에 알맞은 말이 바르게 짝지어진 것은?

① face – pull – stretch
② pull – stretch – face
③ stretch – face – pull
④ face – stretch – pull
⑤ pull – face – stretch

25 위 글의 빈칸 ⓐ와 ⓑ에 알맞은 말이 바르게 짝지어진 것은?

① at – in
② during – at
③ for – at
④ for – with
⑤ during – with

26 위 글에서 다음 영영풀이에 해당하는 단어를 찾아 쓰시오.

the way someone stands, sits, or lies down

➡ _____

27 위 글의 밑줄 친 ⓒ에서 어법상 틀린 부분을 찾아 바르게 고쳐 쓰시오.

_____ ➡ _____

[28~30] 다음 글을 읽고, 물음에 답하시오.

At school you sit for many hours. (①) Do you get tired? (②) Why don't you massage yourself and stretch?
(③) Let's begin with the eyes. (④) Close your eyes and massage them softly with your fingers. (⑤) When you finish, cover your eyes with your hands to block __ⓐ__ the light. ⓑIt will make your eyes to feel more comfortable.

28 위 글의 ①~⑤ 중 주어진 문장이 들어갈 알맞은 곳은?

It will relax your eyes.

①　　　②　　　③　　　④　　　⑤

29 위 글의 빈칸 ⓐ에 알맞은 것은?

① up
② out
③ off
④ into
⑤ over

30 위 글의 밑줄 친 ⓑ에서 어법상 틀린 부분을 찾아 바르게 고쳐 쓰시오.

_____ ➡ _____

INSIGHT
on the textbook
교과서 파헤치기

※ 다음 영어를 우리말로 쓰시오.

01 always	_____
02 warm	_____
03 due	_____
04 easily	_____
05 appointment	_____
06 worried	_____
07 help	_____
08 prepare	_____
09 helpful	_____
10 lesson	_____
11 history	_____
12 remember	_____
13 check	_____
14 while	_____
15 instead	_____
16 join	_____
17 schedule	_____
18 quiz	_____
19 monthly	_____
20 free time	_____
21 planner	_____

22 again	_____
23 try	_____
24 finish	_____
25 attention	_____
26 focus	_____
27 regularly	_____
28 wisely	_____
29 nervous	_____
30 recipe	_____
31 achieve	_____
32 posting	_____
33 practice	_____
34 save	_____
35 all day long	_____
36 stop -ing	_____
37 take[have] a lesson	_____
38 get along with	_____
39 make a plan	_____
40 set the alarm	_____
41 at a time	_____
42 put aside	_____
43 put off	_____

※ 다음 우리말을 영어로 쓰시오.

01 연습하다	
02 ～하기 전에	
03 규칙적으로	
04 끝내다	
05 긴장되는, 불안한	
06 교과서	
07 주의, 집중	
08 현명하게	
09 성취하다, 달성하다	
10 (SNS에 올리는) 글	
11 집중하다	
12 중요한	
13 잊다	
14 요리사	
15 매주의; 매주	
16 ～을 완전히 익히다	
17 걸음, 단계	
18 조리[요리]법	
19 절약하다, 구하다	
20 피곤한	
21 (시간을) 소비하다	

22 (목적·준비) ～을 위해	
23 아마	
24 기억하다	
25 도움이 되는	
26 대신에	
27 약속	
28 따뜻한	
29 준비하다	
30 쉽게	
31 일정	
32 매월의; 매월	
33 자유 시간	
34 확인하다	
35 ～ 때문에	
36 ～ 앞에	
37 온종일	
38 알람을 맞춰 놓다	
39 요즘	
40 목표를 세우다	
41 ～하는 것을 멈추다	
42 ～에 대해 걱정하다	
43 ～을 한쪽에 두다	

※ 다음 영영풀이에 알맞은 단어를 <보기>에서 골라 쓴 후, 우리말 뜻을 쓰시오.

1 _____ : a set of instructions for making food: _____

2 _____ : to use money to pay for something: _____

3 _____ : to get or reach something by working hard: _____

4 _____ : to learn something completely: _____

5 _____ : to make yourself ready for something that you will be doing: _____

6 _____ : an arrangement to meet with someone at a particular time _____

7 _____ : to become a member of a group or organization: _____

8 _____ : to keep something from being lost or wasted: _____

9 _____ : an activity that you do in order to learn something: _____

10 _____ : expected to happen or arrive at a particular time: _____

11 _____ : to direct your attention or effort at something specific: _____

12 _____ : a plan of things that will be done and the times when they will be done: _____

13 _____ : the period of time that will come after the present time: _____

14 _____ : making it easier to do a job, deal with a problem, etc.: _____

15 _____ : the act of listening to, looking at, or thinking about something or someone carefully: _____

16 _____ : something that you give to someone especially as a way of showing affection or thanks: _____

보기			
prepare	schedule	spend	future
present	achieve	due	helpful
appointment	master	focus	attention
join	recipe	lesson	save

※ 다음 우리말과 일치하도록 빈칸에 알맞은 말을 쓰시오.

 해석

Listen & Speak 1 - A

1. **G:** You _____ _____, Sam. What's the _____?

   B: I _____ _____ my alarm in the morning _____ _____.

   G: _____ _____ you _____ _____ _____ on your clock and on your smartphone?

   B: That's a _____ _____.

2. **G:** Phew, _____ _____ I _____?

   B: _____ the matter, Julie?

   G: I _____ money too _____.

   B: Well, I _____ _____ a plan _____ I _____ things.

   G: Maybe I _____ do the _____.

Listen & Speak 2 - A

1. **G:** Jason, are you _____? You _____ _____ _____ _____ today.

   B: I _____ _____ _____.

   G: That's _____ _____. I _____ you _____ _____ _____ a doctor.

   B: _____ _____. Thank you.

2. **G:** You _____ _____. What's _____ _____?

   B: I'm _____ _____ tomorrow's history quiz. _____ _____ _____ _____?

   G: I _____ you _____ _____ your textbook again.

   B: That's _____ _____ _____.

3. **B:** I'm _____ _____.

   G: Why?

   B: I _____ _____ well _____ _____.

   G: _____ _____ you _____ _____ _____ _____ _____ warm milk _____ you sleep. It _____ _____.

   B: Okay, I _____ _____.

Conversation A

B: This is a _____ of book. I write my _____, weekly, and _____ plans here. I also write important dates _____ my friends' birthdays and homework _____ _____ here. Every night, I _____ this for the next day. Do you want _____ _____ things _____? Then I think you _____ _____ this.

Conversation B

Hana: _____ _____ _____, Jiho?

Jiho: I _____ _____ my uniform. I _____ I _____ _____ _____ today.

Hana: Again?

Jiho: My _____ _____ in middle school is _____ _____ my _____ _____, and I _____ _____ things.

Hana: I think _____ _____ _____ a planner. Here's _____.

Jiho: Oh, _____ _____ _____ it?

Hana: Sure. I write my class _____ and _____ in my planner.

Jiho: That's great. _____ I _____ _____ one.

Wrap Up - ❶

W: _____ the matter, Sam? _____ you _____?

B: Ms. Green, _____ _____ I _____ _____ _____.

W: Did you _____ _____ _____ _____ _____ _____ _____?

B: Yes. She _____ I _____ _____ go to the hospital. _____ I _____ school now?

W: Okay, Sam. I'll _____ your mom and _____ _____ about it.

Wrap Up - ❷

B: I'm so _____.

G: Why? Is it _____ _____ the dance contest?

B: Yes. I practiced _____ many days, but I'm _____ nervous. What _____ I _____?

G: I _____ you _____ practice _____ _____ _____ your family. It will be very _____.

B: That's _____ _____. Thank you.

B: 이것은 일종의 책이야. 나는 여기에 매일, 매주, 그리고 월간 계획을 써. 나는 또한 여기에 내 친구들의 생일이나 숙제 예정일과 같은 중요한 날짜를 적어. 매일 밤, 나는 다음 날을 위해 이것을 확인해. 무언가를 쉽게 기억하고 싶니? 그러면 내 생각에 너는 이것을 사용해야 할 것 같아.

하나: 무슨 일 있니, 지호야?
지호: 나는 내 유니폼을 가져오지 않았어. 오늘 축구 연습이 있다는 걸 잊고 있었어.
하나: 또?
지호: 중학교 2학년은 1학년보다 더 바쁘고, 나는 종종 어떤 것들을 잊어버려.
하나: 내 생각에는 너는 일정 계획표를 사용해야 할 것 같아. 여기 내 것이 있어.
지호: 오, 내가 봐도 될까?
하나: 물론. 나는 일정 계획표에 나의 수업 일정과 약속을 적어.
지호: 정말 좋구나. 나도 하나 사야 할까봐.

W: 무슨 일이야, Sam? 어디 아파?
B: Green 선생님, 제가 감기에 걸린 것 같아요.
W: 보건 선생님한테 갔었니?
B: 네. 보건 선생님이 병원에 갈 필요가 있다고 하셨어요. 지금 하교를 해도 될까요?
W: 그럼, Sam. 내가 어머니한테 전화해서 그것에 대해 말할게.

B: 나 너무 긴장돼.
G: 왜? 댄스 경연 대회 때문이니?
B: 응. 며칠 동안 연습을 했지만 여전히 긴장돼. 어떻게 해야 하지?
G: 내 생각에 너는 가족 앞에서 연습을 해야 할 것 같아. 그것은 아주 도움이 될 거야.
B: 좋은 생각이야. 고마워.

※ 다음 우리말에 맞도록 대화를 영어로 쓰시오.

해석

Listen & Speak 1 - A

1. G: _____
   B: _____
   G: _____
   B: _____

2. G: _____
   B: _____
   G: _____
   B: _____
   G: _____

1. G: 걱정이 있어 보여, Sam. 무슨 일 있니?
   B: 요즘 아침에 알람을 못 들어.
   G: 네 시계와 스마트폰에 알람을 맞춰 놓는 게 어때?
   B: 좋은 생각이야.

2. G: 휴, 어떻게 해야 하지?
   B: 무슨 일인데, Julie?
   G: 나는 돈을 너무 빨리 써.
   B: 음, 난 항상 물건을 사기 전에 계획을 세워.
   G: 나도 똑같이 해야 할 것 같아.

Listen & Speak 2 - A

1. G: _____
   B: _____
   G: _____
   B: _____

2. G: _____
   B: _____
   G: _____
   B: _____

3. B: _____
   G: _____
   B: _____
   G: _____
   B: _____

1. G: Jason, 괜찮니? 오늘 안 좋아 보여.
   B: 감기에 걸렸어.
   G: 그거 참 안됐구나. 내 생각에 너는 병원에 가 봐야 할 것 같아.
   B: 네 말이 맞아. 고마워.

2. G: 걱정 있어 보여. 무슨 일이야?
   B: 내일 역사 시험이 걱정돼. 어떻게 해야 하지?
   G: 내 생각에 너는 교과서를 다시 읽어야 할 것 같아.
   B: 좋은 생각이야.

3. B: 나 너무 피곤해.
   G: 왜?
   B: 요즘 잠을 잘 못 자.
   G: 내 생각에는 너는 잠을 자기 전에 따뜻한 우유 한 잔을 마셔야 할 것 같아. 그것은 도움이 될 거야.
   B: 알았어, 한번 해 볼게.

Conversation A

B: _____

_____

_____

_____

Conversation B

Hana: _____

Jiho: _____

Hana: _____

Jiho: _____

_____

Hana: _____

Jiho: _____

Hana: _____

Jiho: _____

Wrap Up - ❶

W: _____

B: _____

W: _____

B: _____

W: _____

Wrap Up - ❷

B: _____

G: _____

B: _____

G: _____

B: _____

B: 이것은 일종의 책이야. 나는 여기에 매일, 매주, 그리고 월간 계획을 써. 나는 또한 여기에 내 친구들의 생일이나 숙제 예정일과 같은 중요한 날짜를 적어. 매일 밤, 나는 다음 날을 위해 이것을 확인해. 무언가를 쉽게 기억하고 싶니? 그러면 내 생각에 너는 이것을 사용해야 할 것 같아.

하나: 무슨 일 있니, 지호야?
지호: 나는 내 유니폼을 가져오지 않았어. 오늘 축구 연습이 있다는 걸 잊고 있었어.
하나: 또?
지호: 중학교 2학년은 1학년보다 더 바쁘고, 나는 종종 어떤 것들을 잊어버려.
하나: 내 생각에는 너는 일정 계획표를 사용해야 할 것 같아. 여기 내 것이 있어.
지호: 오, 내가 봐도 될까?
하나: 물론. 나는 일정 계획표에 나의 수업 일정과 약속을 적어.
지호: 정말 좋구나. 나도 하나 사야 할까 봐.

W: 무슨 일이야, Sam? 어디 아파?
B: Green 선생님, 제가 감기에 걸린 것 같아요.
W: 보건 선생님한테 갔었니?
B: 네. 보건 선생님이 병원에 갈 필요가 있다고 하셨어요. 지금 하교를 해도 될까요?
W: 그럼, Sam. 내가 어머니한테 전화해서 그것에 대해 말할게.

B: 나 너무 긴장돼.
G: 왜? 댄스 경연 대회 때문이니?
B: 응. 며칠 동안 연습을 했지만 여전히 긴장돼. 어떻게 해야 하지?
G: 내 생각에 너는 가족 앞에서 연습을 해야 할 것 같아. 그것은 아주 도움이 될 거야.
B: 좋은 생각이야. 고마워.

※ 다음 우리말과 일치하도록 빈칸에 알맞은 것을 골라 쓰시오.

1 _____ _____ the new _____ _____.

A. year   B. to   C. school   D. welcome

2 _____ the _____ grade, you will have more work _____ _____.

A. do   B. to   C. second   D. in

3 You_____ _____ _____ your time _____.

A. well   B. to   C. need   D. manage

4 _____ do you _____ _____?

A. that   B. do   C. how

5 Subin: I _____ small _____ and _____ them _____ day.

A. every   B. set   C. achieve   D. goals

6 I do _____ say, "I _____ _____ English."

A. master   B. will   C. not

7 With _____ a big goal, I will probably _____ _____ working on it _____ tomorrow, next week, on next month.

A. until   B. off   C. put   D. such

8 _____, I say, "I will learn _____ _____ English words _____ day.

A. every   B. new   C. three   D. instead

9 I will _____ my big _____, one _____ at a time.

A. goal   B. achieve   C. step

10 Minsu: _____ I do something, I give it my _____ _____.

A. attention   B. full   C. when

11 I _____ _____ read SNS postings _____ I was _____ my homework.

A. doing   B. to   C. while   D. used

---

1 새 학년이 된 걸 환영해.

2 2학년에서, 여러분은 할 일이 더 많을 거야.

3 여러분은 시간을 잘 관리할 필요가 있어.

4 여러분은 시간 관리를 어떻게 하는가?

5 수빈: 나는 작은 목표들을 세우고 매일 그것들을 성취해.

6 나는 "나는 영어를 마스터할 거야."라고 말하지 않아.

7 그렇게 큰 목표를 가지면, 나는 아마 그것을 위해 노력하는 걸 내일, 다음 주, 혹은 다음 달까지 미룰 거야.

8 대신에 나는 "나는 매일 세 개의 새로운 영어 단어를 배울 거야."라고 말해.

9 나는 한 번에 한 단계씩 나의 큰 목표를 달성할 거야.

10 민수: 나는 무언가를 할 때 그것에 모든 주의를 기울여.

11 나는 숙제를 하는 동안 SNS 게시 글을 읽곤 했어.

12 It _____ me _____ because I couldn't _____.

A. focus   B. down   C. slowed

13 Now, I _____ _____ my smartphone _____ I do my homework.

A. when   B. aside   C. put

14 It _____ me a _____ of _____.

A. time   B. lot   C. saves

15 These _____, I _____ my homework quickly and _____ my _____ time.

A. free   B. finish   C. enjoy   D. days

16 John: I _____ _____ time _____ toward my dream.

A. working   B. spend   C. regularly

17 I _____ to _____ a _____.

A. chef   B. become   C. want

18 _____ Saturday morning, I go to cooking _____ or _____ _____ recipes.

A. for   B. classes   C. search   D. every

19 I think that _____ my time _____ _____ for my future _____ important.

A. is   B. to   C. using   D. prepare

20 _____ is a _____.

A. present   B. time

21 Everyone _____ the same _____ _____ _____ every day.

A. spend   B. to   C. present   D. has

22 _____ your time well, _____ you will _____ _____ in the new school year!

A. happier   B. and   C. manage   D. be

12 집중할 수 없었기 때문에 그것은 나의 속도를 늦추었어.

13 지금 나는 숙제를 할 때 스마트폰을 한쪽에 치워 놔.

14 그렇게 하면 시간이 많이 절약돼.

15 요즈음, 나는 숙제를 빨리 끝내고 자유 시간을 즐겨.

16 John: 나는 내 꿈을 위해 노력하며 규칙적으로 시간을 사용해.

17 나는 요리사가 되고 싶어.

18 토요일 아침마다 나는 요리 강습에 가거나 요리법을 찾아봐.

19 나는 나의 미래를 준비하기 위해 시간을 쓰는 것이 중요하다고 생각해.

20 시간은 선물이다.

21 모든 사람은 매일 소비할 똑같은 선물을 가지고 있다.

22 시간을 잘 관리하면 여러분은 새 학년에 더 행복해질 것이다!

※ 다음 우리말과 일치하도록 빈칸에 알맞은 말을 쓰시오.

1 _____ _____ the new _____ _____ _____ .

2 _____ the _____ _____ , you will have _____ _____ _____ _____ .

3 You _____ _____ _____ your time _____ .

4 _____ do you _____ that?

5 Subin: I _____ _____ _____ and _____ them every day.

6 I _____ _____ _____ , "I _____ _____ English."

7 _____ such a big goal, I will probably _____ _____ _____ _____ it _____ tomorrow, next week, _____ next month.

8 _____ , I say, "I _____ _____ _____ _____ _____ words _____ _____ ."

9 I _____ _____ my big goal, _____ _____ _____ _____ _____ .

10 Minsu: _____ I do something, I _____ it _____ _____ .

11 I _____ _____ _____ SNS postings _____ I _____ _____ my homework.

1 새 학년이 된 걸 환영해.

2 2학년에서. 여러분은 할 일이 더 많을 거야.

3 여러분은 시간을 잘 관리할 필요가 있어.

4 여러분은 시간 관리를 어떻게 하는가?

5 수빈: 나는 작은 목표들을 세우고 매일 그것들을 성취해.

6 나는 "나는 영어를 마스터할 거야."라고 말하지 않아.

7 그렇게 큰 목표를 가지면, 나는 아마 그것을 위해 노력하는 걸 내일, 다음 주, 혹은 다음 달까지 미룰 거야.

8 대신에 나는 "나는 매일 세 개의 새로운 영어 단어를 배울 거야."라고 말해.

9 나는 한 번에 한 단계씩 나의 큰 목표를 달성할 거야.

10 민수: 나는 무언가를 할 때 그것에 모든 주의를 기울여.

11 나는 숙제를 하는 동안 SNS 게시 글을 읽곤 했어.

12 It _____ me down _____ I _____ _____.

13 Now, I _____ _____ my smartphone _____ I do my homework.

14 It _____ me _____ _____ _____ time.

15 _____ _____, I finish my homework _____ and _____ _____ _____ _____.

16 John: I _____ _____ time _____ toward my dream.

17 I _____ _____ _____ a chef.

18 _____ Saturday morning, I go to _____ _____ or _____ _____ _____.

19 I think that _____ my time _____ _____ _____ my future is important.

20 _____ is a _____.

21 Everyone _____ the _____ present _____ _____ every day.

22 _____ your time well, _____ you will _____ _____ in the _____ _____ _____!

12 집중할 수 없었기 때문에 그것은 나의 속도를 늦추었어.

13 지금 나는 숙제를 할 때 스마트폰을 한쪽에 치워 놔.

14 그렇게 하면 시간이 많이 절약돼.

15 요즈음, 나는 숙제를 빨리 끝내고 자유 시간을 즐겨.

16 John: 나는 내 꿈을 위해 노력하며 규칙적으로 시간을 사용해.

17 나는 요리사가 되고 싶어.

18 토요일 아침마다 나는 요리 강습에 가거나 요리법을 찾아봐.

19 나는 나의 미래를 준비하기 위해 시간을 쓰는 것이 중요하다고 생각해.

20 시간은 선물이다.

21 모든 사람은 매일 소비할 똑같은 선물을 가지고 있다.

22 시간을 잘 관리하면 여러분은 새 학년에 더 행복해질 것이다!

※ 다음 문장을 우리말로 쓰시오.

1 Welcome to the new school year.

➡ _____

2 In the second grade, you will have more work to do.

➡ _____

3 You need to manage your time well.

➡ _____

4 How do you do that?

➡ _____

5 Subin: I set small goals and achieve them every day.

➡ _____

6 I do not say, "I will master English."

➡ _____

7 With such a big goal, I will probably put off working on it until tomorrow, next week, or next month.

➡ _____

8 Instead, I say, "I will learn three new English words every day."

➡ _____

9 I will achieve my big goal, one step at a time.

➡ _____

10 Minsu: When I do something, I give it my full attention.

➡ _____

11 I used to read SNS postings while I was doing my homework.

➡ _____

12 It slowed me down because I couldn't focus.

➡ _____

13 Now, I put aside my smartphone when I do my homework.

➡ _____

14 It saves me a lot of time.

➡ _____

15 These days, I finish my homework quickly and enjoy my free time.

➡ _____

16 John: I regularly spend time working toward my dream.

➡ _____

17 I want to become a chef.

➡ _____

18 Every Saturday morning, I go to cooking classes or search for recipes.

➡ _____

19 I think that using my time to prepare for my future is important.

➡ _____

20 Time is a present.

➡ _____

21 Everyone has the same present to spend every day.

➡ _____

22 Manage your time well, and you will be happier in the new school year!

➡ _____

14 Lesson 1. Manage Yourself!

※ 다음 괄호 안의 단어들을 우리말에 맞도록 바르게 배열하시오.

1 (to / welcome / new / the / year. / school)

➡ _____

2 (the / grade, / in / second / will / you / have / work / do. / to / more)

➡ _____

3 (need / you / to / your / manage / well. / time)

➡ _____

4 (you / do / how / that? / do)

➡ _____

5 (Subin: / set / I / goals / small / and / them / achieve / day. / every)

➡ _____

6 (do / I / say, / not / "I / master / English." / will)

➡ _____

7 (such / with / goal, / big / a / I / probably / will / off / put / working / on / until / it / tomorrow, / next / month. / or / week / next)

➡ _____

_____

8 (say, / I / instead, / "I / learn / will / new / three / words / English / day." / every)

➡ _____

_____

9 (I / achieve / will / my / goal, / big / step / one / time. / a / at)

➡ _____

10 (Minsu: / I / do / when / something, / I / it / give / attention. / full / my)

➡ _____

11 (I / read / to / used / postings / SNS / while / was / I / doing / homework. / my)

➡ _____

1 새 학년이 된 걸 환영해.

2 2학년에서, 여러분은 할 일이 더 많을 거야.

3 여러분은 시간을 잘 관리할 필요가 있어.

4 여러분은 시간 관리를 어떻게 하는가?

5 수빈: 나는 작은 목표들을 세우고 매일 그것들을 성취해.

6 나는 "나는 영어를 마스터할 거야."라고 말하지 않아.

7 그렇게 큰 목표를 가지면, 나는 아마 그것을 위해 노력하는 걸 내일, 다음 주, 혹은 다음 달까지 미룰 거야.

8 대신에 나는 "나는 매일 세 개의 새로운 영어 단어를 배울 거야."라고 말해.

9 나는 한 번에 한 단계씩 나의 큰 목표를 달성할 거야.

10 민수: 나는 무언가를 할 때 그것에 모든 주의를 기울여.

11 나는 숙제를 하는 동안 SNS 게시 글을 읽곤 했어.

12 (slowed / it / down / me / because / I / focus. / couldn't)

➡ _____

13 (now, / I / aside / my / put / smartphone / when / do / I / homework. / my)

➡ _____

14 (it / me / saves / lot / time. / of / a)

➡ _____

15 (days, / these / finish / I / homework / my / quickly / and / my / time. / enjoy / free)

➡ _____

16 (John: / I / spend / regularly / working / time / toward / dream. / my)

➡ _____

17 (I / become / to / want / chef. / a)

➡ _____

18 (Saturday / every / morning, / I / cooking / to / go / classes / or / recipes. / for / search)

➡ _____

19 (think / I / using / that / time / my / prepare / to / for / future / my / important. / is)

➡ _____

20 (present. / a / is / time)

➡ _____

21 (has / everyone / the / present / same / spend / to / day. / every)

➡ _____

22 (your / manage / well, / time / and / will / you / be / in / the / happier / year! / school / new)

➡ _____

12 집중할 수 없었기 때문에 그것은 나의 속도를 늦추었어.

13 지금 나는 숙제를 할 때 스마트폰을 한쪽에 치워 놔.

14 그렇게 하면 시간이 많이 절약돼.

15 요즈음, 나는 숙제를 빨리 끝내고 자유 시간을 즐겨.

16 John: 나는 내 꿈을 위해 노력하며 규칙적으로 시간을 사용해.

17 나는 요리사가 되고 싶어.

18 토요일 아침마다 나는 요리 강습에 가거나 요리법을 찾아봐.

19 나는 나의 미래를 준비하기 위해 시간을 쓰는 것이 중요하다고 생각해.

20 시간은 선물이다.

21 모든 사람은 매일 소비할 똑같은 선물을 가지고 있다.

22 시간을 잘 관리하면 여러분은 새 학년에 더 행복해질 것이다!

※ 다음 우리말을 영어로 쓰시오.

1 새 학년이 된 걸 환영해.

➡ _____

2 2학년에서, 여러분은 할 일이 더 많을 거야.

➡ _____

3 여러분은 시간을 잘 관리할 필요가 있어.

➡ _____

4 여러분은 시간 관리를 어떻게 하는가?

➡ _____

5 수빈: 나는 작은 목표를 세우고 매일 그것들을 성취해.

➡ _____

6 나는 "나는 영어를 마스터할 거야."라고 말하지 않아.

➡ _____

7 그렇게 큰 목표를 가지면, 나는 아마 그것을 위해 노력하는 걸 내일, 다음 주, 혹은 다음 달까지 미룰 거야.

➡ _____

8 대신에 나는 "나는 매일 세 개의 새로운 영어 단어를 배울 거야."라고 말해.

➡ _____

9 나는 한 번에 한 단계씩 나의 큰 목표를 달성할 거야.

➡ _____

10 민수: 나는 무언가를 할 때 그것에 모든 주의를 기울여.

➡ _____

11 나는 숙제를 하는 동안 SNS 게시 글을 읽곤 했어.

➡ _____

12 집중할 수 없었기 때문에 그것은 나의 속도를 늦추었어.

➡ _____

13 지금 나는 숙제를 할 때 스마트폰을 한쪽에 치워 놔.

➡ _____

14 그렇게 하면 시간이 많이 절약돼.

➡ _____

15 요즈음, 나는 숙제를 빨리 끝내고 자유 시간을 즐겨.

➡ _____

16 John: 나는 내 꿈을 위해 노력하며 규칙적으로 시간을 사용해.

➡ _____

17 나는 요리사가 되고 싶어.

➡ _____

18 토요일 아침마다 나는 요리 강습에 가거나 요리법을 찾아봐.

➡ _____

19 나는 나의 미래를 준비하기 위해 시간을 쓰는 것이 중요하다고 생각해.

➡ _____

20 시간은 선물이다.

➡ _____

21 모든 사람은 매일 소비할 똑같은 선물을 가지고 있다.

➡ _____

22 시간을 잘 관리하면 여러분은 새 학년에 더 행복해질 것이다!

➡ _____

※ 다음 우리말과 일치하도록 빈칸에 알맞은 말을 쓰시오.

Enjoy Writing B

1. My Goals for _____ _____

2. I have three _____ _____ _____ this year.

3. The _____ goal is _____ _____ _____ _____ my new _____.

4. The _____ goal is _____ _____ an A _____ the English speaking test.

5. The _____ goal is to _____ _____ smartphone games.

6. I hope _____ this year is _____ _____ last year.

1. 올해의 나의 목표
2. 나는 올해 달성해야 할 목표가 세 가지 있다.
3. 첫 번째 목표는 새로운 반 친구들과 잘 지내는 것이다.
4. 두 번째 목표는 영어 말하기 시험에서 A를 받는 것이다.
5. 마지막 목표는 스마트폰 게임을 중단하는 것이다.
6. 나는 올해가 작년보다 더 낫기를 희망한다.

Project - Step 1

1. A: I _____ we _____ make our group's motto _____ _____ and _____.

2. B: That's a good idea. I _____ that _____ _____ _____ _____ are different.

3. C: Yes. I think that doing _____ _____ _____ _____ dreaming.

4. D: That's _____.

1. A: 나는 우리가 꿈을 꾸고 행동하는 것에 대한 우리 모둠의 좌우명을 만들어야 한다고 생각해.
2. B: 좋은 생각이야. 나는 꿈과 행동이 다르다고 믿어.
3. C: 맞아. 나는 꿈을 꾸는 것보다 하는 것이 더 중요하다고 생각해요.
4. D: 맞아.

Wrap Up - Writing

1. Jenny is _____ to go to the _____ _____ today.

2. She is _____ to buy three apples _____ _____.

3. She is going to buy _____ _____ _____ water _____ _____.

4. She is going to buy _____ _____ _____ _____ _____ _____.

1. Jenny는 오늘 식료품점에 갈 거야.
2. 그녀는 먹을 사과 세 개를 살 거야.
3. 그녀는 마실 물 두 병을 살 거야.
4. 그녀는 읽을 패션 잡지를 하나 살 거야.

구석구석 지문 Test

※ 다음 우리말을 영어로 쓰시오.

Enjoy Writing B

1. 올해의 나의 목표

   ➡ _____

2. 나는 올해 달성해야 할 목표가 세 가지 있다.

   ➡ _____

3. 첫 번째 목표는 새로운 반 친구들과 잘 지내는 것이다.

   ➡ _____

4. 두 번째 목표는 영어 말하기 시험에서 A를 받는 것이다.

   ➡ _____

5. 마지막 목표는 스마트폰 게임을 중단하는 것이다.

   ➡ _____

6. 나는 올해가 작년보다 더 낫기를 희망한다.

   ➡ _____

Project - Step 1

1. A: 나는 우리가 꿈을 꾸고 행동하는 것에 대한 우리 모둠의 좌우명을 만들어야 한다고 생각해.

   ➡ _____

2. B: 좋은 생각이야. 나는 꿈과 행동이 다르다고 믿어.

   ➡ _____

3. C: 맞아. 나는 꿈을 꾸는 것보다 하는 것이 더 중요하다고 생각해요.

   ➡ _____

4. D: 맞아.

   ➡ _____

Wrap Up - Writing

1. Jenny는 오늘 식료품점에 갈 거야.

   ➡ _____

2. 그녀는 먹을 사과 세 개를 살 거야.

   ➡ _____

3. 그녀는 마실 물 두 병을 살 거야.

   ➡ _____

4. 그녀는 읽을 패션 잡지를 하나 살 거야.

   ➡ _____

Step1

※ 다음 영어를 우리말로 쓰시오.

01 shoulder _____

02 luckily _____

03 brave _____

04 lower _____

05 chest _____

06 dangerous _____

07 skill _____

08 degree _____

09 chance _____

10 floor _____

11 training _____

12 announcer _____

13 shake _____

14 practice _____

15 protect _____

16 greatly _____

17 heart _____

18 audience _____

19 around _____

20 save _____

21 late _____

22 zoo keeper _____

23 remember _____

24 excited _____

25 suddenly _____

26 scared _____

27 experience _____

28 CPR _____

29 carefully _____

30 angle _____

31 earthquake _____

32 wet _____

33 forget _____

34 perform _____

35 push down _____

36 bump into _____

37 as ~ as possible _____

38 fall down _____

39 all the time _____

40 get under _____

41 in case of _____

42 hit ~ on the shoulder _____

43 hold on to _____

단어 Test

※ 다음 우리말을 영어로 쓰시오.

01 낮게; 낮은 _____

02 각도 _____

03 주의 깊게 _____

04 외치다 _____

05 심폐소생술 _____

06 경험 _____

07 숨을 쉬다, 호흡하다 _____

08 십대 _____

09 지진 _____

10 무서워하는, 겁먹은 _____

11 젖은 _____

12 무서운, 겁나는 _____

13 장비, 복장 _____

14 잊다 _____

15 학년 _____

16 세게, 힘껏; 어려운 _____

17 중요한 _____

18 인상적인 _____

19 ~ 이내에, ~ 안에 _____

20 함께하다 _____

21 막혀 있지 않은, 개방된 _____

22 행하다, 실시하다 _____

23 안전 _____

24 유지하다 _____

25 (가볍게) 톡톡 두드리다[치다] _____

26 가슴 _____

27 낮추다, 낮아지다 _____

28 위험한 _____

29 용감한 _____

30 교육, 훈련 _____

31 청중, 시청자 _____

32 흔들리다 _____

33 기억하다 _____

34 보호하다 _____

35 ~을 꽉[꼭] 누르다 _____

36 넘어지다 _____

37 가능한 한 ~한[하게] _____

38 ~에 부딪히다 _____

39 항상 _____

40 ~을 입다 _____

41 ~의 경우에 _____

42 위아래로 _____

43 ~에서 내리다 _____

※ 다음 영영풀이에 알맞은 단어를 <보기>에서 골라 쓴 후, 우리말 뜻을 쓰시오.

1 _____ : not yet dry: _____

2 _____ : feeling or showing no fear: _____

3 _____ : the front part of the body between the neck and the stomach: _____

4 _____ : to keep someone or something safe from death, harm, loss, etc.:
   _____

5 _____ : a sudden, violent shaking of the earth's surface: _____

6 _____ : the people who watch, read, or listen to something: _____

7 _____ : a unit for measuring the size of an angle: _____

8 _____ : to keep someone or something from being harmed, lost, etc.: _____

9 _____ : to move air into and out of your lungs: _____

10 _____ : the ability to do something that comes from training, experience, or
   practice: _____

11 _____ : to hit someone or something quickly and lightly: _____

12 _____ : to do an action or activity that usually requires training or skill:
   _____

13 _____ : a person who takes care of the animals in a zoo: _____

14 _____ : the process of doing and seeing things and of having things happen to
   you: _____

15 _____ : to reduce something in amount, degree, strength etc, or to become less:
   _____

16 _____ : to move sometimes violently back and forth or up and down with short,
   quick movements: _____

보기			
save	audience	earthquake	lower
protect	degree	skill	chest
tap	perform	brave	breathe
wet	zoo keeper	experience	shake

대화문 Test

※ 다음 우리말과 일치하도록 빈칸에 알맞은 말을 쓰시오.

Listen & Speak 1 A-1

B: Mom, _____ I _____ some apple juice?

W: Sure, Chris. _____ _____ _____ check the food label.

B: The _____ _____?

W: Yes. Too much sugar is _____ _____ _____ you.

B: Okay, I _____ _____ it.

B: 엄마, 사과 주스 좀 사도 돼요?
W: 물론, Chris. 식품 라벨을 확인하는 것을 잊지 마라.
B: 식품 라벨이요?
W: 그래. 너무 많은 설탕은 너에게 좋지 않아.
B: 네, 확인해 볼게요.

Listen & Speak 1 A-2

G: Dad, I'm _____.

M: You _____ _____ _____ this, Julie. There is _____ _____ _____ _____ in the air today.

G: Oh, I _____ _____ that.

M: It will _____ _____ _____ your health. So _____ _____ _____ this mask.

G: _____ _____. Thank you.

G: 아빠, 저 나가요.
M: Julie, 이걸 쓸 필요가 있어. 오늘은 공기 중에 미세먼지가 많아.
G: 오, 전 몰랐어요.
M: 그것은 건강에 나쁠 거야. 그러니 이 마스크 쓰는 걸 잊지 마라.
G: 알겠습니다, 감사합니다.

Listen & Speak 2 A-1

B: Hi, Amy. _____ _____?

G: I'm here _____ _____ a shirt. _____ _____ you?

B: I _____ a lunch meeting _____ this shopping center. Oh, I _____ _____ now. I'm _____.

G: Okay, but _____ _____ _____ _____ _____. The sign _____ the floor is _____.

B: I _____ _____ it. Thanks.

B: 안녕, Amy. 왠일이야?
G: 셔츠를 사러 왔어. 너는?
B: 이 쇼핑센터에서 점심 모임이 있어. 오, 이만 가 봐야겠어. 늦었어.
G: 그래, 하지만 뛰지 않는 게 좋겠어. 표지판에 바닥이 젖었다고 적혀 있어.
B: 난 못 봤어. 고마워.

Listen & Speak 2 A-2

G: What _____ the sign _____?

B: It means that _____ _____ _____ look at your smartphone _____ you _____ _____.

G: That's _____, _____ why?

B: You can _____ _____ people and _____ _____ many cars _____ here. It's so _____.

G: Now I _____.

G: 그 표지판은 무슨 뜻이니?
B: 걷는 동안 스마트폰을 보지 않는 게 낫다는 뜻이야.
G: 재미있네, 그런데 왜지?
B: 사람들과 부딪힐 수 있고 이 근처에는 차도 많아. 너무 위험해.
G: 이제 알겠어.

24 Lesson 2. All about Safety

Conversation A

B: I was _____ a good time _____ my family last night. Suddenly everything started _____ _____. I _____ stand still and almost _____ _____. Dad shouted, "_____ under the table. _____ _____ to protect your head." _____, the shaking soon _____. It was a _____.

Conversation B

Teacher: I _____ you _____ _____ safety rules for earthquakes today. Now, _____ _____. Are you _____?

Amy & Jiho: Yes.

Teacher: Everything _____ _____. Don't _____ _____ _____ _____ the desk and _____ your body first.

Jiho: It's so _____.

Amy: You're doing fine, Jiho. _____ _____ _____ the leg of the desk.

Jiho: Oh, the shaking stopped _____ _____. Let's get _____!

Teacher: Remember! You'd _____ _____ _____ the elevator. _____ _____ _____.

Amy: _____ _____ we _____ now?

Teacher: You _____ _____ find an open area _____ _____ _____.

Jiho: Then, _____ _____ _____ the park.

Wrap Up - Listening 1

G: Many people use this _____ every day. People _____ _____ _____ to enter this. They _____ _____ others to _____ before they enter. They use this to _____ _____ and _____ floors in a building. _____ _____ _____ this _____ _____ _____ a fire.

Wrap Up - Listening 2

B: I'm _____ _____ _____ _____ Jiri Mountain _____ my dad tomorrow.

G: It _____ great.

B: I'm _____ _____ we are going to stay there _____ two days and _____ _____.

G: That'll be great, but _____ _____ to check the weather.

B: Okay.

B: 나는 어젯밤에 가족과 즐거운 시간을 보내고 있었다. 갑자기 모든 것이 흔들리기 시작했다. 나는 가만히 있을 수가 없어서 하마터면 넘어질 뻔했다. 아빠는 "테이블 밑으로 들어가. 머리를 보호하는 걸 잊지 마."라고 소리쳤다. 다행히도, 흔들림은 곧 멈추었다. 그것은 무서운 경험이었다.

선생님: 오늘 지진에 대한 몇 가지 안전 수칙들을 말했죠. 자, 실습해 봅시다. 준비됐나요?

Amy와 지호: 네.

선생님: 모든 것이 흔들리고 있어요. 책상 밑에 들어가서 먼저 여러분의 몸을 보호하는 것을 잊지 마세요.

지호: 너무 무서워요.

Amy: 너는 잘하고 있어, 지호야. 책상 다리를 꽉 잡아.

지호: 오, 떨림이 잠시 멈췄어. 나가자!

선생님: 기억하세요! 엘리베이터를 이용하면 안 돼요. 계단을 이용하세요.

Amy: 이제 우린 어디로 가야 하죠?

선생님: 건물이 없는 확 트인 곳을 찾아야 해요.

지호: 그럼, 공원에 가자.

G: 많은 사람들이 거의 매일 이것을 사용한다. 사람들이 이것에 들어가기 위해 줄을 선다. 그들은 다른 사람들이 들어오기 전에 내리기를 기다린다. 그들은 건물의 층을 위아래로 움직이기 위해 이것을 사용한다. 화재가 났을 때는 이것을 사용하면 안 된다.

B: 나는 내일 아빠와 지리산에 갈 거야.

G: 멋진데.

B: 우리는 1박 2일 동안 묵을 예정이어서 신나.

G: 그거 좋겠네. 하지만, 날씨를 확인하는 걸 잊지 마.

B: 알았어.

※ 다음 우리말에 맞도록 대화를 영어로 쓰시오.

해석

Listen & Speak 1 A-1

B: _____

W: _____

B: _____

W: _____

B: _____

B: 엄마, 사과 주스 좀 사도 돼요?
W: 물론, Chris. 식품 라벨을 확인하는
   것을 잊지 마라.
B: 식품 라벨이요?
W: 그래. 너무 많은 설탕은 너에게 좋지
   않아.
B: 네, 확인해 볼게요.

Listen & Speak 1 A-2

G: _____

M: _____

G: _____

M: _____

G: _____

G: 아빠, 저 나가요.
M: Julie, 이걸 쓸 필요가 있어. 오늘은
   공기 중에 미세먼지가 많아.
G: 오, 전 몰랐어요.
M: 그것은 건강에 나쁠 거야. 그러니 이
   마스크 쓰는 걸 잊지 마라.
G: 알겠습니다, 감사합니다.

Listen & Speak 2 A-1

B: _____

G: _____

B: _____

G: _____

B: _____

B: 안녕, Amy. 왠일이야?
G: 셔츠를 사러 왔어. 너는?
B: 이 쇼핑센터에서 점심 모임이 있어.
   오, 이만 가 봐야겠어. 늦었어.
G: 그래, 하지만 뛰지 않는 게 좋겠어. 표
   지판에 바닥이 젖었다고 적혀 있어.
B: 난 못 봤어. 고마워.

Listen & Speak 2 A-2

G: _____

B: _____

G: _____

B: _____

G: _____

G: 그 표지판은 무슨 뜻이니?
B: 걷는 동안 스마트폰을 보지 않는 게
   낫다는 뜻이야.
G: 재미있네, 그런데 왜지?
B: 사람들과 부딪힐 수 있고 이 근처에는
   차도 많아. 너무 위험해.
G: 이제 알겠어.

Conversation A

B: _____

_____

_____

_____

B: 나는 어젯밤에 가족과 즐거운 시간을 보내고 있었다. 갑자기 모든 것이 흔들리기 시작했다. 나는 가만히 있을 수가 없어서 하마터면 넘어질 뻔했다. 아빠는 "테이블 밑으로 들어가. 머리를 보호하는 걸 잊지 마."라고 소리쳤다. 다행히도, 흔들림은 곧 멈추었다. 그것은 무서운 경험이었다.

Conversation B

Teacher: _____

Amy & Jiho: _____

Teacher: _____

Jiho: _____

Amy: _____

Jiho: _____

Teacher: _____

Amy: _____

Teacher: _____

Jiho: _____

선생님: 오늘 지진에 대한 몇 가지 안전 수칙들을 말했죠. 자, 실습해 봅시다. 준비됐나요?
Amy와 지호: 네.
선생님: 모든 것이 흔들리고 있어요. 책상 밑에 들어가서 먼저 여러분의 몸을 보호하는 것을 잊지 마세요.
지호: 너무 무서워요.
Amy: 너는 잘하고 있어, 지호야. 책상 다리를 꽉 잡아.
지호: 오, 떨림이 잠시 멈췄어. 나가자!
선생님: 기억하세요! 엘리베이터를 이용하면 안 돼요. 계단을 이용하세요.
Amy: 이제 우린 어디로 가야 하죠?
선생님: 건물이 없는 확 트인 곳을 찾아야 해요.
지호: 그럼, 공원에 가자.

Wrap Up - Listening 1

G: _____

_____

_____

_____

G: 많은 사람들이 거의 매일 이것을 사용한다. 사람들이 이것에 들어가기 위해 줄을 선다. 그들은 다른 사람들이 들어오기 전에 내리기를 기다린다. 그들은 건물의 층을 위아래로 움직이기 위해 이것을 사용한다. 화재가 났을 때는 이것을 사용하면 안 된다.

Wrap Up - Listening 2

B: _____

G: _____

B: _____

G: _____

B: _____

B: 나는 내일 아빠와 지리산에 갈 거야.
G: 멋진데.
B: 우리는 1박 2일 동안 묵을 예정이어서 신나.
G: 그거 좋겠네. 하지만, 날씨를 확인하는 걸 잊지 마.
B: 알았어.

※ 다음 우리말과 일치하도록 빈칸에 알맞은 것을 골라 쓰시오.

1 Announcer: Yesterday, a teenager _____ the _____ of an _____ man.

    A. old   B. life   C. saved

2 The _____ student is _____ the studio _____ us today.

    A. with   B. in   C. brave

3 Please _____ _____.

    A. yourself   B. introduce

4 Sejin: _____ name _____ Kim Sejin.

    A. is   B. my

5 I'm _____ the _____ grade _____ Hanguk Middle School.

    A. at   B. second   C. in

6 Announcer: Could you _____ _____ your _____?

    A. experience   B. us   C. tell

7 Sejin: Sure. I was _____ _____ the bus _____ my friend, Jinho.

    A. for   B. waiting   C. with

8 A man _____ _____ in _____ of us.

    A. front   B. fell   C. suddenly

9 _____ knew _____ to _____.

    A. do   B. what   C. nobody

10 I was _____ _____ as the _____ at first.

    A. others   B. scared   C. as

11 Then, I _____ to him and _____ him _____ the shoulder.

    A. on   B. tapped   C. ran

12 He _____ _____ or _____.

    A. breathing   B. moving   C. wasn't

13 I _____ to Jinho, "_____ 119," and started _____.

    A. CPR   B. call   C. said

14 _____: That's _____.

    A. impressive   B. announcer

---

1 아나운서: 어제, 한 십대가 어떤 노인의 생명을 구했습니다.

2 그 용감한 학생이 오늘 우리와 함께 스튜디오에 있습니다.

3 자기소개를 해 보세요.

4 세진: 제 이름은 김세진입니다.

5 저는 한국중학교 2학년입니다.

6 아나운서: 당신의 경험을 우리에게 말해 줄 수 있나요?

7 세진: 물론이죠. 저는 친구 진호와 버스를 기다리고 있었어요.

8 갑자기 한 남자가 우리 앞에 쓰러졌어요.

9 아무도 무엇을 해야 할지 몰랐어요.

10 저는 처음엔 다른 사람들처럼 겁이 났어요.

11 그러고 나서, 저는 그에게 달려가서 그의 어깨를 두드렸어요.

12 그는 움직이지도 숨을 쉬지도 않았어요.

13 저는 진호에게 "119에 전화해."라고 말하고 심폐소생술을 시작했습니다.

14 아나운서: 인상적이네요.

15 _____ did you learn _____ _____ important _____ ?

A. skill   B. an   C. such   D. when

16 Sejin: We had _____ _____ Day at school _____ week.

A. last   B. Training   C. Safety

17 I _____ _____ to do CPR and had a _____ to _____ .

A. practice   B. how   C. chance   D. learned

18 Announcer: Can you _____ the audience _____ to _____ CPR?

A. perform   B. how   C. show

19 Sejin: Yes. _____ your arms _____ .

A. straight   B. keep

20 Your arms and the _____ person's _____ must be _____ a 90 degree _____ .

A. angle   B. chest   C. at   D. other

21 _____ _____ in the center of the chest _____ and fast _____ an ambulance comes.

A. down   B. until   C. hard   D. push

22 Announcer: Are _____ any _____ things _____ _____ ?

A. remember   B. to   C. other   D. there

23 Sejin: Yes. You _____ to _____ the four _____ of "Golden Time."

A. minutes   B. remember   C. need

24 It means that you _____ start CPR _____ four minutes _____ someone's heart _____ .

A. stops   B. within   C. should   D. after

25 To begin CPR _____ _____ that will greatly _____ the chances of _____ someone's life.

A. saving   B. than   C. lower   D. later

26 Announcer: _____ is as _____ as _____ CPR.

A. doing   B. important   C. timing

27 Thank you _____ _____ _____ .

A. us   B. joining   C. for

28 Sejin: _____ _____ .

A. pleasure   B. my

---

15 언제 그런 중요한 기술을 배웠나요?

16 세진: 지난주에 학교에서 '안전 교육의 날'이 있었어요.

17 저는 심폐소생술을 하는 방법을 배웠고 연습할 기회도 가졌어요.

18 아나운서: 청중들에게 심폐소생술을 어떻게 하는지 보여줄 수 있나요?

19 세진: 네. 팔을 쭉 펴세요.

20 당신의 팔과 다른 사람의 가슴은 90도 각도여야 합니다.

21 구급차가 올 때까지 가슴 중앙을 세게 그리고 빨리 누르세요.

22 아나운서: 기억해야 할 다른 것이 있나요?

23 세진: 네. "골든타임" 4분을 기억해야 합니다.

24 그것은 여러분이 누군가의 심장이 멈춘 후 4분 안에 심폐소생술을 시작해야 한다는 것을 의미합니다.

25 그보다 늦게 심폐소생술을 시작하는 것은 누군가의 생명을 구할 가능성을 크게 낮출 것입니다.

26 아나운서: 타이밍은 심폐소생술을 하는 것만큼이나 중요하군요.

27 저희와 함께 해 주셔서 감사합니다.

28 세진: 제가 더 고맙습니다.

※ 다음 우리말과 일치하도록 빈칸에 알맞은 말을 쓰시오.

1 Announcer: Yesterday, a teenager _____ the _____ of an _____ _____.

2 The _____ student is in the studio _____ _____ today.

3 Please _____ _____.

4 Sejin: _____ name _____ Kim Sejin.

5 I'm _____ the _____ grade _____ Hanguk Middle School.

6 Announcer: Could you _____ _____ _____ _____?

7 Sejin: Sure. I _____ _____ _____ the bus _____ my friend, Jinho.

8 A man _____ _____ _____ _____ us.

9 _____ knew _____ _____ _____.

10 I was _____ _____ the others _____ first.

11 Then, I _____ to him and _____ him _____ the shoulder.

12 He _____ _____ or _____.

13 I _____ _____ Jinho, "Call 119," and _____ _____.

14 Announcer: That's _____.

1 아나운서: 어제, 한 십대가 어떤 노인의 생명을 구했습니다.

2 그 용감한 학생이 오늘 우리와 함께 스튜디오에 있습니다.

3 자기소개를 해 보세요.

4 세진: 제 이름은 김세진입니다.

5 저는 한국중학교 2학년입니다.

6 아나운서: 당신의 경험을 우리에게 말해 줄 수 있나요?

7 세진: 물론이죠. 저는 친구 진호와 버스를 기다리고 있었어요.

8 갑자기 한 남자가 우리 앞에 쓰러졌어요.

9 아무도 무엇을 해야 할지 몰랐어요.

10 저는 처음엔 다른 사람들처럼 겁이 났어요.

11 그러고 나서, 저는 그에게 달려가서 그의 어깨를 두드렸어요.

12 그는 움직이지도 숨을 쉬지도 않았어요.

13 저는 진호에게 "119에 전화해." 라고 말하고 심폐소생술을 시작했습니다.

14 아나운서: 인상적이네요.

15 When did you learn _____ _____ important _____?

16 Sejin: We had _____ _____ Day _____ school last week.

17 I _____ _____ _____ _____ _____ CPR and had a _____ _____ _____.

18 Announcer: Can you _____ the audience _____ _____ _____ _____?

19 Sejin: Yes. _____ your _____ _____.

20 Your arms and the _____ person's chest _____ be _____ _____ _____ _____ _____.

21 _____ _____ in the center of the chest _____ and fast _____ _____ _____.

22 Announcer: _____ _____ any other things _____ _____ _____?

23 Sejin: Yes. You _____ _____ _____ the _____ _____ of "Golden Time."

24 It means _____ you _____ start CPR _____ four minutes _____ _____ _____.

25 _____ _____ CPR _____ _____ that will greatly lower the _____ _____ _____ someone's life.

26 Announcer: Timing is _____ _____ _____ doing CPR.

27 _____ _____ _____ _____ us.

28 Sejin: My _____.

15 언제 그런 중요한 기술을 배웠나요?

16 세진: 지난주에 학교에서 '안전교육의 날'이 있었어요.

17 저는 심폐소생술을 하는 방법을 배웠고 연습할 기회도 가졌어요.

18 아나운서: 청중들에게 심폐소생술을 어떻게 하는지 보여줄 수 있나요?

19 세진: 네. 팔을 쭉 펴세요.

20 당신의 팔과 다른 사람의 가슴은 90도 각도여야 합니다.

21 구급차가 올 때까지 가슴 중앙을 세게 그리고 빨리 누르세요.

22 아나운서: 기억해야 할 다른 것이 있나요?

23 세진: 네. "골든타임" 4분을 기억해야 합니다.

24 그것은 여러분이 누군가의 심장이 멈춘 후 4분 안에 심폐소생술을 시작해야 한다는 것을 의미합니다.

25 그보다 늦게 심폐소생술을 시작하는 것은 누군가의 생명을 구할 가능성을 크게 낮출 것입니다.

26 아나운서: 타이밍은 심폐소생술을 하는 것만큼이나 중요하군요.

27 저희와 함께 해 주셔서 감사합니다.

28 세진: 제가 더 고맙습니다.

※ 다음 문장을 우리말로 쓰시오.

1 Announcer: Yesterday, a teenager saved the life of an old man.

➡ _____

2 The brave student is in the studio with us today.

➡ _____

3 Please introduce yourself.

➡ _____

4 Sejin: My name is Kim Sejin.

➡ _____

5 I'm in the second grade at Hanguk Middle School.

➡ _____

6 Announcer: Could you tell us your experience?

➡ _____

7 Sejin: Sure. I was waiting for the bus with my friend, Jinho.

➡ _____

8 A man suddenly fell in front of us.

➡ _____

9 Nobody knew what to do.

➡ _____

10 I was as scared as the others at first.

➡ _____

11 Then, I ran to him and tapped him on the shoulder.

➡ _____

12 He wasn't moving or breathing.

➡ _____

13 I said to Jinho, "Call 119," and started CPR.

➡ _____

14 Announcer: That's impressive.

➡ _____

15 ▶ When did you learn such an important skill?

➡ _____

16 ▶ Sejin: We had Safety Training Day at school last week.

➡ _____

17 ▶ I learned how to do CPR and had a chance to practice.

➡ _____

18 ▶ Announcer: Can you show the audience how to perform CPR?

➡ _____

19 ▶ Sejin: Yes. Keep your arms straight.

➡ _____

20 ▶ Your arms and the other person's chest must be at a 90 degree angle.

➡ _____

21 ▶ Push down in the center of the chest hard and fast until an ambulance comes.

➡ _____

22 ▶ Announcer: Are there any other things to remember?

➡ _____

23 ▶ Sejin: Yes. You need to remember the four minutes of "Golden Time."

➡ _____

24 ▶ It means that you should start CPR within four minutes after someone's heart stops.

➡ _____

25 ▶ To begin CPR later than that will greatly lower the chances of saving someone's life.

➡ _____

26 ▶ Announcer: Timing is as important as doing CPR.

➡ _____

27 ▶ Thank you for joining us.

➡ _____

28 ▶ Sejin: My pleasure.

➡ _____

※ 다음 괄호 안의 단어들을 우리말에 맞도록 바르게 배열하시오.

1 (Announcer: / a / yesterday, / teenager / the / saved / life / of / man. / old / an)

➡ _____

2 (brave / the / student / is / the / in / with / studio / today. / us)

➡ _____

3 (yourself. / introduce / please)

➡ _____

4 (Sejin: / name / my / Sejin. / is / Kim)

➡ _____

5 (in / I'm / second / the / grade / School. / at / Middle / Hanguk)

➡ _____

6 (Announcer: / you / could / us / tell / experience? / your)

➡ _____

7 (Sejin: sure. // I / waiting / was / the / for / with / bus / Jinho. / friend, / my)

➡ _____

8 (man / a / fell / suddenly / front / us. / in / of)

➡ _____

9 (knew / nobody / do. / to / what)

➡ _____

10 (was / as / I / scared / as / others / the / first. / at)

➡ _____

11 (then, / ran / I / him / to / and / him / tapped / shoulder. / the / on)

➡ _____

12 (wasn't / he / breathing. / or / moving)

➡ _____

13 (said / I / Jinho, / to / "call / and / 119," / CPR. / started)

➡ _____

14 (Announcer: / impressive. / that's)

➡ _____

1 아나운서: 어제, 한 십대가 어떤 노인의 생명을 구했습니다.

2 그 용감한 학생이 오늘 우리와 함께 스튜디오에 있습니다.

3 자기소개를 해 보세요.

4 세진: 제 이름은 김세진입니다.

5 저는 한국중학교 2학년입니다.

6 아나운서: 당신의 경험을 우리에게 말해 줄 수 있나요?

7 세진: 물론이죠. 저는 친구 진호와 버스를 기다리고 있었어요.

8 갑자기 한 남자가 우리 앞에 쓰러졌어요.

9 아무도 무엇을 해야 할지 몰랐어요.

10 저는 처음엔 다른 사람들처럼 겁이 났어요.

11 그러고 나서, 저는 그에게 달려가서 그의 어깨를 두드렸어요.

12 그는 움직이지도 숨을 쉬지도 않았어요.

13 저는 진호에게 " 119에 전화해."라고 말하고 심폐소생술을 시작했습니다.

14 아나운서: 인상적이네요.

15 (you / when / did / learn / an / such / skill? / important)

➡ _____

16 (Sejin: / had / we / Training / Safety / Day / school / week. / at / last)

➡ _____

17 (learned / I / to / how / do / CPR / and / a / had / practice. / to / chance)

➡ _____

18 (Announcer: / you / can / show / audience / the / to / how / CPR? / perform)

➡ _____

19 (Sejin: / yes. // your / straight. / keep / arms)

➡ _____

20 (arms / your / the / and / other / chest / person's / must / at / be / 90 / a / angle. / degree)

➡ _____

21 (down / push / the / in / center / of / chest / the / hard / and / until / fast / comes. / ambulance / an)

➡ _____
_____

22 (Announcer: / there / are / other / any / to / remember? / things)

➡ _____

23 (Sejin: / yes. // need / you / remember / to / four / the / minutes / Time." / of / "Golden)

➡ _____

24 (that / means / it / should / you / start / within / CPR / minutes / four / after / stops. / heart / someone's)

➡ _____
_____

25 (begin / to / CPR / than / later / will / that / lower / greatly / the / saving / of / chances / life. / someone's)

➡ _____
_____

26 (Announcer: / is / important / as / timing / CPR. / doing / as)

➡ _____

27 (you / thank / for / us. / joining)

➡ _____

28 (Sejin: / pleasure. / my)

➡ _____

15 언제 그런 중요한 기술을 배웠나요?

16 세진: 지난주에 학교에서 '안전 교육의 날'이 있었어요.

17 저는 심폐소생술을 하는 방법을 배웠고 연습할 기회도 가졌어요.

18 아나운서: 청중들에게 심폐소생술을 어떻게 하는지 보여줄 수 있나요?

19 세진: 네. 팔을 쭉 펴세요.

20 당신의 팔과 다른 사람의 가슴은 90도 각도여야 합니다.

21 구급차가 올 때까지 가슴 중앙을 세게 그리고 빨리 누르세요.

22 아나운서: 기억해야 할 다른 것이 있나요?

23 세진: 네. "골든타임" 4분을 기억해야 합니다.

24 그것은 여러분이 누군가의 심장이 멈춘 후 4분 안에 심폐소생술을 시작해야 한다는 것을 의미합니다.

25 그보다 늦게 심폐소생술을 시작하는 것은 누군가의 생명을 구할 가능성을 크게 낮출 것입니다.

26 아나운서: 타이밍은 심폐소생술을 하는 것만큼이나 중요하군요.

27 저희와 함께 해 주셔서 감사합니다.

28 세진: 제가 더 고맙습니다.

※ 다음 우리말을 영어로 쓰시오.

1 아나운서: 어제, 한 십대가 어떤 노인의 생명을 구했습니다.

➡ _____

2 그 용감한 학생이 오늘 우리와 함께 스튜디오에 있습니다.

➡ _____

3 자기소개를 해 보세요.

➡ _____

4 세진: 제 이름은 김세진입니다.

➡ _____

5 저는 한국중학교 2학년입니다.

➡ _____

6 아나운서: 당신의 경험을 우리에게 말해 줄 수 있나요?

➡ _____

7 세진: 물론이죠. 저는 친구 진호와 버스를 기다리고 있었어요.

➡ _____

8 갑자기 한 남자가 우리 앞에 쓰러졌어요.

➡ _____

9 아무도 무엇을 해야 할지 몰랐어요.

➡ _____

10 저는 처음엔 다른 사람들처럼 겁이 났어요.

➡ _____

11 그러고 나서, 저는 그에게 달려가서 그의 어깨를 두드렸어요.

➡ _____

12 그는 움직이지도 숨을 쉬지도 않았어요.

➡ _____

13 저는 진호에게 "119에 전화해."라고 말하고 심폐소생술을 시작했습니다.

➡ _____

14 아나운서: 인상적이네요.

➡ _____

15 언제 그런 중요한 기술을 배웠나요?

➡ _____

16 세진: 지난주에 학교에서 '안전 교육의 날'이 있었어요.

➡ _____

17 저는 심폐소생술을 하는 방법을 배웠고 연습할 기회를 가졌어요.

➡ _____

18 아나운서: 청중들에게 심폐소생술을 어떻게 하는지 보여줄 수 있나요?

➡ _____

19 세진: 네. 팔을 쭉 펴세요.

➡ _____

20 당신의 팔과 다른 사람의 가슴은 90도 각도여야 합니다.

➡ _____

21 구급차가 올 때까지 가슴 중앙을 세게 그리고 빨리 누르세요.

➡ _____

22 아나운서: 기억해야 할 다른 것이 있나요?

➡ _____

23 세진: 네. "골든타임" 4분을 기억해야 합니다.

➡ _____

24 그것은 여러분이 누군가의 심장이 멈춘 후 4분 안에 심폐소생술을 시작해야 한다는 것을 의미합니다.

➡ _____

25 그보다 늦게 심폐소생술을 시작하는 것은 누군가의 생명을 구할 가능성을 크게 낮출 것입니다.

➡ _____

26 아나운서: 타이밍은 심폐소생술을 하는 것만큼이나 중요하군요.

➡ _____

27 저희와 함께 해 주셔서 감사합니다.

➡ _____

28 세진: 제가 더 고맙습니다.

➡ _____

※ 다음 우리말과 일치하도록 빈칸에 알맞은 말을 쓰시오.

My Writing B

1. _____ Your Life from a _____

2. Do you know _____ _____ _____ when _____ _____
   a fire?

3. You _____ _____, "Fire!"

4. You _____ _____ _____ your face and body _____
   _____ _____ _____.

5. You _____ _____ _____ as low _____ possible and
   _____ _____.

6. Also, you need to call 119 _____ _____ _____ _____
   _____.

7. _____ _____ _____ _____ the stairs, _____ the
   elevator.

1. 화재로부터 여러분의 생명을 구하라
2. 불이 나면 너는 무엇을 해야 하는지 아니?
3. 여러분은 "불이야!"라고 외쳐야 한다.
4. 여러분은 젖은 수건으로 얼굴과 몸을 가려야 한다.
5. 가능한 한 낮게 유지하고 밖으로 나가야 한다.
6. 또한, 가능한 한 빨리 119에 전화해야 한다.
7. 엘리베이터가 아니라 계단을 이용하는 것을 잊지 마라.

Wrap Up

1. Safety _____ Day

2. Today we had _____ Training Day _____ _____.

3. Teachers _____ _____ _____ _____ _____ when an
   earthquake hits.

4. We learned _____ _____ _____ our heads and bodies.

5. We also learned _____ _____ _____ when the _____
   _____.

1. 안전 교육의 날
2. 오늘은 학교에서 안전 교육의 날이었다.
3. 선생님들은 우리에게 지진이 일어났을 때 무엇을 해야 하는지 가르쳐 주셨다.
4. 우리는 머리와 몸을 보호하는 법을 배웠다.
5. 우리는 또한 흔들림이 멈추었을 때 어디로 가야 하는지 배웠습니다.

Project - Step 3

1. We'll _____ _____ _____ _____ _____ _____ for safety in
   the science room.

2. First, _____ _____ _____ use _____ _____.

3. Second, you'd _____ _____ run _____.

1. 과학실에서 안전을 위해 무엇을 해야 하는지 알려드리겠습니다.
2. 첫째, 보안경을 쓰는 것을 잊지 마세요.
3. 둘째, 뛰어다니면 안 됩니다.

※ 다음 우리말을 영어로 쓰시오.

My Writing B

1. 화재로부터 여러분의 생명을 구하라
   ➡ _____

2. 불이 나면 너는 무엇을 해야 하는지 아니?
   ➡ _____

3. 여러분은 "불이야!"라고 외쳐야 한다.
   ➡ _____

4. 여러분은 젖은 수건으로 얼굴과 몸을 가려야 한다.
   ➡ _____

5. 가능한 한 낮게 유지하고 밖으로 나가야 한다.
   ➡ _____

6. 또한, 가능한 한 빨리 119에 전화해야 한다.
   ➡ _____

7. 엘리베이터가 아니라 계단을 이용하는 것을 잊지 마라.
   ➡ _____

Wrap Up

1. 안전 교육의 날
   ➡ _____

2. 오늘은 학교에서 안전 교육의 날이었다.
   ➡ _____

3. 선생님들은 우리에게 지진이 일어났을 때 무엇을 해야 하는지 가르쳐 주셨다.
   ➡ _____

4. 우리는 머리와 몸을 보호하는 법을 배웠다.
   ➡ _____

5. 우리는 또한 흔들림이 멈추었을 때 어디로 가야 하는지 배웠습니다.
   ➡ _____

Project - Step 3

1. 과학실에서 안전을 위해 무엇을 해야 하는지 알려드리겠습니다.
   ➡ _____

2. 첫째, 보안경을 쓰는 것을 잊지 마세요.
   ➡ _____

3. 둘째, 뛰어다니면 안 됩니다.
   ➡ _____

※ 다음 영어를 우리말로 쓰시오.

01	position	22	download
02	pull	23	backward
03	stretch	24	put
04	difficult	25	show
05	nature	26	waist
06	advice	27	comfortable
07	push	28	bend
08	exercise	29	lower
09	understand	30	habit
10	place	31	fresh
11	count	32	usually
12	second	33	simple
13	shoulder	34	warm
14	activity	35	each other
15	however	36	team up with
16	life	37	block out
17	pour	38	get over
18	switch	39	from top to bottom
19	back	40	focus on
20	massage	41	loosen up
21	neck	42	straighten up
		43	be good for

※ 다음 우리말을 영어로 쓰시오.

01	벌써, 이미	
02	~ 뒤에	
03	편안한	
04	부드럽게	
05	걸음	
06	길	
07	움직이다	
08	넘어지다	
09	~을 향하다; 얼굴	
10	낚시	
11	습관	
12	따뜻한	
13	둘 다	
14	유지하다	
15	구부리다	
16	운동하다	
17	자연	
18	어려운	
19	활동	
20	(근육 등의) 긴장이 풀리다	
21	건강한, 건강에 좋은	

22	~을 낮추다	
23	간단한, 단순한	
24	신선한	
25	스트레스를 받다[주다]	
26	빛	
27	~와 같은, ~처럼	
28	줄이다	
29	보통, 대개	
30	그릇	
31	스트레칭하다	
32	뒤로	
33	목	
34	자세	
35	준비 운동을 하다	
36	위에서 아래까지	
37	~에 집중하다	
38	몇 초 동안	
39	~에 대해 걱정하다	
40	~을 준비하다	
41	(빛을) 가리다[차단하다]	
42	똑바로 하다	
43	회복[극복]하다	

※ 다음 영영풀이에 알맞은 단어를 <보기>에서 골라 쓴 후, 우리말 뜻을 쓰시오.

1 _____ : to say numbers in order: _____

2 _____ : not hard to understand or do: _____

3 _____ : making you feel physically relaxed: _____

4 _____ : to make something smaller in size, amount, number, etc.: _____

5 _____ : an opinion or suggestion about what someone should do: _____

6 _____ : either of the two parts of the body between the top of each arm and the

  neck : _____

7 _____ : to change or replace something with another thing: _____

8 _____ : the part of the body between the head and the shoulders: _____

9 _____ : to move your body so that it is not straight: _____

10 _____ : the way someone stands, sits, or lies down: _____

11 _____ : to become or to cause something to become less tense, tight, or stiff:

  _____

12 _____ : something that a person does often in a regular and repeated way:

  _____

13 _____ : to put your arms, legs, etc., in positions that make the muscles long and

  tight: _____

14 _____ : to do gentle physical exercises to prepare your body for a sport or other

  activity: _____

15 _____ : to hold something firmly and use force in order to move it or try to move

  it toward yourself: _____

16 _____ : the action of rubbing and pressing a person's body with the hands to

  reduce pain in the muscles and joints: _____

보기	stretch	bend	count	habit
	advice	position	switch	massage
	relax	reduce	neck	comfortable
	warm up	shoulder	pull	simple

※ 다음 우리말과 일치하도록 빈칸에 알맞은 말을 쓰시오.

Listen & Speak 1-A-1

B: I want to eat _____ _____. Do you _____ any _____?

G: I _____ _____ fresh salad. It _____ me _____ _____.

B: Really? Do you know _____ _____ _____ it?

G: Yes, it's quite _____. First, _____ many vegetables _____ small pieces. Next, _____ them _____ a bowl. Then, _____ some lemon juice on them. Finally, _____ everything together.

B: That's it? I _____ _____ it.

Listen & Speak 1-A-2

B: People say that we should walk _____ _____ 10,000 _____ every day _____ _____ _____. I can't _____ the number of my _____ _____.

G: You _____ _____ this smartphone app. Do you know _____ _____ _____ it?

B: No. _____ you _____ _____?

G: Sure. First, _____ the app. Then, walk _____ your smartphone. Later, you can _____ the number of _____ _____ _____.

B: Thank you. I _____ _____ _____ it today.

Listen & Speak 2-A-1

G: _____ do you _____ _____ after school?

B: I _____ _____ _____ _____ _____.

G: _____ cool. What _____ you _____?

B: I _____ _____ salad, Bibimbap, and vegetable juice.

Listen & Speak 2-A-2

B: What do you do _____ _____?

G: I _____ _____.

B: _____ _____ of pictures do you _____ _____?

G: I _____ pictures _____ nature, _____ trees and flowers. The beautiful pictures _____ _____ _____.

B: 나는 건강에 좋은 것을 먹고 싶어. 말해 줄 조언이 있니?
G: 나는 신선한 샐러드를 자주 먹어. 그것은 나를 기분 좋게 만들어.
B: 정말? 그것을 어떻게 만드는지 아니?
G: 응, 아주 간단해. 먼저, 많은 채소들을 작은 조각으로 잘라. 다음으로 그것들을 그릇에 담아. 그런 다음. 레몬 주스를 조금 부어. 마지막으로 모든 것을 함께 섞어.
B: 그게 다야? 한번 해 봐야겠다.

B: 사람들은 우리가 건강해지기 위해서 매일 10,000 걸음 이상을 걸어야 한다고 말해. 나는 내 걸음 수를 쉽게 셀 수 없어.
G: 너는 이 스마트폰 앱을 사용할 수 있어. 어떻게 사용하는지 아니?
B: 아니. 내게 보여줄 수 있니?
G: 물론. 먼저 앱을 다운로드해. 그런 다음 스마트폰을 가지고 걸어. 나중에 네가 걸은 걸음 수를 확인할 수 있어.
B: 고마워. 오늘부터 그것을 쓰기 시작해야겠어.

G: 너는 방과 후에 뭐 하는 걸 즐기니?
B: 나는 건강에 좋은 음식을 요리하는 것을 즐겨.
G: 멋지구나. 너는 무엇을 만들 수 있니?
B: 나는 샐러드, 비빔밥 그리고 야채 주스를 만들 수 있어.

B: 너는 주말에 무엇을 하니?
G: 나는 사진을 찍어.
B: 너는 보통 어떤 종류의 사진을 찍니?
G: 나는 나무와 꽃 같은 자연의 사진을 찍는 것을 좋아해. 그 아름다운 사진들은 내 스트레스를 줄여주거든.

Listen & Speak 2-A-3

G: Do you _____ _____ _____?

B: Yes. _____ name is Coco. I _____ _____ her.

G: _____ do you do _____ _____?

B: I _____ _____ a walk with her. It _____ me _____.

Conversation A

B: Tomorrow, I _____ an English _____ contest. I started _____ _____ the contest two weeks _____. I enjoy _____ _____ English, but I _____ _____ _____ the contest. I _____ _____ well.

Conversation B

Karl: Hana, _____ the _____?

Hana: Well, I'm _____ _____ the test _____ _____.

Karl: I understand. I _____ my longboard _____ I'm stressed. Do you _____ _____ _____ _____ a longboard?

Hana: _____, I _____.

Karl: Let's _____ _____! I _____ teach you. _____ one foot _____ the board and _____ hard _____ the other.

Hana: _____ this? Wow! This is fun. I _____ _____ already.

Karl: See? I _____ _____ my longboard _____ it _____ my stress.

Hana: That's _____!

Wrap Up 1

B: You _____ _____. _____ the matter?

G: Well, I _____ _____ _____ _____.

B: Did you _____ _____ _____?

G: Not _____. Do you know how to _____ _____ a cold?

B: Well, I usually drink _____ water _____ I have a cold. It _____ _____ _____ _____.

G: _____ good. I _____ _____ it.

Wrap Up 2

B: My family _____ many activities. My dad enjoys _____. _____ in the morning, he goes to the lake and _____ _____ with some fish. My mom _____ _____ pictures. She likes _____ _____ beautiful mountains and lakes. My brother and I _____ _____ soccer.

G: 너는 강아지를 기르고 있니?

B: 응. 그녀의 이름은 코코야. 난 코코를 아주 좋아해.

G: 너는 코코와 함께 무엇을 하니?

B: 난 코코와 산책하는 걸 즐겨. 그것은 나를 건강하게 만들어.

B: 내일 영어 말하기 대회가 있어. 나는 2주 전에 대회를 준비하기 시작했어. 나는 영어로 말하는 것을 즐기지만, 난 그 대회가 걱정돼. 나는 잠을 잘 못 자.

Karl: 하나야, 무슨 일 있니?

하나: 음, 다음 주에 있을 시험 때문에 스트레스를 받아.

Karl: 난 이해돼. 나는 스트레스를 받을 때 롱보드를 타. 넌 롱보드를 어떻게 타는지 아니?

하나: 아니, 몰라.

Karl: 나가자! 내가 가르쳐 줄 수 있어. 한 발을 보드 위에 올려놓고 다른 한 발로 세게 밀어.

하나: 이렇게? 와! 이거 재밌다. 벌써 기분이 좋아졌어.

Karl: 봤지? 나는 롱보드를 타는 것이 나의 스트레스를 줄여주기 때문에 즐겨.

하나: 정말 멋진데!

B: 너 아파 보여. 무슨 일 있니?

G: 음, 감기에 걸렸어.

B: 병원에 가봤니?

G: 아직. 넌 감기가 나아지는 방법을 아니?

B: 음, 나는 감기에 걸렸을 때 보통 따뜻한 물을 마셔. 그것은 내 기분을 좋아지게 해.

G: 좋아. 한번 해 볼게.

B: 우리 가족은 많은 활동을 즐겨. 우리 아빠는 낚시를 즐기셔. 이른 아침, 그는 호수에 가셔서 약간의 물고기를 가지고 돌아오셔. 우리 엄마는 그림 그리기를 즐기셔. 그녀는 아름다운 산과 호수를 그리는 것을 좋아하셔. 나의 형과 나는 축구를 즐겨.

※ 다음 우리말에 맞도록 대화를 영어로 쓰시오.

Listen & Speak 1-A-1

B: _____

G: _____

B: _____

G: _____
_____
_____

B: _____

B: 나는 건강에 좋은 것을 먹고 싶어. 말해 줄 조언이 있니?
G: 나는 신선한 샐러드를 자주 먹어. 그것은 나를 기분 좋게 만들어.
B: 정말? 그것을 어떻게 만드는지 아니?
G: 응, 아주 간단해. 먼저, 많은 채소들을 작은 조각으로 잘라. 다음으로 그것들을 그릇에 담아. 그런 다음, 레몬 주스를 조금 부어. 마지막으로 모든 것을 함께 섞어.
B: 그게 다야? 한번 해 봐야겠다.

Listen & Speak 1-A-2

B: _____
_____

G: _____

B: _____

G: _____
_____

B: _____

B: 사람들은 우리가 건강해지기 위해서 매일 10,000 걸음 이상을 걸어야 한다고 말해. 나는 내 걸음 수를 쉽게 셀 수 없어.
G: 너는 이 스마트폰 앱을 사용할 수 있어. 어떻게 사용하는지 아니?
B: 아니. 내게 보여줄 수 있니?
G: 물론. 먼저 앱을 다운로드해. 그런 다음 스마트폰을 가지고 걸어. 나중에 네가 걸은 걸음 수를 확인할 수 있어.
B: 고마워. 오늘부터 그것을 쓰기 시작해야겠어.

Listen & Speak 2-A-1

G: _____

B: _____

G: _____

B: _____

G: 너는 방과 후에 뭐 하는 걸 즐기니?
B: 나는 건강에 좋은 음식을 요리하는 것을 즐겨.
G: 멋지구나. 너는 무엇을 만들 수 있니?
B: 나는 샐러드, 비빔밥 그리고 야채 주스를 만들 수 있어.

Listen & Speak 2-A-2

B: _____

G: _____

B: _____

G: _____
_____

B: 너는 주말에 무엇을 하니?
G: 나는 사진을 찍어.
B: 너는 보통 어떤 종류의 사진을 찍니?
G: 나는 나무와 꽃 같은 자연의 사진을 찍는 것을 좋아해. 그 아름다운 사진들은 내 스트레스를 줄여주거든.

Listen & Speak 2-A-3

G: _____

B: _____

G: _____

B: _____

G: 너는 강아지를 기르고 있니?
B: 응. 그녀의 이름은 코코야. 난 코코를 아주 좋아해.
G: 너는 코코와 함께 무엇을 하니?
B: 난 코코와 산책하는 걸 즐겨. 그것은 나를 건강하게 만들어.

Conversation A

B: _____

_____

_____

B: 내일 영어 말하기 대회가 있어. 나는 2주 전에 대회를 준비하기 시작했어. 나는 영어로 말하는 것을 즐기지만, 난 그 대회가 걱정돼. 나는 잠을 잘 못 자.

Conversation B

Karl: _____

Hana: _____

Karl: _____

_____

Hana: _____

Karl: _____

_____

Hana: _____

Karl: _____

Hana: _____

Karl: 하나야, 무슨 일 있니?
하나: 음, 다음 주에 있을 시험 때문에 스트레스를 받아.
Karl: 난 이해돼. 나는 스트레스를 받을 때 롱보드를 타. 넌 롱보드를 어떻게 타는지 아니?
하나: 아니, 몰라.
Karl: 나가자! 내가 가르쳐 줄 수 있어. 한 발을 보드 위에 올려놓고 다른 한 발로 세게 밀어.
하나: 이렇게? 와! 이거 재밌다. 벌써 기분이 좋아졌어.
Karl: 봤지? 나는 롱보드를 타는 것이 나의 스트레스를 줄여주기 때문에 즐겨.
하나: 정말 멋진데!

Wrap Up 1

B: _____

G: _____

B: _____

G: _____

B: _____

G: _____

B: 너 아파 보여. 무슨 일 있니?
G: 음, 감기에 걸렸어.
B: 병원에 가봤니?
G: 아직. 넌 감기가 나아지는 방법을 아니?
B: 음, 나는 감기에 걸렸을 때 보통 따뜻한 물을 마셔. 그것은 내 기분을 좋아지게 해.
G: 좋아. 한번 해 볼게.

Wrap Up 2

B: _____

_____

_____

B: 우리 가족은 많은 활동을 즐겨. 우리 아빠는 낚시를 즐기셔. 이른 아침, 그는 호수에 가셔서 약간의 물고기를 가지고 돌아오셔. 우리 엄마는 그림 그리기를 즐기셔. 그녀는 아름다운 산과 호수를 그리는 것을 좋아하셔. 나의 형과 나는 축구를 즐겨.

※ 다음 우리말과 일치하도록 빈칸에 알맞은 것을 골라 쓰시오.

1 _____ school you sit _____ many _____.
A. hours   B. for   C. at

2 _____ you _____ _____?
A. tired   B. get   C. do

3 Why _____ you massage _____ and _____?
A. stretch   B. yourself   C. don't

4 _____ begin _____ the eyes.
A. with   B. let's

5 _____ your eyes and _____ them _____ with your fingers.
A. softly   B. massage   C. close

6 It _____ _____ your eyes.
A. relax   B. will

7 _____ you finish, _____ your eyes with your hands to _____ _____ the light.
A. out   B. cover   C. block   D. when

8 It will _____ your eyes _____ more _____.
A. comfortable   B. feel   C. make

9 Next, _____ your _____.
A. neck   B. massage

10 _____ your fingers _____ the _____ of your neck.
A. back   B. on   C. put

11 Draw small _____ with your _____ to _____ your neck.
A. massage   B. fingers   C. circles

12 Massage from _____ to _____.
A. bottom   B. top

13 The massage will _____ you _____ _____.
A. better   B. feel   C. help

14 _____ work _____ your _____.
A. waist   B. on   C. let's

15 _____ _____ with a friend.
A. up   B. team

1 학교에서 너는 오랜 시간에 걸쳐 앉아 있다.

2 여러분은 피곤한가?

3 마사지와 스트레칭을 하는 게 어떤가?

4 눈부터 시작하자.

5 눈을 감고 손가락으로 눈을 부드럽게 마사지해라.

6 그것은 여러분의 눈을 편안하게 해줄 것이다.

7 끝나면, 빛을 차단하기 위해 손으로 눈을 가려라.

8 그것은 여러분의 눈을 더 편안하게 해줄 것이다.

9 다음으로, 여러분의 목을 마사지해라.

10 여러분의 목 뒤에 손가락을 대라.

11 여러분의 목을 마사지하기 위해 손가락으로 작은 원을 그려라.

12 위에서 아래로 마사지해라.

13 마사지는 여러분의 기분이 좋아지도록 도울 것이다.

14 허리 운동을 하자.

15 친구와 짝을 이루어라.

16 Stand _____ to each _____ and _____ your partner.
    A. face   B. other   C. close

17 _____ each _____ wrists.
    A. other's   B. hold

18 Slowly _____ your head and _____ _____ .
    A. backward   B. body   C. stretch

19 _____ that position _____ three _____ .
    A. seconds   B. for   C. hold

20 Then, slowly _____ each other _____ a standing position.
    A. to   B. pull

21 You and your partner _____ _____ at the same _____ .
    A. speed   B. move   C. should

22 _____ you don't, _____ of you will _____ !
    A. fall   B. both   C. if

23 _____ the _____ of your right foot _____ the desk _____ you.
    A. behind   B. top   C. on   D. place

24 Then, slowly _____ your left leg and _____ _____ .
    A. yourself   B. lower   C. bend

25 _____ it for a _____ seconds and slowly _____ _____ .
    A. up   B. few   C. straighten   D. hold

26 This _____ will _____ _____ your right leg.
    A. up   B. loosen   C. position

27 _____ your legs and _____ the _____ .
    A. exercise   B. repeat   C. switch

28 _____ do you _____ now?
    A. feel   B. how

29 If you _____ yourself and _____ every day, you will _____ _____ .
    A. healthier   B. stretch   C. massage   D. feel

30 Also, you can _____ _____ your _____ better.
    A. studies   B. on   C. focus

16 서로 가까이 서서 여러분의 파트너를 마주 보아라.

17 서로의 손목을 잡아라.

18 천천히 여러분의 머리와 몸을 뒤로 뻗어라.

19 3초 동안 그 자세를 유지해라.

20 그리고 나서, 천천히 서로 선 자세로 끌어 당겨라.

21 너와 너의 파트너는 같은 속도로 움직여야 한다.

22 그렇지 않으면, 너희 둘 다 넘어질 것이다!

23 여러분의 뒤에 있는 책상 위에 오른쪽 발등을 올려놓아라.

24 그리고 나서, 천천히 왼쪽 다리를 구부리고 몸을 낮추어라.

25 몇 초 동안 그 자세를 유지하다가 천천히 몸을 펴라.

26 이 자세는 여러분의 오른쪽 다리를 풀어 줄 것이다.

27 다리를 바꿔서 운동을 반복해라.

28 지금 기분이 어떤가?

29 매일 마사지와 스트레칭을 하면, 여러분은 더 건강해지는 것을 느낄 것이다.

30 또한, 여러분은 공부에 더 집중할 수 있을 것이다.

Step2

※ 다음 우리말과 일치하도록 빈칸에 알맞은 말을 쓰시오.

1 _____ _____ you sit _____ many hours.

2 Do you _____ _____ ?

3 _____ _____ you massage _____ and _____ ?

4 _____ _____ _____ the eyes.

5 _____ your eyes and _____ them softly _____ your _____ .

6 It _____ _____ your eyes.

7 _____ you finish, _____ your eyes _____ your hands to _____ _____ the light.

8 It will _____ your eyes _____ _____ _____ .

9 Next, _____ _____ _____ .

10 _____ your fingers _____ the _____ of your neck.

11 _____ small circles _____ your fingers _____ _____ your neck.

12 Massage _____ _____ _____ _____ .

13 The massage will _____ _____ _____ _____ .

14 _____ _____ _____ your _____ .

15 _____ _____ _____ a friend.

1 학교에서 너는 오랜 시간에 걸쳐 앉아 있다.

2 여러분은 피곤한가?

3 마사지와 스트레칭을 하는 게 어떤가?

4 눈부터 시작하자.

5 눈을 감고 손가락으로 눈을 부드럽게 마사지해라.

6 그것은 여러분의 눈을 편안하게 해줄 것이다.

7 끝나면, 빛을 차단하기 위해 손으로 눈을 가려라.

8 그것은 여러분의 눈을 더 편안하게 해줄 것이다.

9 다음으로. 여러분의 목을 마사지해라.

10 여러분의 목 뒤에 손가락을 대라.

11 여러분의 목을 마사지하기 위해 손가락으로 작은 원을 그려라.

12 위에서 아래로 마사지해라.

13 마사지는 여러분의 기분이 좋아지도록 도울 것이다.

14 허리 운동을 하자.

15 친구와 짝을 이루어라.

16 Stand close to _____ _____ and _____ your partner.

17 _____ each other's _____.

18 _____ _____ your head and body _____.

19 _____ that position _____ _____ _____.

20 Then, slowly _____ each other _____ a standing position.

21 You and _____ partner should move _____ the same speed.

22 _____ you don't, _____ _____ you _____ _____!

23 _____ the _____ of your right foot _____ the desk _____ you.

24 Then, _____ _____ your left leg and _____ yourself.

25 _____ it for _____ _____ _____ and slowly _____ _____.

26 _____ _____ will _____ _____ your right leg.

27 _____ your legs and _____ _____ _____.

28 _____ do you _____ now?

29 If you _____ yourself and _____ _____ _____, you will _____ _____.

30 Also, you _____ _____ _____ your studies _____.

16 서로 가까이 서서 여러분의 파트너를 마주 보아라.

17 서로의 손목을 잡아라.

18 천천히 여러분의 머리와 몸을 뒤로 뻗어라.

19 3초 동안 그 자세를 유지해라.

20 그리고 나서, 천천히 서로 선 자세로 끌어 당겨라.

21 너와 너의 파트너는 같은 속도로 움직여야 한다.

22 그렇지 않으면, 너희 둘 다 넘어질 것이다!

23 여러분의 뒤에 있는 책상 위에 오른쪽 발등을 올려놓아라.

24 그리고 나서, 천천히 왼쪽 다리를 구부리고 몸을 낮추어라.

25 몇 초 동안 그 자세를 유지하다가 천천히 몸을 펴라.

26 이 자세는 여러분의 오른쪽 다리를 풀어 줄 것이다.

27 다리를 바꿔서 운동을 반복해라.

28 지금 기분이 어떤가?

29 매일 마사지와 스트레칭을 하면, 여러분은 더 건강해지는 것을 느낄 것이다.

30 또한, 여러분은 공부에 더 집중할 수 있을 것이다.

※ 다음 문장을 우리말로 쓰시오.

1 At school you sit for many hours.

➡ _____

2 Do you get tired?

➡ _____

3 Why don't you massage yourself and stretch?

➡ _____

4 Let's begin with the eyes.

➡ _____

5 Close your eyes and massage them softly with your fingers.

➡ _____

6 It will relax your eyes.

➡ _____

7 When you finish, cover your eyes with your hands to block out the light.

➡ _____

8 It will make your eyes feel more comfortable.

➡ _____

9 Next, massage your neck.

➡ _____

10 Put your fingers on the back of your neck.

➡ _____

11 Draw small circles with your fingers to massage your neck.

➡ _____

12 Massage from top to bottom.

➡ _____

13 The massage will help you feel better.

➡ _____

14 Let's work on your waist.

➡ _____

15 Team up with a friend.

➡ _____

16 ▶ Stand close to each other and face your partner.

➡ _____

17 ▶ Hold each other's wrists.

➡ _____

18 ▶ Slowly stretch your head and body backward.

➡ _____

19 ▶ Hold that position for three seconds.

➡ _____

20 ▶ Then, slowly pull each other to a standing position.

➡ _____

21 ▶ You and your partner should move at the same speed.

➡ _____

22 ▶ If you don't, both of you will fall!

➡ _____

23 ▶ Place the top of your right foot on the desk behind you.

➡ _____

24 ▶ Then, slowly bend your left leg and lower yourself.

➡ _____

25 ▶ Hold it for a few seconds and slowly straighten up.

➡ _____

26 ▶ This position will loosen up your right leg.

➡ _____

27 ▶ Switch your legs and repeat the exercise.

➡ _____

28 ▶ How do you feel now?

➡ _____

29 ▶ If you massage yourself and stretch every day, you will feel healthier.

➡ _____

30 ▶ Also, you can focus on your studies better.

➡ _____

※ 다음 괄호 안의 단어들을 우리말에 맞도록 바르게 배열하시오.

1 (school / you / at / sit / hours. / many / for)
➡ _____

2 (get / do / tired? / you)
➡ _____

3 (you / don't / why / massage / stretch? / and / yourself)
➡ _____

4 (begin / with / let's / eyes. / the)
➡ _____

5 (eyes / close / your / and / them / massage / fingers. / with / softly / your)
➡ _____

6 (will / it / relax / eyes. / your)
➡ _____

7 (you / finish, / when / your / cover / with / eyes / hands / your / block / to / light. / the / out)
➡ _____

8 (will / it / make / eyes / your / feel / comfortable. / more)
➡ _____

9 (next, / neck. / your / massage)
➡ _____

10 (fingers / put / your / the / on / back / neck. / your / of)
➡ _____

11 (small / draw / circles / your / with / fingers / massage / neck. / to / your)
➡ _____

12 (from / bottom. / to / massage / top)
➡ _____

13 (massage / the / help / will / better. / feel / you)
➡ _____

14 (work / on / waist. / let's / your)
➡ _____

15 (up / team / friend. / a / with)
➡ _____

1 학교에서 너는 오랜 시간에 걸쳐 앉아 있다.

2 여러분은 피곤한가?

3 마사지와 스트레칭을 하는 게 어떤가?

4 눈부터 시작하자.

5 눈을 감고 손가락으로 눈을 부드럽게 마사지해라.

6 그것은 여러분의 눈을 편안하게 해줄 것이다.

7 끝나면, 빛을 차단하기 위해 손으로 눈을 가려라.

8 그것은 여러분의 눈을 더 편안하게 해줄 것이다.

9 다음으로, 여러분의 목을 마사지해라.

10 여러분의 목 뒤에 손가락을 대라.

11 여러분의 목을 마사지하기 위해 손가락으로 작은 원을 그려라.

12 위에서 아래로 마사지해라.

13 마사지는 여러분의 기분이 좋아지도록 도울 것이다.

14 허리 운동을 하자.

15 친구와 짝을 이루어라.

16 (close / to / stand / other / each / and / partner. / your / face)

➡ _____

17 (each / wrists. / hold / other's)

➡ _____

18 (stretch / slowly / head / your / and / backward. / body)

➡ _____

19 (that / hold / for / position / seconds. / three)

➡ _____

20 (slowly / then, / each / pull / other / to / position. / standing / a)

➡ _____

21 (your / and / you / partner / move / should / the / at / speed. / same)

➡ _____

22 (don't, / you / if / of / you / both / fall! / will)

➡ _____

23 (the / place / of / top / right / your / foot / on / the / desk / you. / behind)

➡ _____

24 (slowly / then, / your / bend / leg / left / yourself. / lower / and)

➡ _____

25 (it / hold / a / for / seconds / few / and / slowly / up. / straighten)

➡ _____

26 (position / this / loosen / will / up / leg. / right / your)

➡ _____

27 (your / switch / legs / and / exercise. / the / repeat)

➡ _____

28 (you / do / how / now? / feel)

➡ _____

29 (you / massage / if / yourself / and / stretch / day, / every / will / you / healthier. / feel)

➡ _____

30 (can / you / also, / on / focus / better. / studies / your)

➡ _____

16 서로 가까이 서서 여러분의 파트너를 마주 보아라.

17 서로의 손목을 잡아라.

18 천천히 여러분의 머리와 몸을 뒤로 뻗어라.

19 3초 동안 그 자세를 유지해라.

20 그러고 나서, 천천히 서로 선 자세로 끌어 당겨라.

21 너와 너의 파트너는 같은 속도로 움직여야 한다.

22 그렇지 않으면. 너희 둘 다 넘어질 것이다!

23 여러분의 뒤에 있는 책상 위에 오른쪽 발등을 올려놓아라.

24 그러고 나서, 천천히 왼쪽 다리를 구부리고 몸을 낮추어라.

25 몇 초 동안 그 자세를 유지하다가 천천히 몸을 펴라.

26 이 자세는 여러분의 오른쪽 다리를 풀어 줄 것이다.

27 다리를 바꿔서 운동을 반복해라.

28 지금 기분이 어떤가?

29 매일 마사지와 스트레칭을 하면, 여러분은 더 건강해지는 것을 느낄 것이다.

30 또한, 여러분은 공부에 더 집중할 수 있을 것이다.

※ **다음 우리말을 영어로 쓰시오.**

1 학교에서 여러분은 오랜 시간에 걸쳐 앉아 있다.

➡ _____

2 여러분은 피곤한가?

➡ _____

3 마사지와 스트레칭을 하는 게 어떤가?

➡ _____

4 눈부터 시작하자.

➡ _____

5 눈을 감고 손가락으로 눈을 부드럽게 마사지해라.

➡ _____

6 그것은 여러분의 눈을 편안하게 해줄 것이다.

➡ _____

7 끝나면, 빛을 차단하기 위해 손으로 눈을 가려라.

➡ _____

8 그것은 여러분의 눈을 더 편안하게 해줄 것이다.

➡ _____

9 다음으로, 여러분의 목을 마사지해라.

➡ _____

10 여러분의 목 뒤에 손가락을 대라.

➡ _____

11 여러분의 목을 마사지하기 위해 손가락으로 작은 원을 그려라.

➡ _____

12 위에서 아래로 마사지해라.

➡ _____

13 마사지는 여러분의 기분이 좋아지도록 도울 것이다.

➡ _____

14 허리 운동을 하자.

➡ _____

15 친구와 짝을 이루어라.

➡ _____

16 서로 가까이 서서 여러분의 파트너를 마주 보아라.

➡ _____

17 서로의 손목을 잡아라.

➡ _____

18 천천히 여러분의 머리와 몸을 뒤로 뻗어라.

➡ _____

19 3초 동안 그 자세를 유지해라.

➡ _____

20 그러고 나서, 천천히 서로 선 자세로 끌어 당겨라.

➡ _____

21 너와 너의 파트너는 같은 속도로 움직여야 한다.

➡ _____

22 그렇지 않으면, 너희 둘 다 넘어질 것이다!

➡ _____

23 여러분의 뒤에 있는 책상 위에 오른쪽 발등을 올려놓아라.

➡ _____

24 그러고 나서, 천천히 왼쪽 다리를 구부리고 몸을 낮추어라.

➡ _____

25 몇 초 동안 그 자세를 유지하다가 천천히 몸을 펴라.

➡ _____

26 이 자세는 여러분의 오른쪽 다리를 풀어 줄 것이다.

➡ _____

27 다리를 바꿔서 운동을 반복해라.

➡ _____

28 지금 기분이 어떤가?

➡ _____

29 매일 마사지와 스트레칭을 하면, 여러분은 더 건강해지는 것을 느낄 것이다.

➡ _____

30 또한, 여러분은 공부에 더 집중할 수 있을 것이다.

➡ _____

Step1

※ 다음 우리말과 일치하도록 빈칸에 알맞은 말을 쓰시오.

Enjoy Writing C

1. My Plan _____ _____ _____

2. _____ _____ my plan to be healthier.

3. I will exercise _____ _____ _____ _____ a week.

4. I will eat breakfast _____ _____ .

5. If I exercise more than _____ _____ _____ _____ , I will _____ _____ .

6. Also, _____ I eat breakfast every day, I _____ _____ _____ in the morning.

7. I will change my _____ , and it will _____ _____ _____ a healthy life.

1. 더 건강해지기 위한 나의 계획
2. 여기 더 건강해지기 위한 나의 계획이 있다.
3. 나는 일주일에 세 번 이상 운동을 할 것이다.
4. 나는 매일 아침을 먹을 것이다.
5. 일주일에 세 번 이상 운동을 하면 더 강해질 것이다.
6. 또한, 매일 아침을 먹으면 아침에 기분이 나아질 것이다.
7. 나는 습관을 바꿀 것이고, 그것은 나를 건강한 삶을 살게 할 것이다.

Project - Step 2

1. Do you know _____ _____ _____ your shoulders?

2. Our _____ _____ _____ _____ "Number Stretching."

3. First, make a number "I" _____ your arm _____ _____ _____ .

4. _____ , make a number "2" _____ your arms.

5. It _____ _____ your _____ .

6. Now, _____ a number "3".

7. If you move your arms _____ _____ _____ , it will _____ _____ .

8. _____ , make a number "4".

9. It is _____ _____ _____ difficult, but it will _____ _____ _____ your shoulders.

1. 여러분은 여러분의 어깨를 어떻게 스트레칭하는지 아니?
2. 우리의 스트레칭 운동은 "숫자 스트레칭"이라고 부른다.
3. "첫 번째, 준비 운동을 하기 위해 팔로 숫자 "1"를 만들어라.
4. 그런 다음, 팔로 숫자 2를 만들어라.
5. 그것은 여러분의 어깨를 쫙 펴줄 것이다.
6. 이제 숫자 3을 만들어라.
7. 팔을 동그랗게 움직이면 기분이 좋아질 것이다.
8. 마지막으로, 숫자 4를 만들어라.
9. 그것은 조금 어렵긴 하지만, 여러분의 어깨에 좋을 것이다.

Wrap Up - Writing

1. Sumi: I feel stressed _____ _____ . What _____ I _____ ?

2. Jiae: When I _____ _____ , I listen to music. It _____ _____ _____ better.

3. If you don't know _____ _____ _____ music, I will show you.

1. 수미: 나는 요즘 스트레스를 받고 있어. 어떻게 해야 하지?
2. 지애: 스트레스를 받을 때, 나는 음악을 들어. 그건 내 기분을 좋아지게 해.
3. 음악을 다운로드하는 방법을 모르면, 내가 가르쳐 줄게.

※ 다음 우리말을 영어로 쓰시오.

Enjoy Writing C

1. 더 건강해지기 위한 나의 계획
   ➡ _____

2. 여기 더 건강해지기 위한 나의 계획이 있다.
   ➡ _____

3. 나는 일주일에 세 번 이상 운동을 할 것이다.
   ➡ _____

4. 나는 매일 아침을 먹을 것이다.
   ➡ _____

5. 일주일에 세 번 이상 운동을 하면 더 강해질 것이다.
   ➡ _____

6. 또한, 매일 아침을 먹으면 아침에 기분이 나아질 것이다.
   ➡ _____

7. 나는 습관을 바꿀 것이고, 그것은 나를 건강한 삶을 살게 할 것이다.
   ➡ _____

Project - Step 2

1. 여러분은 여러분의 어깨를 어떻게 스트레칭하는지 아니?
   ➡ _____

2. 우리의 스트레칭 운동은 "숫자 스트레칭"이라고 부른다.
   ➡ _____

3. "첫 번째, 준비 운동을 하기 위해 팔로 숫자 "1"를 만들어라.
   ➡ _____

4. 그런 다음, 팔로 숫자 2를 만들어라.
   ➡ _____

5. 그것은 여러분의 어깨를 쫙 펴줄 것이다.
   ➡ _____

6. 이제 숫자 3을 만들어라.
   ➡ _____

7. 팔을 동그랗게 움직이면 기분이 좋아질 것이다.
   ➡ _____

8. 마지막으로, 숫자 4를 만들어라.
   ➡ _____

9. 그것은 조금 어렵긴 하지만, 여러분의 어깨에 좋을 것이다.
   ➡ _____

Wrap Up - Writing

1. 수미: 나는 요즘 스트레스를 받고 있어. 어떻게 해야 하지?
   ➡ _____

2. 지애: 스트레스를 받을 때, 나는 음악을 들어. 그건 내 기분을 좋아지게 해.
   ➡ _____

3. 음악을 다운로드하는 방법을 모르면, 내가 가르쳐 줄게.
   ➡ _____

MEMO

MEMO

영어 기출 문제집

적중100

1학기

정답 및 해설

시사 | 박준언

중 2

적중100

Manage Yourself!

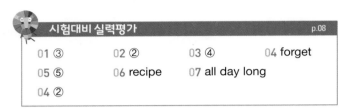

시험대비 실력평가 p.08

01 ③	02 ②	03 ④	04 forget
05 ⑤	06 recipe	07 all day long	
04 ②			

01 ③은 -ous를 붙여 형용사형을 만들고, 나머지는 -ful을 붙여 형용사형을 만든다.

02 in front of: ~ 앞에 / because of: ~ 때문에

03 열심히 일해 뭔가를 얻거나 이루다: 성취하다(achieve)

04 반의어 관계이다. 쉬운 : 어려운 = 기억하다 : 잊다

05 set the alarm: 알람을 맞춰 놓다 / make a plan: 계획을 세우다

06 음식을 만들기 위한 일련의 지시 사항: recipe(조리법)

07 all day long: 하루 종일, 온종일

08 prepare for: ~을 준비하다 / put off: ~을 미루다

서술형 시험대비 p.09

01 (1) warm (2) present (3) helpful
02 (1) be good at (2) get along with (3) stop playing
03 (1) appointment (2) future (3) manage (4) achieve
04 (1) wisely (2) carefully (3) regularly
05 (1) because of (2) put off (3) at a time (4) put aside
06 (1) (l)esson (2) (s)ave (3) (f)ocus (4) (d)ue

01 (1) 반의어 관계이다. ~ 전에 : ~ 후에 = 따뜻한 : 서늘한 (2) 유의어 관계이다. 맛있는 = 선물 (3) '명사 - 형용사' 관계이다. 구름 : 흐린 = 도움 : 도움이 되는

02 (1) be good at: ~에 능숙하다 (2) get along with: ~와 잘 지내다 (3) stop -ing: ~하는 것을 멈추다

03 (1) appointment: 약속 (2) future: 미래 (3) manage: 관리하다 (4) achieve: 달성하다, 성취하다

04 (1) wisely: 현명하게 (2) carefully: 주의 깊게 (3) regularly: 규칙적으로

05 (1) because of: ~ 때문에 (2) put off: ~을 미루다 (3) at a time: 한 번에 (4) put aside: ~을 치우다, ~을 한쪽에 두다

06 (1) lesson: 수업, 강습 (2) save: 절약하다 (3) focus: 집중하다 (4) due: ~하기로 되어 있는[예정된]

핵심 Check p.10~11

1 (1) matter / lost / too bad
 (2) with / hurt, finger / I'm sorry
2 (1) toothache / think, should go
 (2) Let's / better
 (3) Why don't / should drink
 (4) play / ought to

 ## 교과서 대화문 익히기

Check(√) True or False p.12

1 F 2 T 3 F 4 T

교과서 확인학습 p.14~15

Listen & Speak 1 - A
1 worried, matter / hear, these days / Why don't, set / idea
2 should / What's / spend, fast / make, before / should, same

Listen & Speak 2 - A
1 okay, don't look / cold / think, should see / right
2 worried, going on / worried about, What, do / should read / idea
3 tired / these days / I think, a glass of, before, help / will try

Conversation A
type, daily, monthly, like, due dates, check, to remember, easily, should use

Conversation B
matter / didn't bring, forgot / second, busier than, first / you should use, mine / can / schedule, appointment / Maybe, should

Wrap Up - ❶
What's, Are, sick / have a cold / school nurse / need to, Can, leave / call, tell her

Wrap Up - ❷
nervous / because of / for, still, should, do / think, should, in front of, helpful / a good idea

01 ①	02 ④	03 ②	04 ⓓ - ⓑ - ⓒ - ⓐ

01 What's the matter?는 어떤 문제점이 있는지 물어보는 표현으로 What's wrong? / What's the problem? 등으로 바꿔 쓸 수 있다.

02 감기에 걸린 친구에게 알맞은 충고는 ④ '병원에 가보는 게 좋겠다.'가 알맞다.

03 나머지는 모두 '진수에게 무슨 일 있니?'라는 뜻으로 문제점을 파악하는 표현인데, ②는 '진수에 대해서 어떻게 생각하니?'라는 뜻으로 의견을 묻고 있다.

04 ⓓ 너 아파 보여. 괜찮니? - ⓑ 아니. 난 심한 감기에 걸렸어. - ⓒ 너는 병원에 가봐야 해. ⓐ 오, 네 말이 맞아.

시험대비 실력평가　　　　　　　　p.17~18

01 problem	02 busier	03 ③	04 a planner
05 ③	06 on	07 ④	
08 better read	09 She thinks the boy should read his textbook again.	10 ③	11 of
12 소년이 자기 가족 앞에서 연습하는 것		13 ⑤	
14 ⑤	15 ②		

01 What's the matter?는 What's the problem?으로 바꿔 쓸 수 있다.

02 비교급+than: ~보다 더 …한

03 제안이나 권유하는 표현인 「I think you should +동사원형 ~」은 Why don't you ~?로 바꿔 쓸 수 있다.

04 인칭대명사 it은 앞 문장에 나온 단수명사를 가리킨다.

05 ③ 지호가 축구 연습을 하는 장소는 알 수 없다.

06 What's going on?: 무슨 일 있니?

07 What should I do?는 상대방에게 제안이나 충고를 구할 때 사용하는 표현이다.

08 I think you should + 동사원형 ~은 You'd better + 동사원형 ~으로 바꿔 쓸 수 있다.

09 소녀는 소년이 그의 교과서를 다시 읽어야 한다고 생각한다.

10 주어진 문장은 제안이나 충고를 구하는 표현으로 '가족 앞에서 연습해야 한다고 생각해.'라는 문장 앞에 와야 한다.

11 ⓐ because of: ~ 때문에 ⓑ in front of: ~ 앞에서

13 Sam이 요즘 아침에 알람을 듣지 못한다고 말한 것으로 보아 상대방의 상태가 안 좋아 보일 때 무슨 일인지 묻는 표현이 들어가야 한다.

14 Why don't you ~?는 '~하는 게 어때?'라는 말이다.

15 That's a good idea.는 제안이나 권유에 동의하는 표현이다.

서술형 시험대비　　　　　　　　　p.19

01 [모범답안] What's wrong? / What's the matter [problem]? / Is (there) something wrong? 등

02 Why don't

03 그는 내일 역사 시험을 걱정한다.

04 [모범답안] I'm sorry to hear that. / That sounds bad. / What a pity! 등

05 She thinks Jason should see a doctor.

06 I think I have a cold.

07 (A) matter (B) Can

08 She said Sam needs to go to the hospital.

09 감기에 걸린 것 같아 일찍 하교해서 병원에 가는 것

01 슬픔, 불만족, 실망의 원인을 묻는 표현에는 What's wrong? / What's the problem? / What's the matter? / Is (there) something wrong? 등이 있다.

02 I think you should + 동사원형 ~.은 제안이나 충고하기 표현으로 Why don't you + 동사원형 ~?로 바꿔 쓸 수 있다.

03 소년이 'I'm worried about tomorrow's history quiz.'라고 했다.

04 That's too bad.는 유감을 나타낼 때 사용하는 표현으로 I'm sorry to hear that. / That sounds bad. / What a pity! / That's a pity! 등으로 바꿔 쓸 수 있다.

05 소녀는 Jason이 병원에 가야 한다고 충고한다.

06 I think ~: 내 생각에는 ~하다 / have a cold: 감기에 걸리다

07 What's the matter? = What's wrong? / Can I + 동사원형 ~?: 제가 ~해도 될까요?

08 양호 선생님은 Sam에게 병원에 가야 할 필요가 있다고 말했다.

교과서
Grammar

핵심 Check　　　　　　　　　p.20~21

1 (1) to go　(2) to help　(3) to write with　(4) cold to drink
2 (1) to visit　(2) to tell　(3) to listen
3 (1) that　(2) that
4 (1) heard ∨ she　(2) thought ∨ we　(3) says ∨ the

01 ③　　02 (1) many things to do　(2) to help us　03 (1) that Jenny is at home　(2) believed that he would come back.　(3) didn't think that Alice

would like Mason to visit   04 (1) to change   (2) to visit   (3) to solve.

01 접속사 that절 이하의 내용과 자연스럽게 어울리지 않는 단어는 mind이다.

02 (1) '해야 할 많은 일'이라는 뜻으로 to do가 명사 many things를 뒤에서 수식해 준다. (2) to부정사구(to help us)는 앞에 나온 명사 the only person을 꾸며주는 형용사 역할을 한다.

03 that이 접속사로 동사의 목적어가 되는 명사절을 이끄는 경우이다.

04 to부정사구가 앞에 나온 명사(구)를 꾸며주는 형용사 역할을 한다.

시험대비 실력평가   p.23~25

01 ⑤   02 ⑤   03 that   04 ①
05 ⑤   06 believe that   07 ③
08 to eat   09 ②   10 ⑤   11 didn't know that   12 ③   13 I think that Jinwoo will be a great leader.   14 ③   15 Do you have something interesting to read?   16 ③
17 ④   18 something cold to drink   19 a chair to sit on[in]   20 ⑤   21 ③   22 I think (that) James went on a trip. 23 ③   24 The girl has some food to feed the dog.

01 to부정사인 to save가 앞의 명사 a way를 꾸며주는 형용사 역할을 한다.

02 ⑤에서 made 다음에 that이 이끄는 명사절이 나오는 것은 어색하다.

03 절과 절을 연결해 주는 것은 접속사 that이다.

04 빈칸에는 some books를 수식하는 표현이나 책을 산 목적을 나타내는 표현이 올 수 있다.

05 ⑤는 목적어 역할을 하는 to부정사의 명사적 용법으로 쓰였고, 나머지는 to부정사의 형용사적 용법으로 쓰였다.

06 '~라고 믿는다.'라는 의미를 가진 I believe that이 오는 것이 적합하다.

07 ①, ②, ④, ⑤는 명사절을 이끄는 접속사 that이고, ③은 지시형용사이다.

08 명사 snacks을 수식하는 형용사 역할의 to부정사로 써야 한다.

09 good news를 수식하는 to부정사가 와야 한다. (to부정사의 형용사적 용법)

10 ①, ②, ③, ④의 that은 접속사의 목적어 역할로 쓰여서 생략이 가능하고, ⑤는 지시형용사로 쓰였으므로 생략할 수 없다.

11 목적어절을 이끄는 접속사 that이 필요하다.

12 ③은 '~하기 위하여'라는 목적을 나타내는 to부정사의 부사적 용법이고, 나머지는 '~할'의 뜻으로 앞의 명사를 수식하는 to부정사의 형용사적 용법이다.

13 '나는 ~라고 생각한다'는 I think that을 이용해서 나타낸다.

14 ③ something reading → something to read / 그녀는 읽을 것을 찾고 있는 중이다.

15 대명사 something을 수식하기 위해 동사 read를 형용사 역할로 바꿔 준다. (to read)

16 ③은 지시형용사이고, 나머지는 모두 명사절을 이끄는 접속사로 쓰였다.

17 부정사인 to write가 앞의 명사 paper를 수식한다. 이때 paper는 write on의 목적어이므로 write 다음에 전치사 on을 반드시 붙여야 한다.

18 「-thing+형용사+to부정사」의 어순으로 쓴다.

19 to부정사의 수식을 받는 명사가 전치사의 목적어일 경우 to부정사 뒤에 반드시 전치사를 써야 한다.

20 주어진 문장과 ⑤의 that은 접속사로 목적어절을 이끄는 역할을 한다.

21 think 뒤에 절이 올 경우 「that+주어+동사」의 어순으로 쓰고, 이때 접속사 that은 생략 가능하다. ③은 의문문의 어순으로 되어 있으므로 that절 뒤에 이어질 수 없다.

22 여행을 갔다는 것이 목적어이므로 that을 사용한 명사절을 써야 한다.

23 to부정사의 수식을 받는 명사가 전치사의 목적어일 경우 to부정사 뒤에 전치사를 쓴다. ③은 to talk with[to]라고 해야 옳다.

24 주어는 the girl이고 동사는 has, to부정사의 형용사적 용법을 이용하여 some food to feed the dog를 목적어로 쓴다.

서술형 시험대비   p.26~27

01 to   02 that

03 (1) I bought some cookies to eat in the afternoon.
   (2) They need four chairs to sit on.

04 (1) My brother says that he didn't eat the bananas.
   (2) They think that they are proud of themselves.

05 (1) to eat   (2) to drink
   (3) sit on[in]   (4) talk with[to]

06 (1) that you can do everything
   (2) you think that she is pretty

07 (1) a pen to write → a pen to write with
   (2) visiting → to visit

08 (1) I know, she is a wise wife
   (2) I think, he is Chinese
   (3) We believe, we can change the world

09 She needs something to put on.

10 (1) She thinks that her daughter is sick.
   (2) I don't believe that Nick will come to the party.

11 a hotel to stay at[in]

12 (1) She has a strong desire to be a singer.

(2) We had something to talk about.

(3) I want a sheet[piece] of paper to write on.

(4) Please give me something hot to drink.

13 (1) I think (that) my English teacher is pretty.

(2) Many people believe (that) the earth is round.

14 (1) I have a lot of homework to do.

(2) It is your turn to introduce your family.

01 앞의 명사를 수식하는 형용사적 용법의 to부정사가 필요하다.

02 첫 번째 문장의 that은 접속사, 두 번째 문장은 관계대명사, 세 번째 문장은 지시형용사이다.

03 (2) 의미상 to부정사구 뒤에 전치사 on이 와야 한다.

04 주절의 동사 뒤에 접속사 that이 이끄는 목적어절을 쓴다.

05 앞의 명사를 꾸며주는 to부정사의 형용사적 용법을 이용한다.

06 that이 목적어가 되는 명사절을 이끄는 문장이다.

07 (1) to부정사의 수식을 받는 명사가 전치사의 목적어일 경우 to부정사 뒤에 반드시 전치사를 써야 한다. (2) '~할'이라는 의미로 명사를 수식하는 to부정사가 와야 한다. (형용사적 용법)

08 접속사 that은 동사의 목적어절을 이끄는 역할을 한다.

09 명사[대명사]를 수식하는 형용사 역할의 to부정사는 명사[대명사]의 뒤에 위치한다.

10 접속사 that 이하의 내용이 부정일 때, that 앞에 있는 동사를 부정으로 만든다.

11 stay at[in] a hotel의 구조이다.

12 (1), (2) to부정사의 형용사적 용법을 이용해 「명사[대명사]+to부정사」의 형태로 쓴다. (3) to부정사의 목적어가 있고 to부정사의 동사가 자동사일 때는 전치사가 필요하다. (4) -thing으로 끝나는 부정대명사는 「-thing+형용사+to부정사」의 어순을 따른다.

13 (2) 주어 + believe (that): ~라고 믿다

14 (1) 나는 해야 할 숙제가 많다. (2) 네 가족을 소개할 차례야.

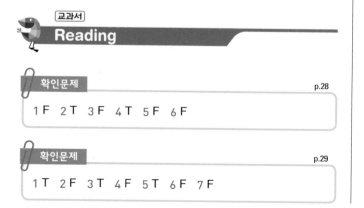

교과서 Reading

확인문제   p.28

1 F 2 T 3 F 4 T 5 F 6 F

확인문제   p.29

1 T 2 F 3 T 4 F 5 T 6 F 7 F

교과서 확인학습 A   p.30~31

01 Welcome to   02 In, second, to do

03 need to, well 04 How, do   05 set, achieve

06 will master   07 With, put off, until, or

08 Instead, will learn, every day

09 will achieve, at a time

10 When, full attention

11 used to read, while

12 slowed, because

13 put aside, when   14 a lot of

15 These days, free time

16 spend, working   17 to become

18 Every, classes, search for

19 that, to prepare   20 present

21 has, to spend 22 Manage, and, be happier

교과서 확인학습 B   p.32~33

1 Welcome to the new school year.

2 In the second grade, you will have more work to do.

3 You need to manage your time well.

4 How do you do that?

5 Subin: I set small goals and achieve them every day.

6 I do not say, "I will master English."

7 With such a big goal, I will probably put off working on it until tomorrow, next week, or next month.

8 Instead, I say, "I will learn three new English words every day."

9 I will achieve my big goal, one step at a time.

10 Minsu: When I do something, I give it my full attention.

11 I used to read SNS postings while I was doing my homework.

12 It slowed me down because I couldn't focus.

13 Now, I put aside my smartphone when I do my homework.

14 It saves me a lot of time.

15 These days, I finish my homework quickly and enjoy my free time.

16 John: I regularly spend time working toward my dream.

17 I want to become a chef.

18 Every Saturday morning, I go to cooking classes or search for recipes.

19 I think that using my time to prepare for my future is important.
20 Time is a present.
21 Everyone has the same present to spend every day.
22 Manage your time well, and you will be happier in the new school year!

01 ②	02 small goals		03 ④
04 ③	05 ⑤	06 to	07 ①
08 working	09 ③	10 ④	11 ④
12 to	13 ⑤	14 숙제를 하는 동안 SNS 게시 글을 읽은 것	
	15 ⑤		16 ③
17 ③	18 to become	19 ①	20 ②
21 are → is	22 ②	23 ④	24 ⑤
25 ③	26 set, achieve, big goal, achieve		
27 ②	28 (a)ttention	29 ④	30 ⑤
31 ④	32 He enjoys his free time.		

01 set a goal: 목표를 세우다
02 인칭대명사 them은 앞에 나온 복수명사를 가리킨다.
03 put off: 미루다(=postpone)
04 instead: 대신에
05 수빈이는 한 번에 한 걸음씩 그녀의 큰 목표를 달성할 것이라고 했다.
06 welcome to: ~이 된 것을 환영하다
07 밑줄 친 ⓑ는 to부정사의 형용사적 용법이다. ① 형용사적 용법 ② 명사적 용법 ③ 부사적 용법 ④ 명사적 용법 ⑤ 부사적 용법
08 spend time -ing: ~하는 데 시간을 소비하다
09 think 다음에 나오는 내용이 목적어의 역할을 하고 있으므로 명사절을 이끄는 접속사 that이 와야 한다.
10 토요일 아침마다 요리법을 찾아본다고 했다.
11 주어진 문장의 It은 '숙제를 할 때 스마트폰을 한 쪽에 치워 놓는 것'을 가리키므로 ④에 와야 한다.
12 수여동사 give는 3형식에서 전치사 to를 쓴다.
13 「used to+동사원형」은 과거에 반복적으로 일어난 행위를 나타낸다.
14 인칭대명사 It은 앞에 나온 문장을 받는다.
15 because: ~ 때문에
16 ③ 스마트폰을 이용해서 숙제를 했는지는 알 수 없다.
17 toward: ~을 위해
18 want는 to부정사를 목적어로 취한다.
19 ⓒ, ①: 수업, 강습 ②, ③, ④: 학급 ⑤: 반 학생들
20 search for: ~을 찾다

21 동명사 주어는 단수 취급하므로 are를 is로 고쳐야 한다.
22 ⓐ, ②: 학년, ①, ③: 성적, ④: 등급, ⑤: 학점
23 2학년에서는 해야 할 일이 많아서 시간을 잘 관리해야 한다는 의미가 자연스러우므로 manage(관리하다)가 알맞다.
24 put off: 미루다
25 문맥상 until(~까지)이 알맞다.
27 주어진 문장의 It은 '숙제를 할 때 SNS 게시 글을 읽었던 것'을 가리키므로 ②에 오는 것이 알맞다.
28 어떤 것 또는 어떤 사람에 대해 주의 깊게 듣고, 보고, 생각하는 행위: attention(주의)
29 used to와 would는 과거에 반복적으로 일어났던 행위를 나타낼 때 쓸 수 있는 표현이다.
30 시간의 접속사 while이 알맞다.
31 ④④: 절약하다, ①③: 구조하다, ②⑤: 저장하다
32 민수는 숙제를 빨리 끝내고 그의 여가 시간을 즐긴다고 했다.

01 you will have more work to do
02 너의 시간을 관리하다
03 She sets small goals and achieves them every day.
04 working
05 She will learn three new English words.
06 나는 한 번에 한 단계씩 나의 큰 목표를 달성할 거야.
07 something
08 (A) used to   (B) because
09 숙제할 때 스마트폰을 한 쪽에 치워 두는 것
10 He used to read SNS postings (while he was doing his homework.)
11 (A) to do   (B) working
12 We need to manage our time well.
13 He wants to become a chef.
14 명사절을 이끄는 접속사 that과 「동명사 주어+동사」 어순이므로 be동사가 들어가는데, 동명사 주어는 단수 취급하므로 is가 알맞다.
15 He goes to cooking classes or search for recipes.
16 선물   17 the same present to spend

01 work를 to do로 수식하여 표현한다.
02 do that = manage your time
03 수빈이는 작은 목표를 세우고 매일 그것들을 성취한다고 했다.
04 put off는 동명사를 목적어로 취한다.
05 수빈이는 매일 세 개의 새로운 단어를 배울 것이라고 했다.
06 achieve: 달성하다, 성취하다 / goal: 목표 / one step at a

time: 한 번에 한 단계씩

07 인칭대명사 it은 something을 가리킨다.v

08 (A) used to+동사원형: ~하곤 했다 (B) because: ~ 때문에

09 인칭대명사 It은 앞 문장을 받는다.

10 민수는 그의 숙제를 하는 동안 SNS 게시 글들을 읽곤 했다.

11 (A) work을 꾸며주는 형용사 역할을 하는 to부정사의 형태가 되어야 한다. (B) spend time -ing: ~하는 데 시간을 보내다

12 2학년에서는 시간 관리를 잘해야 한다고 언급되었다.

13 John은 요리사가 되고 싶어 한다고 했다.

14 명사절을 이끄는 접속사 that과 「동명사 주어+동사」 어순이므로 be동사가 들어가는데, 동명사 주어는 단수 취급하므로 is가 알맞다.

15 John은 토요일 아침마다 요리 강습에 가거나 요리법을 찾아본다고 했다.

16 present: 선물

17 to spend가 앞에 있는 명사구 the same present를 꾸며주는 형용사적 용법이다.

영역별 핵심문제

p.41~45

| 01 ④ | 02 ② | 03 present | 04 ③ |
| 05 ③ | 06 ② | 07 ⑤ | 08 ④ |

09 (D) – (A) – (C) – (B) 10 ②, ⑤ 11 I'm worried about the math test. 12 ④

| 13 ④ | 14 ③ | 15 in | 16 He is |

nervous because of the dance contest. 17 ①

| 18 ⑤ | 19 that | 20 ③ | 21 ⑤ |

22 ② 23 Jane didn't believe that Kevin would come to the party. 24 to write → to write with 25 that → if 26 ③ 27 ④

| 28 ④ | 29 ③ | 30 would | 31 (f)ocus |

32 지금 나는 숙제를 할 때 스마트폰을 한쪽에 치워 놔.

| 33 ④ | 34 ② | 35 ③ | 36 ③ |
| 37 with | 38 playing | 39 ② | 40 ④ |

01 ④는 형용사이고 나머지는 부사이다.

02 관심이나 노력을 특정한 대상에 기울이다: focus(집중하다)

03 반의어 관계이다. 아마 : 아마 = 선물 : 선물

04 be good at: ~을 잘하다, ~에 능숙하다 / at a time: 한 번에

05 • 나는 나의 큰 목표를 달성할 것이다. • 나는 오늘 축구 연습이 있다. • 그는 6학년이다. • 너는 시간을 잘 관리해야 해.

06 put off: 연기하다, 미루다(=postpone)

07 상대방에게 무언가 제안하거나 권유하는 표현을 고른다. ⑤는 '왜 너는 조리법을 찾지 않았니?'라는 의미이다.

08 What's wrong with ~?는 어떤 문제점이 있는지 물을 때 사용하는 표현이므로 ④는 어울리지 않는다.

09 (D) Jason, 너 괜찮아? 오늘 안 좋아 보여. - (A) 감기에 걸렸

어. (C) 그거 참 안됐구나. 내 생각에 너는 병원에 가 봐야 할 것 같아.- (B) 네 말이 맞아. 고마워.

10 B가 좋지 않은 소식을 전하는 것으로 보아 A에는 Kevin에게 무슨 문제가 있느냐고 물어보는 표현이 오는 게 맞다.

11 be worried about: ~에 대해 걱정하다

12 주어진 문장의 It은 '가족 앞에서 연습하는 것'을 가리키므로 ④에 와야 한다.

13 ⓐ because of: ~ 때문에 ⓑ for many days: 여러 날 동안

14 앞뒤 내용이 상반되므로 역접의 접속사 but이 알맞다.

15 in front of: ~ 앞에서

16 소년은 춤 경연대회 때문에 긴장된다고 했다.

17 think 다음에 나오는 내용이 목적어의 역할을 하고 있으므로 명사절을 이끄는 접속사 that이 와야 한다.

18 to부정사인 to live가 앞의 명사 a good house를 수식한다. 수식을 받는 명사가 전치사의 목적어인 경우 to부정사 뒤에 전치사가 와야 한다.

19 명사절을 이끄는 접속사 that이 필요하다.

20 ③은 '~하기 위하여'라는 의미로 목적을 나타내는 to부정사의 부사적 용법이고, 나머지는 앞의 명사를 꾸며주는 to부정사의 형용사적 용법이다.

21 목적어가 되는 명사절을 이끄는 접속사 that은 생략할 수 있다

22 <보기>와 ②는 to부정사의 형용사적 용법 ①, ⑤ 부사적 용법 (목적) ③, ④ 명사적 용법

24 to write가 앞의 명사 a pen을 수식한다. 이때는 write with a pen이라는 전치사의 목적어 관계이므로 write 다음의 전치사 with를 빠뜨리지 않도록 주의한다.

25 don't know의 목적어가 되는 명사절은 접속사 if를 쓴다.

26 ③의 to부정사는 '~하기 위하여'라는 의미로 목적을 나타내는 부사적 용법으로 쓰였고, 나머지는 모두 '~할, ~하는'이라는 뜻으로 앞에 오는 명사나 대명사를 꾸며주는 형용사적 용법으로 쓰였다.

27 ①, ②, ③, ⑤: that / ④: 접속사 when

28 ⓐ, ⓒ to부정사의 형용사적 용법 ⓑ to부정사의 명사적 용법 ⓓ to부정사의 부사적 용법

29 때를 나타내는 접속사 when이 알맞다

30 used to는 '~하곤 했다'는 의미로 would와 바꿔 쓸 수 있다.

31 관심이나 노력을 특정한 대상에 기울이다: 집중하다(focus)

32 put aside: 한쪽에 치워 놓다

33 these days: 요즈음(=nowadays)

34 ⓕ, ②: 자유로운 ①: 사용 중이 아닌, ③: ~이 없는, ④⑤: 무료로

35 ③ 민수가 하루에 얼마나 오랫동안 스마트폰을 사용하는지는 알 수 없다.

36 ⓐ와 ③은 형용사적 용법의 to부정사이고, ①, ②, ④는 명사적 용법, ⑤는 부사적 용법의 to부정사이다.

37 get along with: ~와 잘 지내다

38 stop -ing: ~하는 것을 멈추다

39 hope 다음에 나오는 내용이 목적어의 역할을 하고 있으므로 명사절을 이끄는 접속사 that이 와야 한다.

34 ④ 글쓴이가 작년에 성취한 목표가 무엇인지는 알 수 없다.

단원별 예상문제
p.46~49

01 ③	02 ⑤	03 (1) in front of	(2) all
day long	(3) used to	(4) because of	04 ④
05 ③	06 ①	07 ④	08 worried
09 ⑤	10 ⑤	11 ④	12 ③
13 hang → hang on		14 ③	15 if →
that	16 something hot to drink		17 ⑤
18 ①	19 작은 목표들	20 such a big goal	
21 put off	22 영어를 마스터하는 것		23 ①
24 ①	25 and	26 She says, "I will learn	
three new English words every day."			27 recipes
28 ②	29 ③		

01 ③은 유의어 관계이고 나머지는 반의어 관계이다.

02 get along with: ~와 잘 지내다 / put aside: ~을 한쪽으로 치우다

03 (1) in front of: ~ 앞에서 (2) all day long: 하루 종일 (3) used to: ~하곤 했다 (4) because of: ~ 때문에

04 ④는 spend(소비하다)의 영영풀이다.

05 What should I do?는 상대방에게 충고를 구할 때 사용하는 표현이다.

06 감기에 걸렸을 때 병원에 가보라고 하는 충고가 어울린다.

07 ④ 필기를 하는 게 어떠냐며 조언을 하는데 아직이라며 무엇을 해야 하는지 묻는 건 어색하다.

08 ⓐ look+형용사: ~하게 보이다 ⓑ I'm worried about~: 나는 ~이 걱정이다

09 What's going on?은 '무슨 일 있니?'라는 의미로 문제점을 파악할 때 사용하는 표현이다.

10 '내일 역사 시험이 걱정돼. 어떻게 해야 할까?' 다음에 충고의 의미를 담은 ③ 'Why don't you ~?'가 가장 알맞다.

11 ①, ②, ③ 명사적 용법 ④ 형용사적 용법 ⑤ 부사적 용법

12 첫 번째 빈칸에는 hope의 목적어로 쓰이면서 주절과 종속절을 이어주는 명사절 접속사 that이 적절하다. 두 번째 빈칸에는 '그것(그 말)'이라는 뜻의 지시대명사 that이 적절하다.

13 to부정사의 수식을 받는 명사가 전치사의 목적어일 경우 뒤에 전치사가 온다.

14 ①, ②, ④, ⑤: 지시형용사 / ③: 접속사 that

15 hope 다음에는 접속사 that이 이끄는 명사절이 와야 한다.

16 -thing으로 끝나는 대명사는 형용사가 뒤에서 수식하며, 이를 다시 to부정사가 뒤에서 수식한다.

17 목적어 역할을 하는 명사절을 이끄는 that은 생략 가능하다.

18 ①에서 sit은 자동사이므로 chair를 목적어로 취하기 위해서는 전치사 in이나 on이 필요하다.

19 them은 small goals를 가리킨다.

20 「such + a + 형용사 + 명사」 어순이다.

21 특정 시간에 하기로 계획된 일을 나중에 하기로 결정하다: put off(연기하다, 미루다)

23 at a time: 한 번에

24 본문의 to spend는 형용사적 용법의 to부정사이다. ①은 형용사적 용법, ③은 명사적 용법, ②④⑤는 모두 부사적 용법의 to 부정사이다.

25 명령문 ~, and ...: ~해라, 그러면 ...

26 수빈이는 영어를 마스터하는 대신에 매일 세 개의 새로운 영어 단어를 배울 것이라고 말한다고 했다.

27 음식을 만들기 위한 일련의 지시 사항 : 요리법, 조리법(recipe)

28 ②는 형용사적 용법이고 ⓑ와 나머지는 부사적 용법이다.

29 John이 요리 강습을 어디에서 듣는지는 알 수 없다.

서술형 실전문제
p.50~51

01 ⓐ What's the matter ⓑ What should I do

02 (B)-(C)-(D)-(A)

03 모범답안 What's wrong with you? / What's the problem with you? Is (there) something wrong with you? 등

04 모범답안 You'd better drink some water. / Why don't you drink some water?/ I advise you to drink some water. / How[What] about drinking some water?

05 (1) He believes that it will be a lot of fun.

(2) I think that he is honest.

(3) I know that she was a teacher.

06 to play with

07 I think that he enjoys playing soccer.

08 (1) to tell (2) to live in

09 (1) to answers → to answer

(2) to talk → to talk with[to]

(3) anything drink → anything to drink

10 three goals to achieve

11 to play → playing

12 It is to learn taegwondo.

13 regularly **14** chef

15 for **16** using[to use]

17 He goes to cooking classes every Saturday morning.

01 ⓐ '무슨 일이 있니?'라는 뜻의 What's the matter (with

you)?가 알맞다. ⓑ '내가 어떻게 해야 할까?'라는 뜻의 What should I do?가 알맞다.

02 (B) 무슨 문제 있니? - (C) 음, 이가 아파. - (D) 그것 참 안됐구나. 치과에 가 보는 게 어때? -(A) 알았어. 그럴게.

03 어떤 문제점이 있는지 물을 때 사용하는 표현에는 What's wrong with ~? / What's the matter[problem] with ~? / Is (there) something wrong with ~? 등이 있다.

04 I think you should+동사원형 ~.은 제안이나 충고하기 표현으로 You'd better+동사원형 ~. / Why don't you+동사원형 ~? / How[What] about -ing ~? 등으로 바꿔 쓸 수 있다.

05 that: 명사절(목적어)을 이끄는 접속사

06 앞의 명사를 수식하는 to부정사를 이용하여 한 문장으로 만들도록 한다. 수식을 받는 명사가 전치사의 목적어인 경우 to부정사 뒤에 전치사가 와야 한다.

07 enjoy는 동명사를 목적어로 취하는 동사이다. I think that ~: 나는 ~라고 생각한다

08 (1) to tell이 앞에 있는 명사 good news를 꾸며주는 형용사적 용법이다. (2) to live 앞에 있는 명사 house는 전치사 in의 목적어이므로 in을 써야 한다.

09 (1) 앞에 있는 명사 the questions를 꾸며주는 to부정사(to+동사원형) 형태가 되어야 한다. (2) to부정사의 형용사적 용법으로 앞의 명사 some friends와 연결되려면 전치사 with[to]가 필요하다. (3) '마실 것'의 의미가 되어야 하므로 앞에 나온 대명사를 뒤에서 꾸며주는 '대명사+to부정사' 형태가 되어야 한다.

10 to achieve가 앞에 있는 명사구 three goals를 꾸며주는 형용사적 용법이다.to achieve가 앞에 있는 명사구 three goals를 꾸며주는 형용사적 용법이다.

11 stop -ing: ~하는 것을 멈추다 cf. stop + to부정사: ~하기 위해 멈추다

12 글쓴이의 마지막 목표는 태권도를 배우는 것이다.

13 동사 spend를 수식하므로 부사가 되어야 한다.

14 전문 요리사, 특히 식당, 호텔 등에서 가장 상급의 요리사

15 search for: ~을 찾다 / prepare for: ~을 준비하다

16 주어 역할을 하는 동명사나 to부정사 형태가 되어야 한다.

창의사고력 서술형 문제
p.52

|모범답안|

01 (1) I need something to drink.
   (2) I need a chair to sit on[in].
   (3) He needs friends to talk with[to].
02 (1) He thinks that Jenny is kind.
   (2) She heard that they needed help.
   (3) Mike says that it's delicious.
   (4) They know that many children are hungry.
03 (1) I need a chair to sit on.

   (2) I need friends to talk with.
   (3) I need ski gloves to wear.

01 앞의 명사를 꾸며주는 to부정사의 형용사적 용법을 이용한다.

02 동사의 목적어가 되는 명사절을 이끄는 접속사 that을 사용하여 내용상 어울리는 것끼리 연결한다.

03 앞의 명사를 꾸며주는 to부정사의 형용사적 용법을 이용한다.

단원별 모의고사
p.53~56

01 ④	02 ②	03 ④	
04 remember	05 master	06 ⑤	07 Why
don't you	08 wrong	09 ①	10 (a)
ppointment	11 She thinks he should use a planner.		
12 ③	13 ②	14 ⑤	15 I think
that my English teacher is pretty.			16 ⑤
17 to stay in[at]		18 ④	19 ②
20 ④	21 slowed down me → slowed me		
down	22 ③	23 much	24 No, he
finishes his homework quickly.			25 ②
26 working	27 manage	28 ③	29 different
30 If	31 ④		

01 앞으로 하려는 일을 위해 스스로를 준비시키다: prepare(준비하다)

02 put off: 미루다

03 save: 절약하다; 구하다

04 반의어 관계이다. 미래 : 과거 = 잊다 : 기억하다

05 어떤 것을 완전히 익히다

06 ⑤ A가 B에게 슬퍼 보인다며 무슨 일 있냐고 물었는데, B가 도와주겠다고 대답하는 것은 어색하다.

07 You'd better+동사원형 ~.과 유사한 표현에는 I think you should+동사원형 ~. / I advise you to+동사원형 ~. / I suggest you+동사원형 ~. / Why don't you+동사원형 ~? / How[What] about ~? 등이 있다.

08 What's the matter? = What's wrong?

09 I think you should ~는 상대방에게 제안이나 충고를 하는 표현으로 You had better ~와 바꿔 쓸 수 있다.

10 특정한 때에 어떤 사람을 만나기로 하는 약속: appointment (약속)

11 하나는 지호가 일정 계획표를 사용해야 한다고 생각한다.

12 문맥상 '함께 여행할 친구를 찾고 있다'는 흐름이 자연스러우므로, 빈칸에는 '~와 함께'에 해당하는 with가 알맞다.

13 ①, ③, ④, ⑤의 that은 know, hope, believe 등의 타동사 다음에 목적어가 되는 명사절을 이끄는 접속사 that으로 쓰였으나 ②의 that은 관계대명사이다.

14 to부정사의 형용사적 용법이다.

15 I think that: ~라고 생각한다

16 ⑤ -thing이나 -body로 끝나는 부정대명사의 경우 형용사와 to부정사의 수식을 동시에 받으면 「대명사+형용사+to부정사」의 순서로 써야 한다. something important to tell

17 앞의 명사를 수식해야 하므로 to부정사 형태가 되어야 하고, 호텔 안에 머무는 것이므로 전치사 in[at]을 함께 써야 한다.

18 ①, ②, ③, ⑤: 명사절을 이끄는 접속사 ④: 지시형용사

19 ⓐ, ⓒ: to부정사의 형용사적 용법 ⓑ, ⓓ: to부정사의 명사적 용법 ⓔ to부정사의 부사적 용법

20 「used to+동사원형」은 과거에 반복적으로 일어난 행위를 나타낸다.

21 「타동사 + 부사」의 이어동사의 목적어가 인칭대명사인 경우 「동사 + 인칭대명사 + 부사」의 어순이 된다.

22 밑줄 친 It은 앞에 나온 문장을 받는다.

23 time은 셀 수 없는 명사이므로 much와 바꿔 쓸 수 있다.

24 요즈음 민수는 숙제를 빨리 끝낸다고 했다

25 ⓐ와 ②는 '~할, ~하는'의 의미로 앞의 명사를 수식해 주는 to부정사의 형용사적 용법이고, 나머지는 to부정사의 명사적 용법이다.

26 spend time -ing: ~하는 데 시간을 쓰다

27 시간, 돈 등을 낭비하지 않고 현명하게 사용하다: manage (관리하다)

28 '~하기 위하여'라는 목적을 나타내는 to부정사가 와야 한다.

29 same(같은)의 반의어는 different(다른)이다.

30 「명령문, and ~」구문은 if 조건문으로 바꿔 쓸 수 있다.

31 ④ John이 왜 요리사가 되고 싶어 하는지는 알 수 없다.

All about Safety

01 ⑤   02 possible   03 ④   04 wet
05 ④   06 earthquake   07 ②
08 save

01 <보기>와 ⑤는 동사에 -ive를 붙여 형용사가 되는 단어이 다.

02 as soon as you can(가능한 한 빨리 = as soon as possible)

03 공기를 폐 안으로 들이마셨다가 내쉬다: 숨을 쉬다(breathe)

04 반의어 관계이다. 잘못된 : 옳은 = 마른 : 젖은

05 bump into: ~에 부딪히다 / wait for: ~을 기다리다

06 지구 표면의 갑작스럽고 격렬한 진동: 지진(earthquake)

06 get off: ~에서 내리다 / get under: ~ 밑에 들어가다

08 save: 구하다; 절약하다

01 (1) unimportant   (2) remember   (3) ceiling   (4)
brave   02 (1) in front of   (2) stand in lin   (3)
fall down   (4) all the time   03 (1) hard   (2) save
  (3) grade   04 (1) practice   (2) breathe   (3) scared
05 (1) run around   (2) put on   (3) in case of   06 (1)
(d)egree   (2) (c)hest   (3) (p)erform   (4) (a)udience

01 (1), (2), (3) 반의어 관계이다. (1) 늦게 : 일찍 = 중요한 : 중요하지 않은 (2) 쉬운 : 어려운 = 잊다 : 기억하다 (3) 강한 : 약한 = 바닥 : 천장 (4) 쓰레기 : 쓰레기 = 용감한 : 겁이 없 는

02 '(1) in front of: ~ 앞에 (2) stand in line: 한 줄로 서다 (3) fall down: 넘어지다 (4) all the time: 항상

03 (1) hard: 어려운; 세게 (2) save: 구하다; 저축하다 (3) grade: 학년; 성적

04 (1) 그들은 보통 방과 후에 축구를 연습한다. practice: 연 습하다 (2) 사람은 숨쉬기 위해 산소가 필요하다. breathe: 숨을 쉬다 (3) 그 토끼는 사자를 만났을 때 겁을 먹었다. scared: 겁먹은, 무서워하는

05 (1) run around: 뛰어다니다 (2) put on: ~을 입다 (3) in case of: ~의 경우에

06 (1) degree: (각도의 단위인) 도 (2) chest: 가슴 (3) perform: 수행하다 (4) audience: 청중, 시청자

Conversation

p.62~63

핵심 Check

1 (1) don't forget to (2) borrow / remember to / will
(3) Make[Be] sure / won't
2 (1) think, cold / better not drink (2) Don't eat
(3) shouldn't use / sorry

교과서 대화문 익히기

Check(√) True or False
p.64

1 T 2 F 3 F 4 T

교과서 확인학습
p.66~67

Listen & Speak 1 A-1
can, buy / forget to / food label / for / will check

Listen & Speak 1 A-2
leaving / wear, find dust / didn't know / bad for, don't forget / All right

Listen & Speak 2 A-1
up / to buy, about / have, in, should go, late / better not, says, wet / didn't

Listen & Speak 2 A-2
does, mean / you'd better not, while / but / bump into, there are, around, dangerous / see

Conversation A
having, with, to shake, couldn't, fell down, Get, Don't forget, Luckily, scary experience

Conversation B
told, a few / let's, ready / is shaking, forget to get, protect / scary, Hold on to / for now, out / better not use, Use / should, go / need to, with / let's to

Wrap Up - Listening 1
almost, stand in line, wait for, get off, move up, down, You'd better, in case of

Wrap Up - Listening 2
going to, with / sounds / because, for, on night / don't forget to check

---

시험대비 기본평가
p.68

01 ⑤   02 ⑤   03 ④   04 ②

01 상대에게 상기시키는 표현을 할 때, 「don't forget to+동사원형」의 표현을 써서 잊지 말 것을 당부한다.

02 You'd better not+동사원형 ～은 '～하지 않는 게 좋겠다'라는 뜻의 금지하는 표현으로 You shouldn't + 동사원형 ～.으로 바꿔 쓸 수 있다.

03 Don't forget to + 동사원형: '～하는 것을 잊지 마'라는 의미의 상기시킬 때 사용하는 표현이다.

04 B의 답변으로 보아, 빈칸에는 금지를 나타내는 should not을 사용한 문장이 들어가야 한다.

시험대비 실력평가
p.69~70

01 is   02 ③   03 ④   04 ⑤
05 ④   06 ①   07 ②   08 They
are practicing a few safety rules for earthquakes.
09 ①   10 Remember 11 ③   12 ①, ③
13 ③   14 ③   15 걷는 동안 스마트폰을
보지 않는 게 낫다는 뜻이다.

01 주어 a lot of fine dust가 셀 수 없는 명사이므로 동사는 is가 되어야 한다.

02 so: 그래서

03 잊지 말라고 상기시키는 말이다.

04 ⑤ 소녀는 아빠가 당부하는 말에 알겠다고 했으므로 마스크를 쓸 것이다

05 a few+셀 수 있는 명사의 복수형

06 hold on to: ～을 꼭 잡다

07 계단을 이용하라고 했으므로 빈칸에는 '엘리베이터를 타면 안된다.'는 금지의 표현이 알맞다.

08 Amy와 지호는 지진에 대한 안전 수칙들을 실습하고 있다.

09 주어진 문장은 '갑자기 모든 것이 흔들리기 시작했다.'라는 뜻으로 나는 가만히 서 있을 수 없었고 거의 넘어질 뻔 했다.는 문장 앞에 오는 것이 자연스럽다.

10 Don't forget to + 동사원형 ～: ～하는 것을 잊지 마라 (=Remember+동사원형 ～)

11 ③ 필자와 그의 가족이 어디에 있었는지는 알 수 없다

12 you'd better not ～는 금지를 나타내는 표현으로 ①, ③과 바꿔 쓸 수 있다. you don't have to ～는 '너는 ～할 필요가 없다'는 의미이다.

13 but: 그러나

14 bump into: ～에 부딪히다

11

01 Don't forget to wear your gloves.

02 Make sure to bring your trash back.

03 you'd better not play   04 (B) – (D) – (C) – (A)

05 you shouldn't use / you must not use / don't [do not] use / you can't use

06 to buy   07 She came to buy a shirt.

08 Because the floor is wet.

01 Don't forget to+동사원형 ~: ~하는 것을 잊지 마라.

02 Make sure to + 동사원형 ~: ~하는 것을 명심해라.

03 You'd better not ~.: 너는 ~하지 않는 게 좋겠다.

04 A: 나는 내일 아빠와 지리산에 갈 거야. (B) 멋진데. (D) 우리는 1박 2일 동안 묵을 예정이어서 신나. (C) 그거 좋겠네. 하지만, 날씨를 확인하는 걸 잊지 마. (A) 알았어.

05 You'd better not + 동사원형 ~은 금지하는 표현으로 You shouldn't + 동사원형 ~ / You must not + 동사원형 ~ / Don't[Do not] + 동사원형 ~ / You can't + 동사원형 ~ 등으로 바꿔 쓸 수 있다.

06 목적을 나타내는 to부정사의 부사적 용법이다.

07 소녀는 셔츠를 사러 이 쇼핑센터에 왔다.

08 바닥이 젖었기 때문이다.

 교과서

Grammar

핵심 Check   p.72~73

1 (1) how (2) which (3) where (4) when (5) where

2 (1) as fast as Bora (2) as new as mine
  (3) not as long as the yellow one

 시험대비 기본평가   p.74

01 (1) where to go (2) how to make
   (3) what to eat (4) when to open

02 (1) as heavy as mine
   (2) run as fast as
   (3) as Seoul's (population)
   (4) not as[so] delicious as
   (5) as difficult

03 (1) where I should park
   (2) how they should use the computer

01 (1) where+to부정사: 어디로 ~할지 (2) how+to부정사: ~하는 방법 (3) what+to부정사: 무엇을 ~할지 (4) when+to부정사: 언제 ~할지

02 (1) your bag과 my bag을 비교하는 것이므로 me를 mine으로 고친다. (2) fast의 정도를 비교하는 것이므로 run as fast as ~가 맞다. (3) 도쿄의 인구와 서울의 인구를 비교하는 것이므로 Seoul은 적절하지 않다. (4) as ~ as의 부정문은 not as/so ~ as로 쓴다. (5) 뒤의 비교 대상 앞에 as가 있으므로 동등비교로 만들어야 한다.

03 「의문사+to부정사」는 「의문사+주어+should+동사원형」으로 바꾸어 쓸 수 있다.

01 ①   02 ②   03 ②   04 ③

05 ②   06 as tall as Ted   07 ①

08 where to go   09 as, as   10 ②

11 ②   12 ②   13 they shoul 14 not as[so] cheap as   15 ④   16 (1) cold (2) hotter, than   17 ⑤   18 ②

19 She is not as[so] popular as you.   20 ②

21 ④   22 Can you show me how to use a camera?   23 ④   24 ③

01 '~만큼 …한'의 뜻을 나타내는 동등비교이다.

02 how+to부정사: ~하는 방법, what+to부정사: 무엇을 ~ 할지

03 as ~ as … 동등비교를 쓴다.

04 「의문사+to부정사」 구문으로 첫 번째 문장은 문맥상 '무엇을 입어야 할지'가 되어야 하므로 what이 알맞고, 두 번째 문장은 '~하는 방법'이라는 의미가 되어야 하므로 how가 알맞다.

05 「의문사+to부정사」는 should를 써서 명사절로 바꿔 쓸 수 있다.

06 Eric과 Ted는 키가 같으므로 동등비교 「as + 형용사 + as」를 이용하여 문장을 완성한다.

07 「의문사+to부정사」 구문을 이용한다.

08 '어디로 가야 할지'는 「의문사 where+to부정사」로 나타낼 수 있다.

09 less ~ than …은 not as ~ as 구문으로 바꿔 쓸 수 있다.

10 ② 동사 eat의 목적어로 what이 왔으므로, 뒤에 lunch가 또 올 수 없다. (what → where[when] 또는 lunch → for lunch

11 빨리 달리는 순서는 Mike>Mina>Eric>Junho이다.

12 ②의 what to read는 동사 is의 보어로 쓰였고, 나머지 「의문사+to부정사」는 모두 목적어로 쓰였다.

13 의문사+to부정사 =「의문사+주어+should+동사원형」

14 A is ~ than B: …보다 더 ~하다 = B is not as[so] ~ as A: …만큼 ~하지 않다

15　④ how to make의 목적어가 될 수 있는 말이 와야 한다.

16　(1) 비교급의 문장을 not as ~ as ...의 문장으로 바꾼다. (2) not as ~ as ...의 문장을 비교급의 문장으로 바꾼다.

17　⑤ as ~ as 사이에 동사 speak를 수식하는 부사인 well 을 써야 한다.

18　②에서 '카메라를 사용하는 방법'은 「의문사+to부정사」 구문으로 나타내야 한다.

19　「be동사+not as[so]+형용사 원급+as」: …만큼 ~하지 않다

20　첫 번째 문장은 '~만큼 많이'의 동등비교 표현이고, 두 번째는 'more+원급+than ...'의 비교 표현이다.

21　'서울은 인천보다 크다.'라는 표현은 '인천은 서울만큼 크지 않다.'는 의미이다. not as[so]+형용사의 원급+as: ~만큼 …하지 않은

22　가르쳐 주실래요?: Can you show me ~? / 카메라 사용법: how to use a camera

23　④ 「who+to부정사」 구문은 사용하지 않는다. 대신 Will you tell me who will invite Jack?으로 나타낸다.

24　③은 문맥으로 보아 who가 동사 take의 주어 역할을 하므로 조동사 should가 들어가야 한다. 나머지는 모두 to가 적절하다.

서술형 시험대비
p.78~79

01 (1) how　(2) what　(3) which　(4) where

02 (1) as tall as　(2) taller than　(3) as old as
　(4) not as old as

03 (1) I can't decide what to buy[what I should buy] for my mother's birthday.
　(2) Bill didn't tell us where to stay.

04 (1) Jimin is not as[so] tall as Taemin.
　(2) Jane isn't as[so] heavy as Kirk.

05 (1) as much as I do
　(2) as fast as I could
　(3) not as comfortable as that bed

06 (1) My brother doesn't know where he should go.
　(2) Alice doesn't know what she should cook.
　(3) Please tell me when I should help you.
　(4) The problem is how I should escape from here.

07 (1) where to practice　(2) when to visit
　(3) who(m) to but　(4) what to buy
　(5) which, to buy

08 (1) Ella has as many hats as I have.
　(2) This new tool is as useful as that old one.
　(3) Tom drank as much wine as water.

09 she to take ➡ she should take 또는 to take

10 better, as[so] well as

11 (1) I didn't know when to leave.
　(2) Do you know how to play the guitar?
　(3) I don't know where to meet her.

12 (1) just　(2) wise　(3) twice　(4) early

01 (1) 방법을 나타낼 때는 「how+to부정사」를 쓴다. (2) '몇 시'는 what time ~?을 쓴다. (3) '어느 책'은 which book ~?으로 나타낸다. (4) '이름을 적을 곳'은 장소를 나타내므로 where가 알맞다.

02 (1) Brian은 Kevin만큼 키가 크다. (2) 준호는 Kevin보다 키가 크다. (3) Brian은 준호만큼 나이가 많다. (4) Kevin은 준호와 Brain만큼 나이가 많지 않다.

03 (1) '무엇을 사야 할지'의 의미이므로 「의문사+to부정사」 또는 「의문사+주어+should+동사원형」의 형태로 고쳐야 한다. (2) 「의문사+to부정사」 구문이므로, to 다음에 동사원형 stay가 와야 한다.

04 (2) 'A는 B보다 덜 ~하다'는 A not as[so] ~ as B로 바꾸어 쓸 수 있다.

05 as ~ as ... 구문을 쓴다.

06 「의문사+to부정사」 구문을 「의문사+주어+should+동사」 구문으로 바꿔 쓸 수 있다

07 (3) 목적격 whom 대신 주격 who를 써도 좋다. (5) 'which+명사+to부정사'의 형태이다.

08 (1) Ella has ~와 I have를 동등 비교한다. (2) This new tool과 That old one을 동등 비교한다. one은 tool의 반복을 피하기 위해 쓴 대명사이다. (3) wine과 water를 비교한다.

09 어느 길을 택해야 하는지는 「의문사+to부정사」 구문이나 「의문사+주어+should+동사」 구문을 써서 나타낸다.

10 A 비교급 than B=B not as[so] 원급 as A

11 (1) 의문사(when)+to leave (2) 의문사(how) + to play the guitar (3) 의문사(where)+to meet her

12 (1) 비교 대상의 정도가 완전히 같을 때는 as 앞에 just를 붙인다. (2) '예전만큼 현명하지 않다'의 뜻이므로 wise가 적절하다. (3) '몇 배의 ~'는 배수사를 as 앞에 둔다. (4) 'Ann 만큼 일찍'이므로 early를 쓴다.

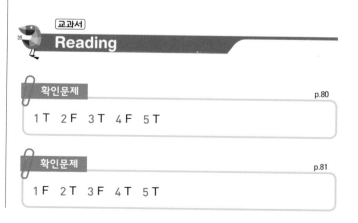

교과서
Reading

확인문제
p.80

1 T　2 F　3 T　4 F　5 T

확인문제
p.81

1 F　2 T　3 F　4 T　5 T

01 saved, life   02 brave, with us

03 yourself   04 My, is   05 in, second, at

06 tell us, experience

07 waiting for, with   08 in front of

09 what to do   10 as, as, at

11 ran, tapped, on

12 wasn't, breathing   13 said to, CPR

14 impressive   15 did, such an

16 Safety Training, at

17 how to do, to practice   18 show, how to

19 Keep, straight 20 other, must, at, angle

21 Push down, hard, until

22 Are there, to remember

23 need to, minutes

24 that, should, within, after, stops

25 To begin, later than, saving

26 as important as   27 for joining

28 pleasure

1 Announcer: Yesterday, a teenager saved the life of an old man.

2 The brave student is in the studio with us today.

3 Please introduce yourself.

4 Sejin: My name is Kim Sejin.

5 I'm in the second grade at Hanguk Middle School.

6 Announcer: Could you tell us your experience?

7 Sejin: Sure. I was waiting for the bus with my friend, Jinho.

8 A man suddenly fell in front of us.

9 Nobody knew what to do.

10 I was as scared as the others at first.

11 Then, I ran to him and tapped him on the shoulder.

12 He wasn't moving or breathing.

13 I said to Jinho, "Call 119," and started CPR.

14 Announcer: That's impressive.

15 When did you learn such an important skill?

16 Sejin: We had Safety Training Day at school last week.

17 I learned how to do CPR and had a chance to practice.

18 Announcer: Can you show the audience how to perform CPR?

19 Sejin: Yes. Keep your arms straights,

20 Your arms and the other person's chest must be at a 90 degree angle.

21 Push down in the center of the chest hard and fast until an ambulance comes.

22 Announcer: Are there any other things to remember?

23 Sejin: Yes. You need to remember the four minutes of "Golden Time."

24 It means that you should start CPR within four minutes after someone's heart stops.

25 To begin CPR later than that will greatly lower the chances of saving someone's life.

26 Announcer: Timing is as important as doing CPR.

27 Thank you for joining us.

28 Sejin: My pleasure.

01 ④   02 in   03 ⑤   04 Nobody knew what to do.   05 ④   06 ⑤

07 the four minutes of "Golden Time"   08 ⑤

09 (l)ower   10 such an important skill   11 to

12 ③   13 perform   14 Our arms and the other person's chest must be at 90 degree angle.

15 ②   16 a man   17 ③   18 breathing

19 CPR   20 She was waiting for the bus with her friend, Jinho.   21 Is → Are   22 ③

23 4분   24 of   25 ⑤   26 joining

27 ②   28 chest   29 at   30 ③

01 명령문의 주어가 You이므로, 주어 You의 재귀대명사는 yourself 이다.

02 be in the second grade: 2학년이다

03 suddenly: 갑자기(=unexpectedly)

04 nobody: 아무도 ~ 않다 / what+to부정사: 무엇을 ~해야 할지

05 ④ 그 남자의 직업은 알 수 없다.

06 ⓐ 명사구 any other things를 꾸며주는 to부정사의 형용사적 용법이므로 to remember가 알맞다. ⓓ 문장의 주어의 역할을 하는 to부정사나 동명사가 와야 한다.

07 인칭대명사 It은 앞 문장의 the four minutes of "Golden Time"를 가리킨다.

08 문맥상 심장이 멈춘 후가 알맞다.

09 어떤 것을 양, 정도, 강도 등을 줄이거나 적게 되다: lower

10 such + a/an + 형용사 + 명사

11 how+to부정사: ~하는 방법, 어떻게 ~해야 할지

12 ⓒ와 ③은 to부정사의 형용사적 용법으로 쓰인 문장이다.

13 대개 훈련이나 기술이 필요한 행동이나 활동을 하다: 행하다, 실시하다(perform)

14 90도 각도가 되어야 한다고 언급되었다.

15 아무도 무엇을 해야 할지 몰랐다고 했으므로 세진이도 처음에는 다른 사람들처럼 겁이 났을 것이다.

16 him은 a man을 가리킨다.

17 tap ~ on the shoulder: ~의 어깨를 가볍게 두드리다

18 or는 앞에 있는 moving과 같은 구조의 단어로 이루어져야 하므로 breathe의 현재분사형 breathing이 되어야 한다.

19 호흡이 멈추고 심장 박동이 정지된 사람의 생명을 구하려고 시행하는 방법: 심폐소생술(CPR)

20 세진이는 그녀의 친구 진호와 함께 버스를 기다리고 있었다.

21 Are there + 복수명사 ~?: ~이 있나요?

22 within: ~ 이내에[안에]

23 the four minutes를 가리킨다.

24 「명사+of+동명사구」 구문으로 이때의 of는 동격을 나타낸다.

25 타이밍은 심폐소생술을 하는 것만큼 중요하다가 문맥상 알맞다.

26 전치사의 목적어로 동명사가 쓰인다.

27 세진이는 심폐소생술 과정을 보여 주고 있다.

28 목과 위 사이의 몸의 앞부분: 가슴(chest)

29 at a 90 degree angle: 90도 각도로

30 문맥상 push down(~을 누르다)가 알맞다.

서술형 시험대비
p.90~91

01 She is in the second grade

02 Could you tell your experience to us?

03 in front of

04 I was as scared as the others at first.

05 on　　06 She said to him, "Call 119."

07 to remember　　08 that

09 누군가의 심장이 멈춘 후 4분 안에 심폐소생술을 시작해야 한다는 것을 의미한다.

10 (c)hances　11 as important as doing CPR

12 so

13 She had Safety Training Day at school last week.

14 I learned how to do CPR.

15 audience　16 will come → comes

17 팔을 쭉 펴고, 팔과 다른 사람의 가슴은 90도 각도로 하고, 구급차가 올 때까지 가슴 중앙을 세게 그리고 빨리 누른다.

01 세진이는 2학년이다.

02 tell+간접목적어+직접목적어 = tell+직접목적어+to+간접 목적어

03 in front of: ~ 앞에

04 as + 형용사의 원급 +as: ~만큼 …한

05 tap ~ on the shoulder: ~의 어깨를 톡톡 치다

06 세진이는 진호에게 119에 전화하라고 말한 후, 심폐소생술을 시작했다. .

07 any other things를 꾸며주는 to부정사의 형용사적 용법이다.

08 명사절을 이끄는 접속사 that이 알맞다.

09 It means that you should start CPR within four minutes after someone's heart stops.를 통해서 알 수 있다.

10 어떤 일이 일어날 가능성: 가능성(chance)

11 as + 형용사의 원급 +as: ~만큼 …한

12 such+a/an+형용사+명사 = so+형용사+a/an+명사

13 지난주 학교에서 안전 교육의 날이 있었다고 언급되었다.

14 how+to부정사: ~하는 방법

15 무언가를 보거나 듣기 위해 모인 사람들(연극, 콘서트, 말하 는 사람 등): 청중(audience)

16 때를 나타내는 부사절은 미래의 일이라도 현재시제를 쓴다.

영역별 핵심문제
p.93~97

01 ⑤	02 ④	03 fall down
04 impressive		05 ③	06 ②
07 ②	08 ①, ②, ④	09 ⑤	10 ②
11 ①	12 Don't forget to check the food label.	
13 ④	14 the food label	15 as[so],
as	16 to	17 ③	18 ⑤
19 He plays tennis as well as Tom.		20 should
begin	21 ②	22 ③	23 ⑤
24 not as[so] diligent as		25 ④	26 ①
27 yourself	28 Could you tell your experience to	
us?	29 ③	30 Nobody knew what	
to do.	31 ①	32 ③	33 are →
is	34 ⑤	35 as low as you can	
36 Remember		37 ⑤	

01 ⑤는 유의어 관계이고, 나머지는 반의어 관계이다.

02 in front of: ~ 앞에 / in case of: ~의 경우에

03 fall down: 넘어지다

04 impressive: 인상적인

05 • 너는 "불이야!"라고 소리쳐야 한다. • 그 표지판은 무엇을 의미하니? • 날씨를 확인하는 것을 잊지 마라. • 너는 젖은 수건으로 너의 얼굴과 몸을 가려야 한다.

06 대개 훈련이나 기술이 필요한 행동이나 활동을 하다: 수행하다(perform)

07 A가 태권도 수업에 간다고 하는 것에 대해 B는 '도복을 입고 가는 것을 잊지 마.'라고 하는 것이 자연스럽다.

08 빈칸에는 대화의 흐름상 상대방에게 상기시키거나 당부를 하는 말이 들어가는 것이 알맞다. 상기를 시키거나 당부를 하는 말에는 「Don't forget to+동사원형 ~.」, 「Make sure to+동사원

15

형 ~.」, 「Remember to+동사원형 ~.」이 있다.

09 금지의 표현은 명령문 「Don't+동사원형 ~.」을 사용하거나 「You shouldn't + 동사원형 ~. / You'd better not + 동사원형 ~.」으로 바꿔 쓸 수 있다.

10 상대에게 무엇인가 상기시키거나 당부하는 표현인 「Don't forget to+동사원형 ~.」에 대한 답은 Okay, thanks., Okay, I see., No, I won't. 등으로 한다.

11 사과 주스를 좀 사도 되겠냐는 요청의 말에 "Sure."는 '물론이지.'라는 뜻으로, 승낙하는 말이다. ①은 승낙의 표현이다.

12 부정명령문은 「Don't + 동사원형 ~.」으로 시작한다. '~하는 것을 잊다'는 「forget + to부정사」로 쓴다.

13 be good for: ~에 좋다

14 인칭대명사 it은 the food label을 가리킨다.

15 not as[so] ~ as: …만큼 ~하지 않다

16 to부정사는 의문사와 함께 쓰여 '~해야 하는지'의 뜻을 나타낸다.

17 「as+형용사+a(n)+명사 as ~」의 어순이므로 as great a statesman as ~가 되어야 한다.

18 ⑤ 「의문사+to부정사」 또는 「의문사+주어+should+동사원형」 (where should go → where to go 또는 where they should go)

19 '~만큼 잘'은 as well as로 나타낸다.

20 「의문사+to부정사」 구문은 「의문사+주어+should+동사원형」 으로 바꿔 쓸 수 있다.

21 ②에서 두 번째 as 뒤에 오는 절의 주어가 George로 3인칭 단 수이므로 do를 does로 바꾸어야 한다.

22 ⓓ 「who+to부정사」는 어색한 표현이므로, Do you know who will tell me about it?으로 바꿔 쓴다. ⓔ when to move는 언제 움직일지 시간에 관한 물음인데, yesterday와 쓰이면, 시간을 나타내는 부사가 중복되어 어색한 문장이 된다.

23 ⑤는 '~할 때'라는 뜻의 접속사이고 나머지는 as ~ as … 구문의 부사로 쓰였다.

24 A is more+형용사의 원급+than B. = B is not as[so]+ 형용사의 원급+as A.

25 「what+to부정사 ~」는 「what+주어+should+동사원형 ~」으로 바꿔 쓸 수 있다.

26 just the same as는 as ~ as로 바꿔 쓸 수 있다.

27 명령문의 주어는 You이므로, You의 재귀대명사 yourself가 알맞다.

28 수여동사가 있는 3형식 문장은 「tell+직접목적어+to+간접 목적어」 어순이다.

29 ⓒ wait for: ~을 기다리다 ⓓ in front of: ~ 앞에서

30 nobody: 아무도 ~ 않다 / what+to부정사: 무엇을 ~해야 할지

31 '~만큼 …한'의 뜻을 나타내는 동등비교이다.

32 그 노인이 어디를 가는 중이었는지는 알 수 없다.

33 there is + 단수명사: ~이 있다

34 with: ~으로

35 as ~ as possible: 가능한 한 ~하게(=as ~ as you can)

36 Don't forget to+동사원형 ~은 상대방에게 상기시키거나 당부하는 표현으로 Remember to+동사원형 ~.으로 바꿔 쓸 수 있다.

37 엘리베이터보다 계단을 이용해야 한다고 상기시키고 있다.

단원별 예상문제 p.98~101

01 ②	02 putting on	03 ④	04 (b) reathe
05 ④	06 dangerous	07 ③	
08 ⑤	09 you'd better not run	10 the sign	
11 ⑤	12 buys → buy		
13 ④	14 I am not as[so] pretty as you.		
15 how to cook	16 ①	17 ③	
18 as much as he used to	19 ②	20 had a chance to practice	
21 ⑤	22 ④		
23 She learned how to do CPR.	24 ④		
25 "골든타임" 4분	26 ③	27 (1) Begin → To begin[Beginning] (2) save → saving	
28 Timing			

01 <보기>와 ②는 동사에 -ive를 붙여 형용사가 되는 단어들이 다.

02 take off: ~을 벗다(↔ put on: ~을 입다)

03 ④는 degree의 영영풀이다.

04 breathe: 호흡하다, 숨을 쉬다

05 at first: 처음에 / in case of: ~의 경우에

06 반의어 관계이다. 바닥 : 천장 = 위험한 : 안전한

07 You'd better not + 동사원형 ~은 '~하지 않는 게 좋겠 다.'라는 의미로 금지하는 표현이다.

08 어떤 일을 상기시켜 주는 표현인 Don't forget to ~는 Remember to ~로 바꿔 쓸 수 있다.

09 You'd better not + 동사원형 ~: 너는 ~하지 않는 게 좋을 거야.

10 인칭대명사 it은 앞에 나온 단수명사를 받는다.

11 must be chosen을 수식해야 하므로 부사 형태가 알맞다.

12 「what to+동사원형」 형태이다.

13 모두 「의문사+to부정사」 구문으로 to가 빈칸에 들어가고, ④는 too ~ to부정사 구문으로 빈칸에 too가 들어간다.

14 A is not as[so] ~ as B: A는 B만큼 ~하지 않다

15 '요리하는 방법'을 배우고 싶다는 뜻이므로 「how+to부정 사」로 나타낼 수 있다.

16 ① 두 번째의 as 뒤에 오는 절의 주어가 Mike로 3인칭 단 수이므로 do를 does로 바꾸어야 한다.

17 '언제 꺼야 할지'라는 뜻으로 목적어 역할을 하는 「의문사 +to부 정사」 형태가 되어야 한다.

18 '예전만큼 많이'는 as much as he used to로 나타낸다.

19 how to+동사원형: ~하는 방법

20 to부정사 to practice가 명사 a chance를 꾸며주는 역할 을 한다.

21 「keep+목적어+목적격보어」 순으로 와야 한다.

22 until: ~때까지

23 세진이는 안전 교육의 날에 심폐소생술을 배웠다고 했다.

24 ④는 to부정사의 부사적 용법으로 목적을 나타내지만, ⓐ와 나 머지는 앞에 나온 명사를 수식하는 형용사적 용법으로 사 용되 었다.

25 인칭대명사 It은 the four minutes of "Golden Time" 을 가 리킨다.

26 누군가의 심장이 멈춘 후가 되어야 하므로 after가 알맞다.

27 (1) 동사 will의 주어 역할을 해야 하므로 To begin[Beginning] 이 되어야 한다. (2) 전치사의 목적어로 동명사 형태가 되어야 한다.

28 특히 결과에 좋거나 나쁜 영향을 미칠 것으로 여겨지는 어떤 것 이 일어나거나 행해지는 시간: 타이밍(timing)

서술형 실전문제 p.102~103

01 Remember / Don't forget

02 you shouldn't eat / you must not eat / don't eat

03 Don't forget to wear safety gear.

04 (C) – (E) – (A) – (D) – (B)

05 (1) Meg sings as well as you (do).

 (2) This street is just as wide as that one.

 (3) Seoul Tower is about three times as high as this tower.

 (4) I can't[cannot] cook as well as my sister.

06 (1) I couldn't make up my mind which to choose.

 (2) He doesn't know when to study/play and when to play/study.

07 when there is a fire

08 with 09 wet

10 No, we should use the stairs.

11 to 12 Keep your arms straight.

13 We push down in the center of the chest when we perform CPR. |

---

01 '~하는 것을 잊지 마.'라는 표현은 「Make sure to+동사원형 ~.」, 「Remember to+동사원형 ~.」, 「Don't forget to+동사 원형 ~.」 등이다.

02 You'd better not + 동사원형 ~.은 금지를 나타내는 표현으 로 You shouldn't + 동사원형 ~. / You must not + 동사원 형 ~. / Don't+동사원형 ~. 등으로 나타낼 수 있다.

03 Don't forget to + 동사원형 : ~하는 것을 잊지 마라.

04 (C) 엄마, 사과 주스 좀 사도 돼요? - (E) 물론, Chris. 식품 라 벨을 확인하는 것을 잊지 마라. - (A) 식품 라벨요? - (D) 그래.

너 무 많은 설탕은 너에게 좋지 않아. - (B) 네, 확인해 볼게요.

05 as ~ as ...는 동등비교를 나타낸다.

06 (1) '어느 것을 ~할 것인지'는 which to ~로 쓴다. make up one's mind 결정하다 (2) '언제 공부해야/놀아야 하는지'는 when to study/play로 나타낸다.

07 when: ~할 때 / there is + 단수명사: ~이 있다

08 with: ~으로

09 마르지 않은: 젖은(wet)

10 우리는 엘리베이터 대신에 계단을 사용해야 한다.

11 ⓐ how to+동사원형: ~하는 방법 ⓑ a chance를 꾸며 주는 형용사적 용법의 to부정사가 되어야 한다.

12 keep+목적어+목적격보어: ~을 …하게 유지하다

13 우리는 심폐소생술을 할 때 가슴 중앙을 눌러야 한다고 언급 되 었다.

창의사고력 서술형 문제 p.104

|모범답안|

01 A: Excuse me. May I use this computer?

 B: Yes, you may. But don't forget to turn it off.

 A: All right.

 A: Excuse me. May I borrow this book?

 B: Yes, you may. But don't forget to return it.

 A: All right.

 A: Excuse me. May I ride my bike?

 B: Yes, you may. But don't forget to ride slowly.

 A: All right.

 A: Excuse me. May I use my cell phone here?

 B: Yes, you may. But don't forget to talk quietly.

 A: All right.

 A: Excuse me. May I eat here?

 B: Yes, you may. But don't forget to pick up any trash.

 A: All right.

02 (1) I am as popular as you.

 (2) I run as fast as my brother does.

 (3) I study as hard as you do.

 (4) I am not as beautiful as Kate.

03 (1) I want to know how to make *gimbap*.

 (2) I didn't know what to choose.

 (3) I didn't decide where to stay during my trip.

 (4) I told him when to leave.

---

02 「as+형용사/부사의 원급+as」와 「not as+형용사/부사의 원급 +as」의 구문을 활용하여 자신의 입장에서 자유롭게 써 보도록 한다.

17

01 ④	02 ④	03 zoo keeper	04 ⑤
05 wait for	06 as, as, possible		07 ②
08 ④	09 ③	10 ②, ④	11 ①, ③
12 ④	13 ①	14 ④	15 what to say
16 ⑤	17 should go there		
18 harder → hard	19 ④	20 as fast as	
21 ⑤	22 what to do	23 (s)cared	
24 ⑤	25 ③	26 the four minutes of "Golden Time"	
27 ⑤	28 where		
29 They taught us what to do when an earthquake hits			

01 ④는 유의어 관계이고 나머지는 반의어 관계이다.

02 hold on to: ~을 꽉 잡다 / bump into: ~에 부딪히다

03 특히 동물원에서 동물을 돌보는 일을 하는 사람 : 동물원 사육사[관리인](zoo keeper)

04 wear: 입다, 쓰다 / touch: 만지다 / pick: 고르다 / cross: 건너다

05 wait for: ~을 기다리다

06 as ~ as possible: 가능한 한 ~하게

07 상기시키거나 당부하는 말에 대한 대답은 OK, I won't (forget). / Don't worry. I won't forget. 등으로 표현한다.

08 You'd better not to ~는 금지하는 표현으로 You're not permitted to로 바꿔 쓸 수 있다.

09 Don't forget to ~. (~하는 것을 잊지 마.)는 꼭 해야 할 중요한 것을 상기시킬 때 쓰는 표현이다.

10 '~하는 것을 잊지 마라'라는 표현은 「Don't forget to+동사원형」, 「Remember to+동사원형」, 「Make sure to+ 동사원형」으로 한다.

11 '~하는 것을 잊지 마라'라는 「Don't forget to+동사원형」에 대한 응답은 Okay, I see., Thank you for reminding me., No, I won't. 등으로 한다.

12 B가 자기의 행동을 사과하고 있으므로 잘못된 행동을 금지하는 말이 와야 알맞다. ④ leave computers on: 컴퓨터를 켠 채로 두다

13 '어디서 경기하는지', '어떻게 가는지'라는 의미로 where와 how가 알맞다.

14 ④ 원급 비교 「as+원급+as」: as와 as 사이에는 형용사나 부사의 원급이 와야 한다. heavier를 heavy로 고쳐야 한다.

15 「의문사+주어+should+동사원형」은 「의문사+to부정사」와 같은 의미이다.

16 ⑤ 동등 비교이므로 as ~ as ... 구문이 되어야 한다.

17 의문사 why는 to부정사와 함께 쓰이지 않는다. 대신 why로 「의문사+to부정사」의 의미를 나타내고자 할 때는 「why+주어+should+동사」로 나타낸다.

18 동등 비교 as와 as 사이에는 형용사/부사의 원급 형태가 와야 한다.

19 ④ 「what+to부정사」의 구문으로 what이 to read의 목적어가 되므로 a book은 삭제해야 한다

20 '~만큼 …할 수 있다'는 as ~ as를 이용한 원급 비교로 나타낼 수 있다.

21 ⓐ be in the second grade: 2학년이다 ⓓ tap ~ on the shoulder: ~의 어깨를 가볍게 두드리다

22 what to+동사원형: 무엇을 ~해야 할지

23 뭔가를 두려워하거나 뭔가 나쁜 일이 일어날까봐 두려워하는: scared(무서워하는, 두려워하는)

24 세진이는 그 남자의 어깨를 가볍게 두드렸고 그가 움직이거나 숨을 쉬고 있지 않다는 것을 알게 되었다.

25 (A) such an + 형용사 + 명사 (B) keep + 목적어 + 목적격 보어(형용사) (C) any other things를 꾸며주는 to부정사의 형용사적 용법이다.

26 인칭대명사 It은 the four minutes of "Golden Time"을 가리킨다.

28 뒤에 go가 나왔으므로, 장소에 관한 내용이 와야 한다. 따라서 where to go가 어울린다.

29 선생님들은 우리에게 지진이 일어났을 때 무엇을 해야 하는지 가르쳐 주셨다고 언급되었다.

Living a Healthy Life

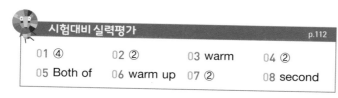

시험대비 실력평가
p.112

| 01 ④ | 02 ② | 03 warm | 04 ② |
| 05 Both of | 06 warm up | 07 ② | 08 second |

01 ④는 -ive를 붙여 형용사형을 만들고 나머지는 -able을 붙여 형용사형을 만든다.

02 be good for: ~에 좋다 / focus on: ~에 집중하다

03 반의어 관계이다. 강한 : 약한 = 서늘한 : 따뜻한

04 신체적으로 편안함을 느끼게 하는: 편안한(comfortable)

05 both of: ~ 둘 다

06 운동이나 다른 활동을 위해 당신의 몸을 준비하기 위해 가벼운 운동을 하다: 준비 운동을 하다(warm up)

07 get over: 회복하다

08 second: (시간 단위인) 초. 두 번째의

서술형 시험대비
p.113

01 (1) forward (2) increase (3) advice (4) uncomfortable

02 (1) each other (2) more than (3) a little bit

03 (1) ride (2) reduce (3) count (4) download

04 (1) healthy (2) movable (3) comfortable

05 (1) get over (2) prepare for (3) am worried about

06 (1) (s)tretch (2) (h)abit (3) (s)witch (4) (r)elax

01 (1) 반의어 관계이다. ~ 전에 : ~ 후에 = 뒤로 : 앞으로 (2) 반의어 관계이다. 잘못된 : 틀린 = 줄다 : 증가하다 (3) 유의어 관계이다. 맛있는 : 맛있는 = 조언 : 조언 (4) 나타나다 : 사라지다 = 편안한 : 불편한

02 (1) each other: 서로 (2) more than: ~ 이상 (3) a little bit: 조금

03 (1) ride: 타다 (2) reduce: 줄이다 (3) count: 세다 (4) download: 다운로드하다

04 (1) healthy: 건강에 좋은 (2) movable: 움직이는 (3) comfortable: 편안한

05 (1) get over: 회복하다 (2) prepare for: ~을 준비하다 (3) be worried about: ~에 대해 걱정하다

06 (1) stretch: 스트레칭하다 (2) habit: 습관 (3) switch: 바꾸다 (4) relax: (근육 등의) 긴장을 풀다

교과서 Conversation

핵심 Check
p.114~115

1 (1) how to / not good at (2) how to make

2 (1) What / like to / riding

(2) what, enjoy doing / fishing

(3) do you do / enjoy drawing / How

교과서 대화문 익히기

Check(√) True or False
p.116

1 T 2 F 3 T 4 F

교과서 확인학습
p.118~119

Listen & Speak 1 A-1

something healthy, have, adivce / often eat, makes, good / how to / cut, into, put, into, pour, mix / should try

Listen & Speak 1 A-2

more than / to be, count, steps / can use, how to use / Can, show / download, with, check / will, using

Listen & Speak 2 A-1

What, doing / enjoy cooking / Sounds, can / can make

Listen & Speak 2 A-2

on weekends / take / What kind, take / taking, of, like / reduce

Listen & Speak 2 A-3

puppy / Her, really / with / enjoy taking, makes, healthy

Conversation A

have, speaking, preparing, for, ago, speaking in, about, cannot sleep

Conversation B

matter / stressed about / ride, when / how to ride / go out, can, Put, on, push, with / Like, feel better / riding, because

시험대비 기본평가　　　　　　　　　　p.120

01 ②　　　02 ⑤　　　03 ②　　　04 ⓒ － ⓑ － ⓐ － ⓓ

01 건강에 좋은 주스를 만드는 방법을 아는지 묻고 있으므로 how to make가 들어가야 한다.

02 건강해지기 위해 하는 것으로 적절하지 않은 것을 고른다

03 Do you know how to + 동사원형 ～?은 능력 여부를 묻는 표현으로 Can you + 동사원형 ～?으로 바꿔 쓸 수 있다.

04 ⓒ 너는 강아지가 있니? - ⓑ 응. 그 강아지의 이름은 코코야. 난 강아지를 정말 좋아해. - ⓐ 너는 강아지와 함께 무엇을 하니? - ⓓ 난 강아지와 산책하는 걸 즐겨. 그것은 나를 건강하게 만들어.

시험대비 실력평가　　　　　　　　　p.121~122

01 ⑤　　　02 ⑤　　　03 ⓑ to ride　ⓓ riding

04 riding[to ride] my longboard　　　05 ②

06 ③　　　07 ③　　　08 (감기에 걸렸을 때) 따뜻한 물을 마시는 것　09 I want to eat something healthy.

10 Eating[To eat] fresh salad　　　11 ①, ③

12 ②　　　13 ②　　　14 ③

01 주어진 문장은 '난 벌써 기분이 더 좋아졌어.'라는 의미로 롱보드를 타는 것이 재미있다는 문장 다음에 와야 한다.

02 ⓐ be stressed about: ～에 대해 스트레스를 받다 ⓒ with: ～로

03 ⓑ how+to부정사: ～하는 방법 ⓓ enjoy -ing: ～하는 것을 즐기다

04 인칭대명사 it은 riding[to ride] my longboard를 가리킨다.

05 ② 하나가 스트레스를 받을 때 무엇을 하는지는 알 수 없다.

06 How have you been?은 안부를 묻는 표현이고, 나머지는 슬픔, 불만족, 실망의 원인을 묻는 표현이다.

07 Do you know how to ～?: 상대방에게 어떤 일을 할 수 있는지 묻는 표현이다.

08 인칭대명사 It은 drinking warm water를 의미한다.

09 -thing으로 끝나는 부정대명사는 형용사가 뒤에서 수식한다.

10 인칭대명사 It은 Eating[To eat] fresh salad를 가리킨다.

11 능력 여부를 묻는 문장에는 Do you know how to ～?, Can you ～?, Are you good at ～? 등이 있다.

12 ⓐ prepare for: ～을 준비하다 ⓒ be worried about: ～에 대해 걱정하다

13 앞뒤 내용이 상반되므로 but이 알맞다.

14 글쓴이는 내일 있을 영어 시험이 걱정된다고 했으므로 스트레스를 받고 있을 것이다.

서술형 시험대비　　　　　　　　　　p.123

01 People say that we should walk more than 10,000 steps.

02 너는 그것(스마트폰 앱)을 어떻게 사용하는지 아니? / |모범답안| Can you use it? / Are you good at using it?

03 app　　　04 It is to download the app.

05 taking

06 She enjoys taking pictures of nature, like trees and flowers.

07 such as　　　08 (r)educe

01 매일 10,000 걸음 이상을 걸어야 한다고 말한다.

02 Do you know how to + 동사원형 ～?은 능력 여부를 묻는 표현으로 Can you + 동사원형 ～? / Are you good at + (동)명사 ～? 등으로 바꿔 쓸 수 있다.

03 특정한 일을 하도록 고안된 컴퓨터 프로그램, 특히 스마트폰에서 사용할 수 있는 프로그램: app(앱)

04 스마트폰 앱을 사용하는 첫 번째 단계는 앱을 다운로드하는 것이라고 언급되었다.

05 enjoy는 동명사를 목적어로 취한다.

06 소녀는 나무와 꽃 같은 자연의 사진을 찍는 것을 즐긴다고 했다.

07 like: ～ 같은(=such as)

08 어떤 것의 크기, 양, 수 등이 작아지게 하다: reduce(줄이다)

교과서
Grammar

핵심 Check　　　　　　　　　　p.124~125

1 (1) melt　(2) do　(3) ring　(4) to come

2 (1) will give　(2) If　(3) takes　(4) drink

01 (1) If I go to France   (2) If it rains tomorrow

02 (1) to look → look   (2) to write → write

    (3) to go → go

03 (1) Unless you leave   (2) If it doesn't rain

04 (1) me go out after dinner

    (2) the children play outside

    (3) the bear stand on the ball

01 조건의 부사절은 「If+주어+동사 ~」의 어순으로 쓴다.

02 사역동사 have, make, let은 목적격 보어로 동사원형을 취한다.

03 「if+주어+don't[doesn't]+동사원형 ~」은 「unless+주어+동사의 현재형 ~」으로 바꿔 쓸 수 있다.

04 「사역동사(let, have, make)+목적어+동사원형」의 형태에 유의하여 주어진 문장을 「목적어+동사원형」 형태로 완성한다.

01 ③	02 ①	03 ⑤	04 ⑤

05 to do → do   06 ③   07 I helped my mom (to) do the dishes. 08 ③   09 ③

10 ④   11 ④   12 will rain → rains

13 ③   14 His smile always makes me smile.

15 ③   16 ③   17 ②   18 you stop   19 ②   20 Judy makes her brother study math.   21 ③   22 Unless you like the food   23 My father helped me carry the heavy bag.   24 ⑤

01 「주어+동사+목적어+목적격보어」로 구성된 5형식 문장이므로 사역동사 have의 목적격보어로 쓰일 수 있는 동사원형의 형태가 알맞다.

02 '만약 ~하면'의 조건절을 이끄는 접속사와 '~인지 아닌지'의 명사절을 이끄는 접속사 역할을 하는 if가 적절하다.

03 make가 5형식 문장에 쓰이면 목적격 보어로 형용사 또는 동사원형이 올 수 있다.

04 가까운 미래의 상황을 가정하거나 조건을 나타낼 때 if절은 현재시제로, 종속절은 미래시제로 써야 한다.

05 사역동사 make는 목적격 보어로 동사원형을 취한다.

06 if 조건절은 의미가 미래이더라도 현재시제를 쓴다.

07 help는 준사역동사로 목적격 보어로 동사원형이나 to부정사 둘 다 취할 수 있다.

08 조건을 나타내는 if절에서는 현재시제가 미래의 일을 나타내므로 ③이 알맞다.

09 let, have, make, help는 모두 목적격보어로 동사원형을 취한다. want는 to부정사를 목적격보어로 취한다.

10 If ~ not은 Unless와 의미가 같다.

11 ④는 4형식 문장에 쓰인 수여동사이며, 나머지는 5형식 문장에 쓰인 불완전 타동사이다.

12 조건을 나타내는 if는 미래시제 will과 쓰지 못한다.

13 조건을 나타내는 if 부사절에서는 미래의 일이라도 현재시제를 사용한다.

14 make+목적어+동사원형

15 두 빈칸 모두 동사의 자리이고, 다음에 him이라는 목적어가 나온다. 목적격보어로 'to+동사원형'이 나왔으므로 get이 들어가야 맞다. 동사원형이 목적격보어로 오는 경우 사역동사는 해당되지 않는다. help는 의미상 어울리지 않는다.

16 if ~ not = unless: 만약 ~하지 않으면

17 첫 번째 빈칸에는 사역동사가 들어가야 하고, 두 번째 빈칸에는 사역동사의 목적격보어인 동사원형이 들어가야 한다. 사역동사 let, have, make는 모두 뒤에 동사원형을 동반한다. take care of: ~를 돌보다

18 if ~ not = unless

19 사역동사 make, let과 help는 모두 목적격보어로 동사원형을 쓴다. (② to go → go) ③ 「ask+목적어+to부정사」 형태이다.

21 ③ 조건을 나타내는 if절에서는 현재시제가 미래시제를 대신한다. will leave → leave

22 '만약 ~하지 않는다면'이라는 의미의 「If+주어+don't[doesn't]+동사원형 ~」은 「Unless+주어+동사의 현재형 ~」으로 바꿔 쓸 수 있다.

23 사역동사 help 다음에는 동사원형이나 to부정사가 쓰인다.

24 대화 속의 밑줄 친 make와 ⑤는 사역동사이다.

01 (1) (to) carry   (2) get   (3) help   (4) to show

02 (1) If   (2) when   (3) Unless

03 (1) to explain → explain   (2) fell → fall

    (3) played → play

04 (1) If I am late for class, my teacher gets very angry.

    (2) If the weather is nice, I always walk to school.

    (3) If it rains on weekends, we watch TV.

05 Mom doesn't let me go out at night.

06 I made my younger[little] brother turn off the TV.

07 (1) If you study hard   (2) If it rains

08 (1) Finally, the police let the thief go.

    (2) Love makes people do unusual things.

    (3) I got my dog to wear strange glasses.

    (4) My English teacher helps us (to) write a diary every day.

09 (1) you'll pass → you pass

    (2) I won't be → I'm not / I am not

10 (1) My parents let me play computer games every Friday.

(2) My teacher made me wash my hands.

(3) My mom didn't let me go out. |

11 (1) If it rains tomorrow, we won't go hiking.

(2) Unless you hurry, you will miss the train.

12 (1) Eddie lets his brother play with his toys.

(2) She makes her children study English.

(3) Dad has us cook breakfast on Sundays.

13 If she doesn't study hard, she will fail the exam.

01 (1) help+목적어+(to)동사원형 (2) get+목적어+to부정사 (3) let+목적어+동사원형 (4) 보여줄 그림들이라는 의미의 to부정사의 형용사적 용법이 적절하다.

02 when은 때, if는 조건을 나타낸다. unless는 if ~ not의 뜻이다.

03 5형식 문장에서 사역동사 let, make, have의 목적격보어는 동사원형을 써야 한다.

04 if는 종속절을 이끄는 접속사이다.

06 「사역동사+목적어+목적격보어(동사원형)」 어순으로 써야 한다.

07 '만약 ~한다면'이라는 의미로 조건을 나타내는 표현은 「if+ 주어+동사의 현재형」으로 나타낸다.

08 (1), (2) let, make는 사역동사로 목적격보어 자리에는 동사원형이 와야 한다. (3) get은 목적격보어 자리에 'to+동사원형'이 온다. (4) help는 목적격보어로 동사원형 또는 to부정사를 쓴다.

09 조건의 if절에서는 미래의 일을 현재시제로 나타낸다.

10 (1) 「let+목적어+동사원형(…이 ~하도록 허락하다)」 (2) 「make+목적어+동사원형(…이 ~하게 하다)」 (3) 「don't let+목적어+동사원형(…이 ~하도록 허락하지 않다)」

11 (1) if 이하가 조건절이므로, 현재시제가 미래시제를 대신한다.
(2) unless는 '만약 ~하지 않으면'의 뜻이므로 not을 붙일 필요가 없다

12 사역동사 have, make, let은 목적격 보어로 동사원형을 사용한다.

13 콤마가 있으므로 if절을 주절 앞에 둔다.

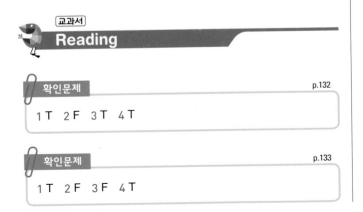

교과서
Reading

확인문제	p.132

1 T 2 F 3 T 4 T

확인문제	p.133

1 T 2 F 3 F 4 T

01 At, for   02 get tired

03 Why don't, yourself   04 Let's, with

05 Close, massage, with   06 will relax

07 When, cover, with, block out

08 make, feel, comfortable   09 massage

10 Put, on   11 Draw, with, to 12 from, to

13 help, feel   14 Let's, waist 15 Team up

16 each other, faces   17 Hold

18 stretch, backward   19 Hold, for

20 pull, to   21 your, at 22 If, both of

23 Place, on, behind   24 bend, lower

25 Hold, a few, up   26 loosen up

27 Switch, repeat 28 How, feel

29 massage, stretch, feel healthier 30 focus on, better

1 At school you sit for many hours.

2 Do you get tired?

3 Why don't you massage yourself and stretch?

4 Let's begin with the eyes.

5 Close your eyes and massage them softly with your fingers.

6 It will relax your eyes.

7 When you finish, cover your eyes with your hands to block out the light.

8 It will make your eyes feel more comfortable.

9 Next, massage your neck.

10 Put your fingers on the back of your neck.

11 Draw small circles with your fingers to massage your neck.

12 Massage from top to bottom.

13 The massage will help you feel better.

14 Let's work on your waist.

15 Team up with a friend.

16 Stand close to each other and face your partner.

17 Hold each other's wrists.

18 Slowly stretch your head and body backward.

19 Hold that position for three seconds.

20 Then, slowly pull each other to a standing position.

21 You and your partner should move at the same speed.

22 If you don't, both of you will fall!

23 Place the top of your right foot on the desk

behind you.

24 Then, slowly bend your left leg and lower yourself.

25 Hold it for a few seconds and slowly straighten up.

26 This position will loosen up your right leg.

27 Switch your legs and repeat the exercise.

28 How do you feel now?

29 If you massage yourself and stretch every day, you will feel healthier.

30 Also, you can focus on your studies better.

시험대비 실력평가

p.138~141

01 ③	02 ②	03 your eyes	04 stretch
05 ⑤	06 ③	07 ⓑ for ⓔ of	
08 position	09 ②	10 ⑤	11 ③
12 ③	13 slowly	14 ④	15 ⓑ → ⓒ
→ ⓐ	16 softly	17 눈을 감고 손으로 눈을	

부드럽게 마사지하는 것   18 ③   19 ④

20 make your eyes feel more comfortable   21 ②

22 ③   23 feeling → feel[to feel]   24 waist

25 ③   26 ②   27 ④   28 ③

29 yourself   30 switch   31 ⑤

01 for many hours: 오랜 시간 동안 / block out: (빛을) 차단하다

02 get tired: 피곤하다

03 인칭대명사 them은 your eyes를 가리킨다.

04 팔, 다리 등을 근육이 길고 단단해지도록 하는 자세에 놓다: stretch(스트레칭하다)

05 인칭대명사 It은 앞에 나온 문장 cover your eyes with your hands to block out the light를 가리킨다.

06 ⓐ, ③: 마주보다, ①, ④: 얼굴, ②: 직면하다, ⑤: 표면

07 for three seconds: 3초 동안 / both of: ~ 둘 다

08 어떤 사람이 서거나 앉거나 눕는 방식 : position(자세)

09 '만약 ~하면'의 뜻으로 조건절을 이끄는 접속사 if가 알맞다.

10 두 사람이 같은 속도로 움직이지 않으면, 두 사람은 넘어질 것이라고 언급되어 있다.

11 명령문은 상대방, 즉 2인칭에게 하는 말이므로 재귀대명사는 yourself가 되어야 한다.

12 ③ bend(구부리다): 몸을 움직여 구부리다 ① mix ② switch ④ place ⑤ stretch

13 동사를 수식하는 부사 형태가 되어야 한다

14 straighten up: 똑바로 하다 / loosen up: (몸 • 근육을) 풀어 주다

15 뒤에 있는 책상 위에 오른쪽 발등을 올려놓고 천천히 왼쪽 다리를 구부리고 몸을 낮추고 그 상태로 몸을 낮춘 상태로 몇 초 동안 유지한다.

16 동사를 수식하는 부사 형태가 되어야 한다.

17 인칭대명사 It은 앞 문장 Close your eyes and massage them softly with your fingers.를 가리킨다.

18 빛을 차단하기 위해 눈을 가려라가 문맥상 적절하므로 cover가 알맞다.

19 목적을 나타내는 부사적 용법의 to부정사 형태가 되어야 한다.

20 make + 목적어 + 목적격 보어(동사원형): ~을 …하게 하다 / feel+형용사: ~하게 느끼다

21 목을 맛사지하는 방법은 '목 뒤에 손가락을 대고(Put), 목을 마사지하기 위해 손가락으로 작은 원을 그리고(Draw), 위에서 아래로 마사지해라(Massage)'는 순서가 알맞다.

22 <보기>와 ③은 목적을 나타내는 부사적 용법의 to부정사이다. 나머지는 명사적 용법이다

23 동사 help는 목적격 보어로 동사원형이나 to부정사를 쓸 수 있다.

24 갈비뼈와 엉덩이 사이의 신체 중앙 부분: 허리

25 머리와 몸을 뒤로 뻗어라가 알맞다. forward → backward

26 ⓑ, ②: (시간 단위인) 초 ①: 두 번째로 ③,⑤: 두 번째의 ④: 둘째의[제2의]

27 ⓒ should: ~해야 한다 ⓓ 조건을 나타내는 접속사 if 문장에서 주절에는 미래형을 쓴다.

28 주어진 문장의 it은 왼쪽 다리를 구부리고 몸을 낮춘 자세를 가리키므로 ③이 알맞다.

29 재귀대명사 yourself가 되어야 한다.

30 어떤 것에서 다른 것으로 바꾸다[전환하다]: 바꾸다 (switch)

31 문맥상 몸을 풀어 주라는 의미를 가진 loosen up이 알맞다.

서술형 시험대비

p.142~143

01 Why don't you massage

02 massage   03 comfortably → comfortable

04 We can cover our eyes with our hands.

05 to massage   06 from

07 The massage will help you feel better.

08 ⓒ → ⓐ → ⓑ   09 (l)ower

10 왼쪽 다리를 구부리고 몸을 낮춘 자세   11 up

12 이 자세는 여러분의 오른쪽 다리를 풀어 줄 것이다.

13 (f)ace   14 여러분의 머리와 몸을 뒤로 뻗은 자세

15 push → pull   16 They will fall.

01 Why don't you + 동사원형 ~?: ~하는 게 어때?

02 근육의 긴장을 풀어 주거나 근육과 관절의 통증을 완화 시키기

위해 몸을 문지르거나 눌러 주다: 마사지하다 (massage)

03 feel+형용사: ~하게 느끼다

04 빛을 막기 위해 우리는 우리의 눈을 가릴 수 있다고 언급되었다.

05 목적을 나타내는 to부정사의 부사적 용법이다.

06 from A to B: A부터 B까지

07 help+목적어+목적격보어(동사원형/to+동사원형); ~가 …하는 것을 돕다 / feel better: 기분이 나아지다

08 목 뒷부분에 손가락을 대고, 목을 마사지하기 위해 손가락으로 작은 원을 그린 후, 위에서 아래로 마사지한다.

09 뭔가를 위쪽에서 아래로 이동시키다: 낮추다(lower)

11 straighten up: 똑바로 하다

12 loosen up: 몸을 풀어 주다

13 얼굴과 몸을 어떤 것 또는 어떤 사람을 향해 서거나 앉다: 마주 보다

14 밑줄 친 부분은 stretching your head and body backward 를 가리킨다.

15 천천히 서로 서 있는 위치로 끌어당겨라가 문맥상 알맞다. push → pull

16 같은 속도로 움직이지 않으면, 두 사람은 넘어질 것이라고 언급 되어 있다.

영역별 핵심문제

p.145~149

01 ④　　02 ②　　03 team up
04 massage　05 ③　　06 ⑤　　07 ④
08 ②　　09 ③　　10 ③　　11 (C) – (A) – (D) – (B)　　12 ⓐ feel　ⓑ to make
13 ④　　14 ③　　15 It is to put small pieces of vegetables into a bowl.　　16 ③
17 ⑤　　18 ③　　19 What will you do if he visits your home tomorrow? 20 ②　　21 ②
22 She has the children play soccer.　　23 ④
24 ③　　25 changing → change　　26 If Jenny does not get up now, she will miss the train. 또는 Jenny will miss the train if she does not get up now.　　27 ⑤　　28 ⑤　　29 with
30 ④　　31 make your eyes feel　　32 ④
33 wrists　34 ④　　35 ⑤　　36 how to stretch　　37 (A) First　(B) Then　(C) Finally
38 너의 팔로 숫자 2를 만드는 것　　39 ④

01 ④는 유의어 관계이고 나머지는 반의어 관계이다.

02 몸을 움직여 구부리다: 구부리다(bend)

03 team up with: ~와 협력하다

04 근육과 관절의 통증을 줄이기 위해 손으로 사람의 몸을 문지르고 누르는 행동: 마사지(massage)

05 • 시청에 가려면 어떤 방법이 가장 좋을까요?. • 나는 경기장으

06 loosen up: (몸을) 풀어 주다 / block out: (햇빛을) 차단 하다

07 방과 후에 무엇을 하는 것을 즐기냐고 물었으므로, 대답으로는 방과 후에 할 수 있는 활동에 대해 말하는 것이 적절하다.

08 '~하는 방법'은 「how to+동사원형」으로 나타낸다.

09 음악의 종류로 답했으므로 '너는 어떤 종류의 음악을 좋아하 니?'라고 묻는 것이 알맞다.

10 A: 수학 문제 푸는 것 잘하니? B: 아니, 나 수학 잘 못해.

11 (C) 방과 후에 뭐 하는 걸 즐기니? (A) 나는 건강에 좋은 음식을 요리하 는 것을 즐겨. (D) 멋지구나. 너는 무엇을 만들 수 있니? (B) 나는 샐러드, 비빔 밥 그리고 야채 주스를 만들 수 있어.

12 ⓐ 사역동사 make의 목적격보어로 동사원형을 쓴다. ⓑ how+to부정사: ~하는 방법

13 cut A into B: A를 B로 자르다

14 순서를 열거하는 문장이므로 First, Then, Finally 순으로 오 는 것이 알맞다.

15 신선한 샐러드를 만드는 두 번째 단계는 채소의 작은 조각들을 그릇에 담는 것이다.

16 문장의 구조로 보아 목적어와 목적격보어(원형부정사)를 갖는 5 형식 문장이므로 사역동사 made가 빈칸에 들어가야 한다.

17 접속사 if가 '~한다면'으로 해석되면 부사절을 이끌고, '~인지 아닌지'로 해석되면 명사절을 이끈다. 주어진 문장과 ⑤ 의 if는 명사절을 이끄는 접속사이다.

18 ①, ②, ④, ⑤의 밑줄 친 동사는 모두 사역동사로 쓰였으나, ③ 의 have는 '가지고 있다'의 일반동사로 쓰였다.

19 미래의 일이므로 주절에서는 미래시제를 나타낸다.

20 ①, ③, ④, ⑤는 사역동사 구문인데, ②의 told는 목적격보 어로 to부정사를 사용하는 동사이다.

21 '만약 ~하면'의 뜻으로 조건절을 이끄는 접속사와 '~인지 아 닌지'의 뜻으로 명사절을 이끄는 접속사 역할을 하는 if가 알 맞다.

22 사역동사 have는 목적격보어로 동사원형을 쓴다.

23 <보기>와 ④는 사역동사로 '(목적어)를 ~하게 만들다'라는의미 로 쓰였다. ① make it: 해내다 ② make money: 돈을 벌다 ③ make: 만 들어 주다(수여동사) ⑤ make an effort: 노력 하다

24 ③ 조건을 나타내는 if절에서는 현재시제가 미래시제를 대신 한다.

25 어떤 것도 나의 마음을 바꾸게 하지 않을 것이다.

26 첫 문장이 두 번째 문장의 조건이 되므로 접속사 if를 이용하 여 연결한다.

27 ①~④는 내용상 조건을 나타내는 접속사 if가 와야 하고, ⑤는 동사 think의 목적어 역할을 하는 접속사 that이 적절하다.

28 (A) for + 숫자를 나타내는 기간 (B) 목적어가 주어 자신이 므 로 재귀대명사 yourself가 알맞다. (C) 목적을 나타내는 to부 정사 형태가 되어야 한다.

29 ⓐ begin with: ~부터 시작하다 ⓑ with: ~으로

30 빛을 차단하기 위해서 눈을 가리라는 의미가 되는 것이 흐름 상 알맞다. open → close

31 make+목적어+목적격 보어(동사원형)

32 team up with: ～와 협력하다

33 손과 팔이 잇닿은 부분: 손목(wrist)

34 that position은 여러분의 머리와 몸을 뒤로 뻗는 것을 가리키므로 ④번이 알맞다.

35 미래를 표현할 때 주절에서는 미래시제를 쓴다.

36 '～하는 방법'이라는 뜻으로 「how to+동사원형」을 쓴다.

37 순서를 열거할 때 First(우선, 먼저), Then(그런 다음), Finally(마지막으로) 순으로 표현한다.

38 인칭대명사 It은 앞 문장의 내용을 받는다.

39 앞뒤 내용이 상반되는 내용이므로 but이 알맞다.

단원별 예상문제
p.150~153

01 ③ 02 bottom 03 ⑤ 04 ④
05 (1) a few seconds (2) take a walk (3) What kind of 06 ③ 07 ② 08 to be
09 Do you know how to use it? 10 Later
11 the smartphone app 12 ⑤ 13 ④
14 ② 15 ④ 16 ⑤ 17 ⑤
18 If it is, will go 19 had Martin read
20 top 21 ④ 22 ⑤ 23 ④
24 to 25 warm up 26 for 27 ⓐ Place ⓑ bend ⓒ Hold 28 ① 29 ⑤
30 ④

01 <보기>와 ③은 -able를 붙여 형용사형이 되는 단어이고, 나머지는 -ive를 붙여 형용사가 되는 단어들이다.

02 반의어 관계이다. 단순한 : 복잡한 = 꼭대기 : 맨 아래

03 focus on: ～에 집중하다 / straighten up: 똑바로 하다

04 어떤 것이 긴장, 팽팽함, 경직성이 줄어들게 하다: relax(근육 등의) 긴장을 풀다

05 (1) for a few seconds: 몇 초 동안 (2) take a walk: 산책하다 (3) what kind of: 어떤 종류의

06 Do you know how to + 동사원형 ～?은 능력 여부를 묻는 표현이다.

07 여가 시간에 무엇을 하느냐는 질문에 나는 영어와 수학 공부하는 것을 싫어한다는 대답은 어색하다.

08 목적을 나타내는 to부정사의 부사적 용법이다.

09 Do you know how to + 동사원형 ～?: ～하는 방법을 아니?(능력 여부를 묻는 표현)

10 later: 나중에

11 인칭대명사 it은 the smartphone app을 가리킨다.

12 사역동사 let은 목적격보어로 동사원형을 취한다.

13 ④ make는 5형식을 이끄는 사역동사이므로 practicing을

practice로 바꿔야 한다.

14 if로 시작하는 조건절에서는 현재시제가 미래시제를 대신한다.

15 ④ 사역동사 make는 목적어 다음에 목적격보어로 동사원 형이 온다.

16 '주말마다'는 반복적인 습관을 나타내므로 현재시제를 사용한다.

17 첫 번째 문장은 이유, 두 번째 문장은 조건을 나타낸다.

18 조건의 부사절에서는 현재시제가 미래시제를 대신한다. 날씨를 말할 때는 비인칭 주어 it을 사용한다.

19 「have+목적어+동사원형」의 사역동사 구문이다.

20 어떤 것의 윗면

21 place A on B: A를 B 위에 놓다

22 a few+복수 명사

23 주어진 문장의 This position은 몇 초 동안 왼쪽 다리를 구부리고 몸을 낮추는 자세를 가리키므로 ④번이 알맞다.

24 ⓐ how to부정사: ～하는 방법 ⓑ 목적을 나타내는 to부정사의 부사적 용법

25 스포츠나 그 밖의 활동을 준비하려고 하는 운동이나 일련의 운동을 하다: 준비 운동을 하다(warm up)

26 be good for: ～에 좋다

27 ⓐ place: 놓다, 두다 ⓑ bend: 구부리다 ⓒ hold: 유지하다

28 straighten up: 똑바로 하다 / focus on: ～에 집중하다

29 문맥상 여러분의 오른쪽 다리를 풀어줄 것이라는 내용이 알맞다.

30 also: 또한

서술형 실전문제
p.154~155

01 Do you know how to massage

02 I enjoy playing catch.

03 I am not good at math. |

04 (D) – (C) – (A) – (B)

05 (1) I will have my brother clean my room.
　(2) Inhui made her daughter do the dishes.
　(3) My mother let me watch the TV drama.

06 (1) If you have a fever, you should see a doctor.
　(2) If it rains tomorrow, I will go to a movie.
　(3) If you add yellow to blue, it becomes green.

07 (1) My mother makes me clean my room.
　(2) The librarian helped me find a book.
　(3) They let her go safely.

08 We massage our eyes softly.

09 그것은 여러분의 눈을 더 편안하게 해 줄 것이다.

10 We can draw small circles with our fingers.

11 The massage will help you feel better.

12 are → is

13 He[She] plans to exercise more than three times a week.

25

14 나의 습관을 바꾸는 것

15 make me live a healthy life

01 Do you know how to + 동사원형 ~?: 너는 ~하는 방법을 아니?

02 I enjoy -ing ~.: 나는 ~하는 것을 즐긴다.

03 능력을 부인하는 표현으로 I'm not good at을 사용할 수 있다.

04 (D) 너는 방과 후에 뭐 하는 걸 즐기니? (C) 나는 건강에 좋은 음식을 요리하는 것을 즐겨. (A) 멋지구나. 너는 무엇을 만들 수 있니? (B) 나는 샐러드, 비빔밥 그리고 야채 주스를 만들 수 있어.

05 have, make, let 등 사역동사는 목적어 다음에 목적격보어로 동사원형을 쓴다.

06 (1) see a doctor: 진찰을 받다 (2) go to a movie: 영화 보러 가다 (3) add A to B: B에 A를 섞다

07 (1) makes가 사역동사이므로 목적격보어로 clean이 들어 가야 한다. (2) help는 목적격보어로 동사원형을 쓴다. (3) let은 사역동사로 목적격보어는 동사원형이 온다.

08 눈을 손가락으로 부드럽게 마사지한다.

09 사역동사 make+목적어+목적격보어(동사원형): ~을 ...하게 만들다 / feel+형용사: ~하게 느끼다

10 목을 마사지하기 위해 손가락으로 작은 원을 그릴 수 있다.

11 help+목적어+목적격보어(동사원형/to부정사): ~가 ...하는 것을 돕다 / feel better: 기분이 좋아지다

12 Here is + 단수 명사 ~: 여기 ~이 있다

13 글쓴이는 일주일에 세 번 이상 운동할 것이라고 했다.

14 인칭대명사 it은 changing[to change] my habits를 가리킨다.

15 사역동사 make+목적어+목적격보어(동사원형) / live a healthy life: 건강한 삶을 살다

창의사고력 서술형 문제
p.156

|모범답안|

01 (1) Do you know how to shop on the Internet? / No, I don't how to shop on the Internet.

(2) Do you know how to cook instant noodles? / Yes, I know how to cook instant noodles.

02 (1) If I go to Paris, I can see the Eiffel Tower.

(2) If it is sunny tomorrow, I will go hiking with my friends.

(3) If I find an abandoned dog on the street, I will take it to the animal center.

03 (1) My mother let me go to the amusement park.

(2) Jenny made my brother run fast.

(3) My friend helped me (to) do my homework.

(4) My grandparents had me wait so long.

단원별 모의고사
p.157~160

01 ⑤	**02** ③	**03** ④	**04** simple
05 (a)dvice	**06** ⑤	**07** ②, ⑤	**08** ②
09 ②, ④	**10** ③	**11** 한쪽 발을 보드 위에	

11 올려 놓고 다른 한 발로 세게 민다. **12** ③

13 feels → feel		**14** ①	**15** ④

16 My brother had me clean[sweep] the room.

17 Unless	**18** ②	**19** ①	**20** ①
21 ④	**22** ①	**23** Massage from top to	

23 bottom. **24** ④ **25** ③ **26** position

27 won't → don't		**28** ⑤	**29** ②

30 to feel → feel

01 각각의 팔 끝과 목 사이에 있는 신체의 두 부분 중 하나: 어깨 (shoulder)

02 ③ for a few seconds: 수 초 동안

03 face: 얼굴; ~와 마주 보다

04 반의어 관계이다. 배고픈 : 배부른 = 복잡한 : 단순한

05 누군가에게 어떻게 하라고 알려 주는 말이나 제안: 조언, 충고 (advice)

06 능력 여부를 묻는 말에는 Do you know how to ~?, Can you ~?, Are you good at ~? 등이 있다.

07 I enjoy -ing ~는 좋아하는 것을 말하는 표현으로 I like to + 동사원형 ~. / I feel great when I + 동사원형 ~ 으로 바꿔 쓸 수 있다.

08 when: ~할 때 / because: ~ 이기 때문에

09 Do you know how to + 동사원형 ~?은 능력 여부를 묻는 표현으로 ①, ③, ⑤와 바꿔 쓸 수 있다.

10 the other: (둘 중에서) 다른 하나

11 Put one foot on the board and push hard with the other.에서 알 수 있다.

12 '~하면'이라는 조건의 접속사가 필요하다.

13 make는 사역동사로 목적격보어로 동사원형을 쓴다. 따라서 동사 feels는 원형인 feel로 써야 한다.

14 사역동사 let은 목적격보어로 동사원형(cross)을 쓴다.

15 ④ 조건을 나타내는 if절은 미래의 의미이더라도 현재시제로 써야 한다.

16 사역동사 have+목적어+동사원형: ~하도록 시키다

17 If ~ not은 '~하지 않는다면'이라는 의미로 Unless와 같다.

18 ②는 직접목적어와 간접목적어가 있는 4형식 문장이고 나머지는 모두 5형식 문장이다.

19 ② 미래의 일이므로 조건을 나타내는 문장의 주절은 미래시제를 사용한다.

20 의미상 오른쪽 발등이 되어야 한다. ⓐ bottom → top

21 loosen up: (근육을) 풀어 주다

22 put A on B: A를 B 위에 놓다[대다]

23 from top to bottom: 위에서 아래로

24 파트너를 마주 보고(face), 머리와 몸을 뒤로 뻗고 (stretch), 서로 서 있는 자세로 끌어당긴다(pull)가 옳다.

25 for three seconds: 3초 동안 / at the same speed: 같은 속도로

26 어떤 사람이 서거나 앉거나 눕는 방식: 자세(position)

27 조건의 부사절에서는 미래시제 대신 현재시제를 사용한다.

28 주어진 문장의 It은 massaging[to massage] your eyes softly with your fingers를 가리키므로 ⑤번이 알 맞다.

29 block out: (빛을) 차단하다

30 make+목적어+목적격보어(동사원형)

교과서 파헤치기

단어 TEST Step 1   p.02

01 항상	02 따뜻한	
03 ~하기로 되어 있는[예정된]		04 쉽게
05 약속	06 걱정하는	07 도움이 되다; 도움
08 준비하다	09 도움이 되는	10 수업, 강습
11 역사	12 기억하다	13 확인하다
14 ~하는 동안	15 대신에	16 가입하다
17 일정	18 퀴즈, 시험	19 매월의; 매월
20 자유 시간	21 일정 계획표, 플래너	
22 다시	23 해 보다, 노력하다	24 끝내다
25 주의, 집중	26 집중하다	27 규칙적으로
28 현명하게	29 긴장되는, 불안한	30 조리[요리]법
31 성취하다, 달성하다		
32 (인터넷이나 SNS에 올리는) 글, 포스팅		33 연습하다
34 절약하다, 구하다	35 온종일	
36 ~하는 것을 멈추다		37 수업[강습]을 받다
38 ~와 잘 지내다	39 계획을 세우다	40 알람을 맞춰 놓다
41 한 번에	42 ~을 한쪽에 두다	43 미루다, 연기하다

단어 TEST Step 2   p.03

01 practice	02 before	03 regularly
04 finish	05 nervous	06 textbook
07 attention	08 wisely	09 achieve
10 posting	11 focus	12 important
13 forget	14 chef	15 weekly
16 master	17 step	18 recipe
19 save	20 tired	21 spend
22 toward	23 probably	24 remember
25 helpful	26 instead	27 appointment
28 warm	29 prepare	30 easily
31 schedule	32 monthly	33 free time
34 check	35 because of	36 in front of
37 all day long	38 set the alarm	39 these days
40 set a goal	41 stop -ing	41 be worried about
43 put aside		

1 recipe, 요리[조리]법   2 spend, (돈을) 쓰다

3 achieve, 성취하다, 달성하다   4 master, ~을 완전히 익히다

5 prepare, 준비하다   6 appointment, 약속

7 join, 가입하다   8 save, 절약하다   9 lesson, 수업, 강습

10 due, ~하기로 되어 있는[예정된]   11 focus, 집중하다

12 schedule, 일정   13 future, 미래

14 helpful, 도움이 되는   15 attention, 주의

16 present, 선물

Listen & Speak 1 - A

1 look worried, matter / don't hear, these days / Why don't, set the alarm / good idea

2 what should, do / What's / spend, fast / always make, before, buy / should, same

Listen & Speak 2 - A

1 okay, don't look good / have a cold / too bad, think, should see / You're right

2 look worried, going on / worried about, What should I do / think, should read / a good idea

3 so tired / don't sleep, these days / I think, should drink a glass of, before, will help / will try

Conversation A

type, daily, monthly, like, due dates, check, to remember, easily, should use

Conversation B

What's the matter / didn't bring, forgot, have soccer practice / second year, busier than, first year, often forget / you should use, mine / can I see / schedule, appointment / Maybe, should buy

Wrap Up - ❶

What's, Are, sick / I think, have a cold / go to the school nurse / said, need to, Can, leave / call, tell her

Wrap Up - ❷

nervous / because of / for, still, should, do / think, should, in front of, helpful / a good idea

Listen & Speak 1 - A

1 G: You look worried, Sam. What's the matter?

   B: I don't hear my alarm in the morning these days.

   G: Why don't you set the alarm on your clock and on your smartphone?

   B: That's a good idea.

2 G: Phew, what should I do?

   B: What's the matter, Julie?

   G: I spend money too fast.

   B: Well, I always make a plan before I buy things.

   G: Maybe I should do the same.

Listen & Speak 2 - A

1 G: Jason, are you okay? You don't look good today.

   B: I have a cold.

   G: That's too bad. I think you should see a doctor.

   B: You're right. Thank you.

2 G: You look worried. What's going on?

   B: I'm worried about tomorrow's history quiz. What should I do?

   G: I think you should read your textbook again.

   B: That's a good idea.

3 B: I'm so tired.

   G: Why?

   B: I don't sleep well these days.

   G: I think you should drink a glass of warm milk before you sleep. It will help.

   B: Okay, I will try.

Conversation A

B: This is a type of book. I write my daily , weekly, and monthly plans here. I also write important dates like my friends' birthdays and homework due dates here. Every night, I check this for the next day. Do you want to remember things easily? Then I think you should use this.

Conversation B

Hana: What's the matter, Jiho?

Jiho: I didn't bring my uniform. I forgot I have soccer practice today.

Hana: Again?

Jiho: My second year in middle school is busier than my first year, and I often forget things.

Hana: I think you should use a planner. Here's mine.

Jiho: Oh, can I see it?

Hana: Sure. I write my class schedule and appointment in my planner.

Jiho: That's great. Maybe I should buy one.

Wrap Up - ❶

W: What's the matter, Sam? Are you sick?

B: Ms. Green, I think I have a cold.

W: Did you go to the school nurse?

B: Yes. She said I need to go to the hospital. Can I leave school now?

W: Okay, Sam. I'll call your mom and tell her about it.

B: I'm so nervous.

G: Why? Is it because of the dance contest?

B: Yes. I practiced for many days, but I'm still nervous. What should I do?

G: I think you should practice in front of your family. It will be very helpful.

B: That's a good idea. Thank you.

본문 TEST Step 1   p.09~10

01 Welcome to, school year   02 In, second, to do

03 need to manage, well   04 How, do that

05 set, goals, achieve, every

06 not, will master

07 such, put off, until

08 Instead,three new, every

09 achieve, goal, step

10 When, full attention

11 used to, while, doing

12 slowed, down, focus

13 put aside, when

14 saves, lot, time

15 days, finish, enjoy, free

16 regularly spend, working

17 want, become, chef

18 Every, classes, search for

19 using, to prepare, is   20 Time, present

21 has, present to spend

22 Manage, and, be happier

본문 TEST Step 2   p.11~12

01 Welcome to, school year

02 In, second grade, more work to do

03 need to manage, well   04 How, do

05 set small goals, achieve

06 do not say, will master

07 With put off working on, until, or

08 Instead, will learn three new English, every day

09 will achieve, one step at a time

10 When, give, my full attention

11 used to read, while, was doing

12 slowed, because, couldn't focus

13 put aside, when   14 saves, a lot of

15 These days, quickly, enjoy my free time

16 regularly spend, working

17 want to become

18 Every, cooking classes, search for recipes

19 using, to prepare for   20 Time, present

21 has, same, to spend

22 Manage, and, be happier, new school year

본문 TEST Step 3   p.13~14

1 새 학년이 된 걸 환영해.

2 2학년에서, 여러분은 할 일이 더 많을 거야.

3 여러분은 시간을 잘 관리할 필요가 있어.

4 여러분은 시간 관리를 어떻게 하는가?

5 수빈: 나는 작은 목표를 세우고 매일 그것들을 성취해.

6 나는 "나는 영어를 마스터할 거야."라고 말하지 않아.

7 그렇게 큰 목표를 가지면, 나는 아마 그것을 위해 노력하는 걸 내일, 다음 주, 혹은 다음 달까지 미룰 거야.

8 대신에 나는 "나는 매일 세 개의 새로운 영어 단어를 배울 거야."라고 말해.

9 나는 한 번에 한 단계씩 나의 큰 목표를 달성할 거야.

10 민수: 나는 무언가를 할 때 그것에 모든 주의를 기울여.

11 나는 숙제를 하는 동안 SNS 게시 글을 읽곤 했어.

12 집중할 수 없었기 때문에 그것은 나의 속도를 늦추었어.

13 지금 나는 숙제를 할 때 스마트폰을 한쪽에 치워 놔.

14 그렇게 하면 시간이 많이 절약돼.

15 요즈음, 나는 숙제를 빨리 끝내고 자유 시간을 즐겨.

16 John: 나는 내 꿈을 위해 노력하며 규칙적으로 시간을 사용해.

17 나는 요리사가 되고 싶어.

18 토요일 아침마다 나는 요리 강습에 가거나 요리법을 찾아봐.

19 나는 나의 미래를 준비하기 위해 시간을 쓰는 것이 중요하다고 생각해.

20 시간은 선물이다.

21 모든 사람은 매일 소비할 똑같은 선물을 가지고 있다.

22 시간을 잘 관리하면 여러분은 새 학년에 더 행복해질 것이다!

본문 TEST Step 4-Step 5   p.15~18

1 Welcome to the new school year.

2 In the second grade, you will have more work to do.

3 You need to manage your time well.

4 How do you do that?

5 Subin: I set small goals and achieve them every day.

6 I do not say, "I will master English."

7 With such a big goal, I will probably put off

29

working on it until tomorrow, next week, or next month.

8 Instead, I say, "I will learn three new English words every day."

9 I will achieve my big goal, one step at a time.

10 Minsu: When I do something, I give it my full attention.

11 I used to read SNS postings while I was doing my homework.

12 It slowed me down because I couldn't focus.

13 Now, I put aside my smartphone when I do my homework.

14 It saves me a lot of time.

15 These days, I finish my homework quickly and enjoy my free time.

16 John: I regularly spend time working toward my dream.

17 I want to become a chef.

18 Every Saturday morning, I go to cooking classes or search for recipes.

19 I think that using my time to prepare for my future is important.

20 Time is a present.

21 Everyone has the same present to spend every day.

22 Manage your time well, and you will be happier in the new school year!

Enjoy Writing B

1. My Goals for This Year

2. I have three goals to achieve this year.

3. The first goal is to get along with my new classmates.

4. The second goal is to get an A on the English speaking test.

5. The last goal is to stop playing smartphone games.

6. I hope that this year is better than last year.

Project - Step 1

1. A: I think we should make our group's motto about dreaming and doing.

2. B: That's a good idea. I believe that dreaming and doing are different.

3. C: Yes. I think that doing is more important than dreaming.

4. D: That's right.

Wrap Up - Writing

1. Jenny is going to go to the grocery store today.

2. She is going to buy three apples to eat.

3. She is going to buy two bottles of water to drink.

4. She is going to buy one fashion magazine to read.

Enjoy Writing B

1. This Year

2. goals to achieve

3. first, to get along with, classmates

4. second, to get, on

5. last, stop playing

6. that, better than

Project - Step 1

1. think, should, about dreaming, doing

2. believe, dreaming and doing

3. is more important than

4. right

Wrap Up - Writing

1. going, grocery store

2. going, to eat

3. two bottles of, to drink

4. one fashion magazine to read

10 skill, 기술　11 tap, (가볍게) 톡톡 두드리다[치다]

12 perform, 행하다, 실시하다　13 zoo keeper, 동물원 사육사

14 experience, 경험　15 lower, 낮추다, 낮아지다

16 shake, 흔들리다

단어 TEST Step 1　　　　p.21

01 어깨	02 다행히도	03 용감한
04 낮추다, 낮아지다	05 가슴	06 위험한
07 기술	08 (각도의 단위인) 도	09 기회, 가능성
10 바닥	11 교육, 훈련	12 아나운서
13 흔들리다	14 연습하다	15 보호하다
16 대단히, 크게	17 심장	18 청중, 시청자
19 ~ 주위에	20 구하다	21 늦게
22 동물원 사육사	23 기억하다	24 신이 난
25 갑자기	26 무서워하는, 겁먹은	
27 경험	28 심폐소생술	29 주의 깊게
30 각도	31 지진	32 젖은
33 잊다	34 행하다, 실시하다	35 ~을 꽉[꼭] 누르다
36 ~에 부딪히다	37 가능한 한 ~한[하게]	
38 넘어지다	39 항상	
40 밑에 들어가다, 밑에 숨다		41 ~의 경우에
42 ~의 어깨를 치다	43 ~을 꼭 잡다, ~을 붙잡다	

단어 TEST Step 2　　　　p.22

01 low	02 angle	03 carefully
04 shout	05 CPR	06 experience
07 breathe	08 teenager	09 earthquake
10 scared	11 wet	12 scary
13 gear	14 forget	15 grade
16 hard	17 important	18 impressive
19 within	20 join	21 open
22 perform	23 safety	24 stay
25 tap	26 chest	27 lower
28 dangerous	29 brave	30 training
31 audience	32 shake	33 remember
34 protect	35 push down	36 fall down
37 as ~ as possible		38 bump into
39 all the time	40 put on	41 in case of
42 up and down	43 get off	

단어 TEST Step 3　　　　p.23

1 wet, 젖은　2 brave, 용감한　3 chest, 가슴

4 save, 구하다　5 earthquake, 지진

6 audience, 청중, 시청자　7 degree, (각도의 단위인) 도

8 protect, 보호하다　9 breathe, 숨을 쉬다, 호흡하다

대화문 TEST Step 1　　　　p.24~25

Listen & Speak 1 A-1

can, buy / Don't forget to / food label / not good for / will check

Listen & Speak 1 A-2

leaving / need to wear, a lot of find dust / didn't know / be bad for, don't forget to wear / All right

Listen & Speak 2 A-1

What's up / to buy. What about / have, in, should go, late / you'd better not run, says, wet / didn't see

Listen & Speak 2 A-2

does, mean / you'd better not, while, are walking / interesting, but / bump into, there are, around, dangerous / see

Conversation A

having, with, to shake, couldn't, fell down, Get, Don't forget, Luckily, scary experience

Conversation B

told, a few / let's practice, ready / is shaking, forget to get under, protect / scary / Hold on to / for now, out / better not use, Use the stairs / Where should, go / need to, with no buildings / let's go to

Wrap Up - Listening 1

almost, stand in line, wait for, get off, move up, down, You'd better not use, in case of

Wrap Up - Listening 2

going to go to, with / sounds / excited because, for, on night / don't forget

대화문 TEST Step 2　　　　p.26~27

Listen & Speak 1 A-1

B: Mom, can I buy some apple juice?

W: Sure, Chris. Don't forget to check the food label.

B: The food label?

W: Yes. Too much sugar is not good for you.

B: Okay, I will check it.

Listen & Speak 1 A-2

G: Dad, I'm leaving.

M: You need to wear this, Julie. There is a lot of fine dust in the air today.

G: Oh, I didn't know that.

M: It will be bad for your health. So don't forget to wear this mask.

G: All right . Thank you.

B: Hi, Amy. What's up?

G: I'm here to buy a shirt. What about you?

B: I have a lunch meeting in this shopping center. Oh, I should go now. I'm late .

G: Okay, but you'd better not run . The sign says the floor is wet.

B: I didn't see it. Thanks.

G: What does the sign mean?

B: It means that you'd better not look at your smartphone while you are walking.

G: That's interesting, but why?

B: You can bump into people and there are many cars around here. It's so dangerous.

G: Now I see .

B: I was having a good time with my family last night. Suddenly everything started to shake. I couldn't stand still and almost fell down. Dad shouted, "Get under the table. Don't forget to protect your head." Luckily, the shaking soon stopped. It was a scary experience.

Teacher: I told you a few safety rules for earthquakes today. Now, let's practice. Are you ready?

Amy & Jiho: Yes.

Teacher: Everything is shaking. Don't forget to get under the desk and protect your body first.

Jiho: It's so scary.

Amy: You're doing fine, Jiho. Hold on to the leg of the desk.

Jiho: Oh, the shaking stopped for now. Let's get out!

Teacher: Remember! You'd better not use the elevator. Use the stairs .

Amy: Where should we go now?

Teacher: You need to find an open area with no buildings.

Jiho: Then, let's go to the park.

G: Many people use this almost every day. People stand in line to enter this. They wait for others to get off before they enter. They use this to move up and down floors in a building. You'd better not use this in case of a fire.

B: I'm going to go to Jiri Mountain with my dad tomorrow.

G: It sounds great.

B: I'm excited because we are going to stay there for two days and one night.

G: That'll be great, but don't forget to check the weather.

B: Okay.

본문 TEST Step 1   p.28~29

01 saved, life, old 02 brave, in, with

03 introduce yourself   04 My, is

05 in, second, at   06 tell us, experience

07 waiting for, with

08 suddenly, fell, front

09 Nobody, what, do

10 as, scared, others

11 ran, tapped, on

12 wasn't moving, breathing

13 said, Call, CPR

14 Announcer, impressive

15 When, such as, skill

16 Safety Training, last

17 learned how, chance, practice

18 show, how, perform   19 Keep, straight

20 other, chest, at, angle

21 Push down, hard, until

22 there, other, to remember

23 need, remember, minutes

24 should, within, after, stops

25 later than, lower, saving

26 Timing, important, doing   27 for joining us

28 My pleasure

본문 TEST Step 2   p.30~31

01 saved, life, old man   02 brave, with us

03 introduce yourself   04 My, is

05 in, second, at   06 tell us your experience

07 was waiting for, with

08 suddenly fell in front of

09 Nobody, what to do

10 as scared as, at

11 ran, tapped, on

12 wasn't moving, breathing

13 said to, started CPR   14 impressive

15 such as, skill

16 Safety Training, at

17 learned how to do, chance to practice

18 show, how to perform CPR

19 Keep, arms straight

20 other, must, at a 90 degree angle

21 Push down, hard, until an ambulance comes

22 Are there, to remember

23 need to remember, four minutes

24 that, should, within, after someone's heart stops

25 To begin, later than, chances of saving

26 as important as

27 Thank you for joining   21 pleasure

---

25 그보다 늦게 심폐소생술을 시작하는 것은 누군가의 생명을 구할 가능성을 크게 낮출 것입니다.

26 아나운서: 타이밍은 심폐소생술을 하는 것만큼이나 중요하군요.

27 저희와 함께 해 주셔서 감사합니다.

28 세진: 제가 더 고맙습니다.

본문 TEST Step 3   p.32~33

1 아나운서: 어제, 한 십대가 어떤 노인의 생명을 구했습니다.

2 그 용감한 학생이 오늘 우리와 함께 스튜디오에 있습니다.

3 자기소개를 해 보세요.

4 세진: 제 이름은 김세진입니다.

5 저는 한국중학교 2학년입니다.

6 아나운서: 당신의 경험을 우리에게 말해 줄 수 있나요?

7 세진: 물론이죠. 저는 친구 진호와 버스를 기다리고 있었어요.

8 갑자기 한 남자가 우리 앞에 쓰러졌어요.

9 아무도 무엇을 해야 할지 몰랐어요.

10 저는 처음엔 다른 사람들처럼 겁이 났어요.

11 그러고 나서, 저는 그에게 달려가서 그의 어깨를 두드렸어요.

12 그는 움직이지도 숨을 쉬지도 않았어요.

13 저는 진호에게 "119에 전화해."라고 말하고 심폐소생술을 시작했습니다.

14 아나운서: 인상적이네요.

15 언제 그런 중요한 기술을 배웠나요?

16 세진: 지난주에 학교에서 '안전 교육의 날'이 있었어요.

17 저는 심폐소생술을 하는 방법을 배웠고 연습할 기회를 가졌어요.

18 아나운서: 청중들에게 심폐소생술을 어떻게 하는지 보여줄 수 있나요?

19 세진: 네. 팔을 쭉 펴세요.

20 당신의 팔과 다른 사람의 가슴은 90도 각도여야 합니다.

21 구급차가 올 때까지 가슴 중앙을 세게 그리고 빨리 누르세요.

22 아나운서: 기억해야 할 다른 것이 있나요?

23 세진: 네. "골든타임" 4분을 기억해야 합니다.

24 그것은 여러분이 누군가의 심장이 멈춘 후 4분 안에 심폐소생술을

본문 TEST Step 4~Step 5   p.34~37

1 Announcer: Yesterday, a teenager saved the life of an old man.

2 The brave student is in the studio with us today.

3 Please introduce yourself.

4 Sejin: My name is Kim Sejin.

5 I'm in the second grade at Hanguk Middle School.

6 Announcer: Could you tell us your experience?

7 Sejin: Sure. I was waiting for the bus with my friend, Jinho.

8 A man suddenly fell in front of us.

9 Nobody knew what to do.

10 I was as scared as the others at first.

11 Then, I ran to him and tapped him on the shoulder.

12 He wasn't moving or breathing.

13 I said to Jinho, "Call 119," and started CPR.

14 Announcer: That's impressive.

15 When did you learn such an important skill?

16 Sejin: We had Safety Training Day at school last week.

17 I learned how to do CPR and had a chance to practice.

18 Announcer: Can you show the audience how to perform CPR?

19 Sejin: Yes. Keep your arms straights.

20 Your arms and the other person's chest must be at a 90 degree angle.

21 Push down in the center of the chest hard and fast until an ambulance comes.

22 Announcer: Are there any other things to remember?

23 Sejin: Yes. You need to remember the four minutes of "Golden Time."

24 It means that you should start CPR within four minutes after someone's heart stops.

25 To begin CPR later than that will greatly lower the chances of saving someone's life.

26 Announcer: Timing is as important as doing CPR.

27 Thank you for joining us.

28 Sejin: My pleasure.

2. First, don't forget to use safety glasses.

3. Second, you'd better not run around.

My Writing B

1. Save, Fire

2. what to do, there is

3. should shout

4. need to cover, with a wet towel

5. have to stay, as, get out

6. as soon as you can

7. Don't forget to use, not

Wrap Up

1. Training

2. Safety, at school

3. taught us what to do

4. how to protect

5. where to go, shaking stops

Project - Step 3

1. tell you what to do

2. don't forget to, safety glasses

3. better not, around

My Writing B

1. Save Your Life from a Fire

2. Do you know what to do when there is a fire?

3. You should shout, "Fire!"

4. You need to cover your face and body with a wet towel.

5. You have to stay as low as possible and get out.

6. Also, you need to call 119 as soon as you can.

7. Don't forget to use the stairs, not the elevator.

Wrap Up

1. Safety Training Day

2. Today we had Safety Training Day at school.

3. Teachers taught us what to do when an earthquake hits.

4. We learned how to protect our heads and bodies.

5. We also learned where to go when the shaking stops.

Project - Step 3

1. We'll tell you what to do for safety in the science room.

10 position, 자세　11 relax, (근육 등의) 긴장을 풀다
12 habit, 습관　13 stretch, 스트레칭하다
14 warm up, 준비 운동을 하다　15 pull, 당기다
16 massage, 마사지

단어 TEST Step 1　p.40

01 자세	02 끌다, 당기다	03 스트레칭하다
04 어려운	05 자연	06 조언, 충고
07 밀다	08 운동하다	09 이해하다, 알다
10 놓다, 두다	11 세다	12 (시간 단위인) 초
13 어깨	14 활동	15 그러나
16 삶	17 붓다	18 바꾸다
19 뒤쪽, 뒷부분	20 마사지; 마사지를 하다	
21 목	22 다운로드하다	23 뒤로
24 놓다, 두다	25 보여[가르쳐] 주다	
26 허리	27 편안한	28 구부리다
29 ~을 낮추다, ~을 낮게 하다		30 습관
31 신선한	32 보통, 대개	33 간단한, 단순한
34 따뜻한	35 서로	36 ~와 협력하다
37 (빛을) 가리다[차단하다]		38 회복[극복]하다
39 위에서 아래까지	40 ~에 집중하다	41 몸을 풀어 주다
42 똑바로 하다	43 ~에 좋다	

단어 TEST Step 2　p.41

01 already	02 behind	03 comfortable
04 softly	05 step	06 way
07 move	08 fall	09 face
10 fishing	11 habit	12 warm
13 both	14 hold	15 bend
16 exercise	17 nature	18 difficult
19 activity	20 relax	21 healthy
22 lower	23 simple	24 fresh
25 stress	26 light	27 like
28 reduce	29 usually	30 bowl
31 stretch	32 backward	33 neck
34 position	35 warm up	
36 from top to bottom		37 focus on
38 for a few seconds		39 be worried about
40 prepare for	41 block out	42 straighten up
43 get over		

단어 TEST Step 3　p.42

1 count, 세다　2 simple, 간단　3 comfortable, 편안한
4 reduce, 줄이다　5 advice, 조언　6 shoulder, 어깨
7 switch, 바꾸다　8 neck, 목　9 bend, 구부리다

대화문 TEST Step 1　p.43~44

Listen & Speak 1 A-1

something healthy, have, adivce / often eat, makes,
feel / how to make / simple, cut, into, put, into, pour,
mix / should try

Listen & Speak 1 A-2

more than / steps, to be healthy, count, steps easily
/ can use, how to use / Can, show me / download,
with, check, steps you took / will start using

Listen & Speak 2 A-1

What, enjoy doing / enjoy cooking healthy food /
Sounds, can, make / can make

Listen & Speak 2 A-2

on weekends / take pictures / What kind, usually
take / enjoy taking, of, like / reduce my stress

Listen & Speak 2 A-3

have a puppy / Her, really like / What, with her /
enjoy taking, makes, healthy

Conversation A

have, speaking, preparing, for, ago, speaking in, am
worried about, cannot sleep

Conversation B

what's matter / stressed about, next week / ride,
when / know how to ride / No, don't / go out, can,
Put, on, push, with / Like, feel better / enjoy, riding,
because, reduces / great

Wrap Up 1

look sick, What's / have a cold / see a doctor / yet,
get over / warm, when, makes me feel better /
Sounds, will try

Wrap Up 2

enjoys, fishing, Early, comes back, enjoys drawing,
to draw, enjoy playing

대화문 TEST Step 2　p.45~46

Listen & Speak 1 A-1

B: I want to eat something healthy. Do you have any
　adivce?
G: I often eat fresh salad. It makes me feel good.

B: Really? Do you know how to make it?

G: Yes, it's quite simple. First, cut many vegetables into small pieces. Next, put them into a bowl. Then, pour some lemon juice on them. Finally, mix everything together.

B: That's it? I should try it.

Listen & Speak 1 A-2

B: People say that we should walk more than 10,000 steps every day to be healthy. I can't count the number of my steps easily.

G: You can use this smartphone app. Do you know how to use it?

B: No. Can you show me?

G: Sure. First, download the app. Then, walk with your smartphone. Later, you can check the number of steps you took.

B: Thank you. I will start using it today.

Listen & Speak 2 A-1

G: What do you enjoy doing after school?

B: I enjoy cooking healthy food.

G: Sounds cool. What can you make?

B: I can make salad, Bibimbap, and vegetable juice.

Listen & Speak 2 A-2

B: What do you do on weekends?

G: I take pictures.

B: What kind of pictures do you usually take?

G: I enjoy taking pictures of nature, like trees and flowers. The beautiful pictures reduce my stress.

Listen & Speak 2 A-3

G: Do you have a puppy?

B: Yes. Her name is Coco. I really like her.

G: What do you do with her?

B: I enjoy taking a walk with her. It makes me healthy.

Conversation A

B: Tomorrow, I have an English speaking contest. I started preparing for the contest two weeks ago. I enjoy speaking in English, but I am worried about the contest. I cannot sleep well.

Conversation B

Karl: Hana, what's the matter?

Hana: Well, I'm stressed about the test next week.

Karl: I understand. I ride my longboard when I'm stressed. Do you know how to ride a longboard?

Hana: No, I don't.

Karl: Let's go out! I can teach you. Put one foot on the board and push hard with the other.

Hana: Like this? Wow! This is fun. I feel better already.

Karl: See? I enjoy riding my longboard because it reduces my stress.

Hana: That's great!

Wrap Up 1

B: You look sick. What's the matter?

G: Well, I have a cold.

B: Did you see a doctor?

G: Not yet. Do you know how to get over a cold?

B: Well, I usually drink warm water when I have a cold. It makes me feel better.

G: Sounds good. I will try it.

Wrap Up 2

B: My family enjoys many activities. My dad enjoys fishing . Early in the morning, he goes to the lake and comes back with some fish. My mom enjoys drawing pictures. She likes to draw beautiful mountains and lakes. My brother and I enjoy playing soccer.

본문 TEST Step 1   p.47~48

01 At, for, hours   02 Do, get tired

03 don't, yourself, stretch   04 Let's, with

05 Close, massage, softly   06 will relax

07 When, cover, block out

08 make, feel, comfortable

09 massage, neck   10 Put, on, back

11 circles, fingers, massage   12 top, bottom

13 help, feel better

14 Let's, on, waist   15 Team up

16 close, other, faces   17 Hold, other's

18 stretch, body backward

19 Hold, for, seconds   20 pull, to

21 should move, speed   22 If, both, fall

23 Place, top, on, behind

24 bend, lower yourself

25 Hold, few, straighten up

26 position, loosen up

27 Switch, repeat, exercise   28 How, feel

29 massage, stretch, feel healthier

30 focus on, studies

본문 TEST Step 2   p.49~50

01 At school, for   02 get tired

03 Why don't, yourself, stretch

04 Let's begin with

05 Close, massage, with, fingers   06 will relax

07 When, cover, with, block out

08 make, feel more comfortable

09 massage your neck   10 Put, on, back

11 Draw, with to massage

12 from top to bottom

13 help you feel better

14 Let's work on, waist   15 Team up, with

16 each other, faces   17 Hold, wrists

18 Slowly stretch, backward

19 Hold, for three seconds   20 pull, to

21 your, at   22 If, both of, will fall

23 Place, top, on, behind

24 slowly bend, lower

25 Hold, a few seconds, straighten up

26 The position, loosen up

27 Switch, repeat the exercise   28 How, feel

29 massage, stretch every day, feel healthier

30 can focus on, better

---

23 여러분의 뒤에 있는 책상 위에 오른쪽 발등을 올려놓아라.

24 그러고 나서, 천천히 왼쪽 다리를 구부리고 몸을 낮추어라.

25 몇 초 동안 그 자세를 유지하다가 천천히 몸을 펴라.

26 이 자세는 여러분의 오른쪽 다리를 풀어 줄 것이다.

27 다리를 바꿔서 운동을 반복해라.

28 지금 기분이 어떤가?

29 매일 마사지와 스트레칭을 하면, 여러분은 더 건강해지는 것을 느낄 것이다.

30 또한, 여러분은 공부에 더 집중할 수 있을 것이다.

---

1 학교에서 여러분은 오랜 시간에 걸쳐 앉아 있다.

2 여러분은 피곤한가?

3 마사지와 스트레칭을 하는 게 어떤가?

4 눈부터 시작하자

5 눈을 감고 손가락으로 눈을 부드럽게 마사지해라.

6 그것은 여러분의 눈을 편안하게 해줄 것이다.

7 끝나면, 빛을 차단하기 위해 손으로 눈을 가려라.

8 그것은 여러분의 눈을 더 편안하게 해줄 것이다.

9 다음으로, 여러분의 목을 마사지해라.

10 여러분의 목 뒤에 손가락을 대라.

11 여러분의 목을 마사지하기 위해 손가락으로 작은 원을 그려라.

12 위에서 아래로 마사지해라.

13 마사지는 여러분의 기분이 좋아지도록 도울 것이다.

14 허리 운동을 하자.

15 친구와 짝을 이루어라.

16 서로 가까이 서서 여러분의 파트너를 마주 보아라.

17 서로의 손목을 잡아라.

18 천천히 여러분의 머리와 몸을 뒤로 뻗어라.

19 3초 동안 그 자세를 유지해라.

20 그러고 나서, 천천히 서로 선 자세로 끌어 당겨라.

21 너와 너의 파트너는 같은 속도로 움직여야 한다.

22 그렇지 않으면, 너희 둘 다 넘어질 것이다!

---

1 At school you sit for many hours.

2 Do you get tired?

3 Why don't you massage yourself and stretch?

4 Let's begin with the eyes.

5 Close your eyes and massage them softly with your fingers.

6 It will relax your eyes.

7 When you finish, cover your eyes with your hands to block out the light.

8 It will make your eyes feel more comfortable.

9 Next, massage your neck.

10 Put your fingers on the back of your neck.

11 Draw small circles with your fingers to massage your neck.

12 Massage from top to bottom.

13 The massage will help you feel better.

14 Let's work on your waist.

15 Team up with a friend.

16 Stand close to each other and face your partner.

17 Hold each other's wrists.

18 Slowly stretch your head and body backward.

19 Hold that position for three seconds.

20 Then, slowly pull each other to a standing position.

21 You and your partner should move at the same speed.

22 If you don't, both of you will fall!

23 Place the top of your right foot on the desk behind you.

24 Then, slowly bend your left leg and lower yourself.

25 Hold it for a few seconds and slowly straighten up.

26 This position will loosen up your right leg.

27 Switch your legs and repeat the exercise.

28 How do you feel now?

29 If you massage yourself and stretch every day, you will feel healthier.

30 Also, you can focus on your studies better.`

2 Our stretching exercise is called "Number Stretching."

3 First, make a number "I" with your arm to warm up.

4 Then, make a number "2" with your arms. 5

5 It will stretch your shoulders.

6 Now, make a number "3".

7 If you move your arms in a circle, it will feel nice.

8 Finally, make a number "4".

9 It is a little bit difficult, but it will be good for your shoulders.

구석구석지문 TEST Step 1
p.57

Enjoy Writing C

1. to Be Healthier

2. Here is

3. more than three times

4. every day

5. three times a week, become stronger

6. if, will feel better,

7. habits, make me live

Project - Step 2

1. how to stretch

2. stretching exercise is called

3. with, to warm up

4. Then, with

5. will stretch, shoulders

6. make

7. in a circle, feel nice

8. Finally

9. a little bit, be good for

Wrap Up - Writing

1. these days, should, go

2. get stressed, makes me feel

3. how to download

Wrap Up - Writing

1. Sumi: I feel stressed these days. What should I do?

2. Jiae: When I get stressed, I listen to music. It makes me feel better.

3. If you don't know how to download music, I will show you.

구석구석지문 TEST Step 2
p.58

Enjoy Writing C

1. My Plan to Be Healthier

2. Here is my plan to be healthier

3. I will exercise more than three times a week.

4. I will eat breakfast every day.

5. If I exercise more than three times a week, I will become stronger.

6. Also, if I eat breakfast every day, I will feel better in the morning.

7. I will change my habits, and it will make me live a healthy life.

Project - Step 2

1. Do you know how to stretch your shoulders?

MEMO

적중 100

영어 기출 문제집

정답 및 해설

시사 | 박준언